INTERNATIONAL CHEMICAL SERIES

H. P. TALBOT, Ph.D., Sc.D., Consulting Editor

THE HYDROUS OXIDES

INTERNATIONAL CHEMICAL SERIES

(H. P. TALBOT, PH.D., SC.D., CONSULTING EDITOR)

Bancroft—
**APPLIED COLLOID CHEM-
ISTRY**
Second Edition

Bingham—
FLUIDITY AND PLASTICITY

Cady—
INORGANIC CHEMISTRY

Cady—
GENERAL CHEMISTRY
Second Edition

Griffin—
**TECHNICAL METHODS OF
ANALYSIS**
As Employed in the Labora-
tories of Arthur D. Little, Inc.

Hall and Williams—
**CHEMICAL AND METALLO-
GRAPHIC EXAMINATION
OF IRON, STEEL AND
BRASS**

Hamilton and Simpson—
**CALCULATIONS OF QUAN-
TITATIVE CHEMICAL
ANALYSIS**

Loeb—
**PROTEINS AND THE
THEORY OF COLLOIDAL
BEHAVIOR**
Second Edition

Lord and Demorest—
**METALLURGICAL ANALY-
SIS**
Fifth Edition

Mahin—
QUANTITATIVE ANALYSIS
Third Edition

Mahin and Carr—
**QUANTITATIVE AGRICUL-
TURAL ANALYSIS**

Millard—
**PHYSICAL CHEMISTRY FOR
COLLEGES**
Second Edition

Moore—
HISTORY OF CHEMISTRY

Norris—
**TEXTBOOK OF INORGANIC
CHEMISTRY FOR COL-
LEGES**

Norris and Mark—
**LABORATORY EXERCISES
IN INORGANIC CHEMIS-
TRY**

Norris—
ORGANIC CHEMISTRY
Second Edition

Norris—
**EXPERIMENTAL ORGANIC
CHEMISTRY**
Second Edition

Parr—
**ANALYSIS OF FUEL, GAS,
WATER AND LUBRICANTS**
Third Edition

Robinson—
**THE ELEMENTS OF FRAC-
TIONAL DISTILLATION**

White—
**TECHNICAL GAS AND FUEL
ANALYSIS**
Second Edition

Williams—
**PRINCIPLES OF METALLO-
GRAPHY**

Woodman—
FOOD ANALYSIS
Second Edition

Long and Anderson—
CHEMICAL CALCULATIONS

Bogue—
**THE THEORY AND APPLI-
CATION OF COLLOIDAL
BEHAVIOR**
Two Volumes

Reedy—
**ELEMENTARY QUALITA-
TIVE ANALYSIS FOR
COLLEGE STUDENTS**

Leighou—
**CHEMISTRY OF ENGINEER-
ING MATERIALS**
Second Edition

Adkins and McElvain—
**PRACTICE OF ORGANIC
CHEMISTRY**

Eucken, Jette and LaMer—
**FUNDAMENTALS OF PHY-
SICAL CHEMISTRY**

Underwood—
**PROBLEMS IN ORGANIC
CHEMISTRY**

Schorger—
**THE CHEMISTRY OF CELLU-
LOSE AND WOOD**

Weiser—
THE HYDROUS OXIDES

THE HYDROUS OXIDES

BY

HARRY BOYER WEISER

Professor of Chemistry at the Rice Institute

FIRST EDITION

McGRAW-HILL BOOK COMPANY, Inc.

NEW YORK: 370 SEVENTH AVENUE

LONDON: 6 & 8 BOUVERIE ST., E. C. 4

1926

THE MAPLE PRESS COMPANY, YORK, PA.

PREFACE

The scientific foundation of modern colloid chemistry was laid by Thomas Graham more than three score years ago as a result of his basic researches on the colloidal behavior of albumin, gums, and gelatin, and of the hydrous oxides of silicon, iron, aluminum, chromium, tin, titanium, molybdenum, and tungsten. Since Graham's time a great many investigators, van Bemmelen in particular, have studied the colloidal character and application of the hydrous oxides. So far as the author is aware, the present volume represents the first endeavor to correlate systematically and summarize critically the numerous scattered facts in an old but increasingly important field.

No group of substances presents a greater variety of colloidal properties than the hydrous oxides. For this reason they have been employed frequently in the investigation of colloid chemical phenomena and applied in widely diversified ways to the industrial arts. There is little doubt that a more intimate acquaintanceship with this group of substances will serve to extend their field of usefulness rapidly. It is hoped, therefore, that the book may prove of value alike to scientist and industrialist.

Portions of the manuscript of the book have been read and criticized by several gentlemen. Special acknowledgment of this sort is gratefully made to W. D. Bancroft of Cornell University, R. H. Bogue of the Bureau of Standards, F. L. Browne of the United States Forest Products Laboratory, E. M. Chamot of Cornell University, P. L. Gile of the U. S. Department of Agriculture, and C. L. Parsons, Secretary of the American Chemical Society.

HARRY B. WEISER.

HOUSTON, TEXAS.
  Feb. 1, 1926

CONTENTS

CHAPTER VI

CHAPTER VII

CHAPTER VIII

CHAPTER IX

CHAPTER X

CHAPTER XI

CHAPTER XII

CHAPTER XIII

CHAPTER XIV

CHAPTER XV

CHAPTER XVI

CHAPTER XVII

CHAPTER XVIII

CHAPTER XIX

THE HYDROUS OXIDES

INTRODUCTION

When a solution of a ferric salt is treated with an alkali, there is formed a voluminous, gelatinous precipitate which is commonly called ferric hydroxide and assigned the formula $Fe(OH)_3$. The extent to which this terminology is fixed in our chemical literature is evidenced by its almost universal use in our textbooks, although four decades ago van Bemmelen[1] showed not only that there is no definite hydrate of the formula $Fe(OH)_3$ or $Fe_2O_3 \cdot 3H_2O$, but that no other hydrate is formed by the usual method of precipitating the oxide. The viscous voluminous precipitate when first formed may be represented approximately by the formula $Fe_2O_3 \cdot \pm 2OH_2O$, but it loses water, gradually attaining a composition that varies with the time, the temperature, and the pressure of the water vapor in contact with it. A composition corresponding to a definite hydrate is, therefore, purely accidental, depending as it does on the exact method of formation, the method of drying, the temperature, and the age of the sample. Precipitated oxides like ferric oxide which contain varying amounts of water adsorbed by the oxide particles are called hydrous oxides to distinguish them from hydrates, in which the water is chemically combined in definite stoichiometric proportions. There are a few hydrated oxides, such as $Al_2O_3 \cdot 3H_2O$ and $BeO \cdot H_2O$, which may adsorb varying amounts of water, depending on the conditions of formation. Such preparations may be termed hydrous hydrated oxides. On standing, the primary colloidal particles of the hydrous oxides grow and lose water spontaneously, causing the mass to assume a less gelatinous and more granular character. This spontaneous transformation from a loose voluminous precipitate to a granular mass is accompanied by a decrease in the solubility, the adsorbability, and the peptizability of the compounds.

[1] *Rec. trav. chim.*, **7**, 106 (1888).

Although the rapid precipitation of a hydrous oxide usually gives a gelatinous mass with a supernatant liquid, it is frequently possible to bring about uniform precipitation throughout the entire solution with the formation of a jelly which differs from a gelatinous precipitate in that all the liquid is enclosed by the precipitated phase. Since the hydrous oxides are obtained so frequently in the form of gelatinous precipitates, and since the latter are produced when jellies contract spontaneously or are broken up by stirring, the first chapter deals in a general way with the structure, preparation, and properties of gels. This is followed by separate chapters devoted to the typical oxides of iron, chromium, and aluminum, after which the remaining oxides are taken up by families in the approximate order in which the elements appear in the periodic table. The last five chapters are concerned with some of the more important industrial applications of the hydrous oxides.

CHAPTER I

JELLIES AND GELATINOUS PRECIPITATES

Gelatinous precipitates and jellies are the two forms of solid or semisolid colloids that are commonly included under the term gel. Gels of the hydrous oxides, such as ferric oxide and chromic oxide, which lose their elasticity and become powdery on drying, are called rigid or non-elastic gels in contradistinction to the elastic gels, such as gelatin, albumin, and agar, which are characterized by perfect elasticity through certain narrow limits and by retaining their elasticity and coherence on drying. Although a detailed discussion of the properties of elastic gels lies beyond the scope of this book, any adequate theory of gels must take them into account. Moreover, the vast majority of the work on gel structure has been done with gelatin, and a survey of the results of these investigations throws considerable light on the nature of gels of the hydrous oxides.

STRUCTURE

Since a working theory of the structure of gels is necessary for a systematic discussion of their preparation and properties, we shall take up first the question of the structure of the two forms, beginning with jellies. This question has doubtless received more attention at the hands of investigators than any other single problem in the field of colloid chemistry; but, in spite of this, opinions differ as to the exact nature of a jelly. Thus Robertson, Procter,[1] and Katz[2] regard jellies as homogeneous single-phase systems, solid solutions, or semisolid solutions "of the exterior solution in the colloid in which both constituents are within the range of the molecular attraction of the mass."

[1] *J. Chem. Soc.*, **105**, 313 (1914).
[2] *Kolloidchem. Beihefte*, **9**, 1 (1918).

Wolfgang Ostwald[1] considers gels to be two-phase liquid-liquid systems possessing an interfacial tension. The vast majority of investigators, however, incline to the view that jellies are two-phase solid-liquid systems in which there is a network or cellular arrangement of solid phase permeated by liquid.

The Solid-solution Theory.—The evidence in support of the solid-solution theory of jelly structure has been drawn largely from investigations on the swelling of substances. Thus in an exhaustive monograph, published in 1917, Katz points out the close similarity between the phenomena associated with swelling and the changes which accompany the formation of binary liquid mixtures. This parallelism would indicate that the swelling process is simply the formation of a solid solution between water and the swelling substance. Later, however, Katz[2] studied the effect of swelling on the x-ray spectrum of a number of substances to determine whether the taking up of liquid is intermicellar or intramolecular. If the liquid is held between the particles, the crystal lattice should not be altered by swelling, whereas if a solid solution is formed, the dimensions of the lattice should be increased. In practically all cases investigated, Katz observed no change in the x-ray spectrum, indicating that, as a rule, the swelling process is not a solid-solution phenomenon.

From a study of the swelling of gelatin in acid solution, Procter concludes that gelatin combines with acid, forming easily soluble, highly-ionized salts, and that the volume of a swollen jelly under equilibrium conditions is determined by the osmotic pressure of the salts and the Donnan equilibrium. This view seems inadequate to account for the marked increase in viscosity and the loss of mobility when a warm gelatin solution is cooled. In order to get around this difficulty, Procter postulates the formation of tenuous and possibly flexible crystals which interlace and anastomose when a warm solution sets to a jelly on cooling. These crystals are assumed to be so very minute and the network so extremely fine that both solvent and crystals are within the

[1] *Pflüger's Arch.*, **109**, 277 (1905); **111**, 581 (1906). "Theoretical and Applied Colloid Chemistry," translated by Fischer, 103 (1917).

[2] *Koninklijke Akad. Wetenschappen Amsterdam*, **33**, 281 (1924); *Physik. Z.*, **25**, 321 (1924); KATZ and MARK: *Ibid.*, **33**, 294 (1924); *Chem. Zentr.*, **II**, 442 (1924); *Z. physik. Chem.*, **115**, 385 (1925).

range of each other's molecular attraction. From those consid-erations, it would appear that the only essential difference between the solid-solution theory and the two-phase solid-liquid theory is in the size of the particles constituting the network. Since these particles are not infrequently of microscopic dimen-sions, the solid-solution theory cannot be of general application.

The Emulsion Theory.—Wolfgang Ostwald's theory that jellies are simple emulsions of spherical or more or less distorted glob-ules in a liquid medium meets with serious objection at the outset, since there are no emulsions known that have really the properties of jellies. The inorganic jellies certainly could not be looked upon as emulsions particularly in those cases where a rigid crystalline structure has been detected. Recalling the applicability of Boltzmann's theory[1] which considers molecules to be completely elastic material particles incapable of much deformation, and van der Waals' view[2] that the properties of molecules must be compared with those of solids, Zsigmondy[3] assumes, as seems necessary, that the larger ultramicrons of a solid are themselves solid. The liquid properties of gels rich in water are explained by assuming that the ultramicrons are surrounded by water layers and have a certain free path and motion. Hatschek[4] examined the emulsion hypothesis critically and found it untenable if the assumptions necessary to allow of mathematical treatment are granted.

The Cellular or Honeycomb Theory.—The oldest theories of jelly structure were alike in picturing the bodies as two-phase solid-liquid systems; but there has long existed a fundamental difference of opinion as to the exact nature of the solid framework which is assumed to entrain the liquid phase and the manner in which this framework is formed.

From an extended investigation first on foams and emulsions and later on gelatin, agar, and silicic acid jellies, Bütschli[5] concluded that the droplets of liquid were held in a cell-like

---

[1] "Vorlesungen über Gastheorie," Leipsig, 34 (1896).

[2] "Die Kontinuität des gasförmigen und flussigen Zustandes," Leipsig, 34 (1899).

[3] "Chemistry of Colloids," translated by Spear, 138 (1917).

[4] *Trans. Faraday Soc.*, **12**, 17 (1916).

[5] "Untersuchungen über Strukturen," Leipsig (1898).

frameworĸ comparable to a honeycomb, an idea suggested, in all probability, by the cellular structure of the stems of young plants which enclose a relatively high percentage of water and still possess considerable rigidity. The walls of the cells in a silica jelly appeared to be about 0.3 μ in diameter and the pockets which held the liquid from 1 to 1.5μ in diameter. Gelatin jellies that appeared homogeneous under the microscope were hardened with alcohol or chromic acid to make their structure visible, and these likewise appeared to be made up of thin films.

Bütschli's general concept of jelly structure was supported by van Bemmelen,[1] Quincke,[2] and Hardy.[3] According to the latter, gelatin consists of two phases separated by a well-defined surface; one phase a solid solution of gelatin in water and the other a solution of water in gelatine. Like van Bemmelen, he assumes that both phases are liquid at first; but with fall of temperature, one becomes solid. The solid solution forms on the concave side of the surface of separation when the proportion of gelatin is small and on the convex side when the proportion of gelatin is large. In the latter case the drops of liquid are held in a solid gelatin-rich phase. As Bancroft[4] points out, such a jelly consists merely of a viscous medium in which liquid is dispersed and so does not have a honeycomb structure in the same sense that an emulsion has a honeycomb structure. The view entertained by Bancroft is that both phases in a gelatin jelly are colloidal rather than solid solutions. Since water peptizes gelatin under certain conditions, there is no reason why gelatin or a gelatin-rich phase should not peptize water. The separate phases will, therefore, in the nature of things, never be homogeneous.

The investigations of Bütschli, van Bemmelen, and Hardy seemed so conclusive that a decade ago the honeycomb theory was generally looked upon as established.[5] But later investigations of Zsigmondy and his pupils disclosed errors in the optical observations of Bütschli and Hardy and showed the heterogeneity of jellies to be of an entirely different order of magnitude from that

[1] *Z. anorg. Chem.*, **18**, 14 (1898).
[2] *Drude's Ann.*, **9**, 793, 969 (1902); **10**, 478, 673 (1903).
[3] *Z. physik. Chem.*, **33**, 326 (1900).
[4] "Applied Colloid Chemistry," 241 (1921).
[5] *Cf.* FREUNDLICH: "Kapillarchemie," 475 (1909).

which the latter supposed. By applying the laws of capillarity to van Bemmelen's[1] results on the hydration and dehydration of silica gel, Zsigmondy[2] estimated the diameter of the pores to be $0.5\mu\mu$, that is, 200 or 300 times smaller than Bütschli observed. This was confirmed by Anderson[3] who showed that the pores vary in size, some being as small as $10\mu\mu$ in diameter. Working by the same method, Bachmann[4] found that gelatin jellies hardened by alcohol or chromic acid contained very much finer spaces than Bütschli supposed. Apparently the structure observed by Bütschli and Hardy were artifacts produced by the action of the hardening agents on the much finer structure already existing.[5]

In the light of the work of Zsigmondy and his pupils, Lloyd[6] postulates a porous but continuous, solid cellular framework to enclose the liquid. The gelatin is assumed to exist in two chemical states: gelatin, *per se*, and gelatin in the form of soluble salts. On cooling a solution containing isoelectric gelatin and gelatin salts in equilibrium with free electrolytes, the insoluble isoelectric gelatin is believed to precipitate not as crystals but in a state of suspended crystallization forming a solid framework which is kept extended by the osmotic pressure of the soluble gelatin salts in solution. In support of this hypothesis, isoelectric gelatin and water, in the absence of so-called gelatin salts in solution, were found to form an unstable clot that contracted and squeezed out liquid. It would seem, therefore, that an electrolyte must be present to form a stable gelatin jelly in accord with the view of Jordis.[7] J. Alexander[8] suggests that what Lloyd calls "suspended crystallization" may be a manifestation of the protective or crystal-inhibiting action of a portion of the gelatin solution. This would account for the fact that a jelly

---

[1] "Die Absorption," 198 (1910).

[2] *Z. anorg. Chem.*, **71**, 356 (1911).

[3] *Z. physik. Chem.*, **88**, 191 (1914).

[4] *Z. anorg. Chem.*, **100**, 1 (1917).

[5] *Cf.* PAULI: "Der kolloidale Zustand und die Vorgänge in der Lebendigen Substanz," Braunschweig (1902); A. FISCHER: "Fixerung, Färbung, und Bau des Protoplasms," 312 (1899).

[6] *Biochem. J.*, **14**, 165 (1920), *cf.* THOMSON: *J. Soc. Leather Trades' Chem.*, **3**, 299 (1919).

[7] *Z. Elektrochem.*, **8**, 677 (1902).

[8] "Glue and Gelatin," 71 (1923).

formed of isoelectric gelatin and water alone is apparently unstable in the sense that it contracts and squeezes out some of the water. But because of the slight inherent tendency of gelatin to crystallize, it is doubtful whether the alleged increase in stability of a jelly in the presence of a trace of electrolyte is due to inhibition of the crystallization of the gelatin phase. It seems more probable that the presence of an adsorbed ion may influence the nature and size[1] of the agglomerated particles and so may have an effect on the stability. If an electrolyte is necessary to form a stable jelly, the amount is apparently very slight indeed, since Field[2] prepared such a jelly from a very highly purified gelatin. Sheppard and Elliott[3] see no need of postulating the existence of osmotic pressure to keep the jelly extended, if the isoelectric gelatin forms a rigid solid framework.

The Micellar Theory.—The investigations of Zsigmondy and Bachmann which disproved the observations of Bütschli and Hardy resulted in a resuscitation of the micellar theory of Frankenheim[4] and Nägeli.[5] According to this, the earliest theory of jelly structure, distensible bodies were assumed to consist of small anisotropic crystal-like molecular aggregates which retain their identity even when the substance goes into (colloidal) solution. The micelles, as Nägeli called the molecular aggregates, take up water in such a manner that they are surrounded by a water layer, the thickness of which is determined by the relative intensity of the attraction of the micelles for water and for each other. Zsigmondy's earliest investigations with the ultramicroscope led him to conclude with Nägeli that the jelly structure is granular or flocculent; but later, Zsigmondy and Bachmann[6] observed a fibrilar structure in addition to the apparently grainy structure met with in diluted gels of gelatin, agar, and hydrous silica. The fibrils or threads are quite sharply defined in soap jellies studied by Bachmann and later by McBain

[1] Weiser: *J. Phys. Chem.*, **21**, 314 (1917).

[2] *J. Am. Chem. Soc.*, **43**, 667 (1921).

[3] *J. Am. Chem. Soc.*, **44**, 373 (1922).

[4] "Die Lehre von der Kohäsion," Breslau (1835).

[5] "Pfanzenphysiologischen Untersuchungen," Zurich (1858); "Theorie der Garung," Munich (1879).

[6] *Kolloid-Z.*, **11**, 150 (1912).

and his coworkers,[1] and in barium malonate jellies studied by
Flade.[2] The latter noted the crystalline character of the fibrils
and suggested that jellies in general probably consist of a network of crystalline threads.[3] Gortner[4] prepared a jelly of
di-benzoyl-l-cystine which was found to consist of minute
crystalline needle-like fibrils. Büchner[5] showed that jellies,
obtained from myricyl alcohol dissolved in chloroform and in
amyl alcohol, consist of a conglomerate of very fine crystals
which retain a large amount of liquid in the meshes.[6] Bradford[7]
champions the theory that the reversible sol-gel transformation
is merely an extreme case of crystallization. Ultramicroscopic
examination of a gelatin jelly reveals the presence of spherites
which Bradford believes are made up of crystalline particles.
Moeller[8] likewise believes gelatinization to be a kind of crystallization in which there is formed a lattice of crystal threads that
entrains the liquid; and von Weimarn[9] concludes from his investigations that a jelly is a sponge composed of highly dispersed,
crystalline granules soaked in dispersive medium.

While Bradford, Moeller, and von Weimarn may have sufficient evidence to convince them of the crystalline character of all
jellies, it is difficult for me to accept the view that there is no
such thing as an amorphous precipitate of the flocculent, gelatinous or jelly-like type. The theory that jelly formation is merely
a process of crystallization seems to be contradicted by the
work of Bogue, McBain, and Barratt, although all of the latter
are strong supporters of a filamentous structure. Bogue[10] believes
the elastic jellies such as gelatin to be made up of streptococcal

---

[1] LAING and McBAIN: *J. Chem. Soc.*, **117**, 1506 (1920); DARKE, McBAIN,
and SALMON: *Proc. Roy. Soc. (London)*, **98A**, 395 (1921).

[2] *Z. anorg. Chem.*, **82**, 173 (1913).

[3] *Cf.* STÜBEL: *Pflüger's Arch.*, **156**, 361 (1914); HOWELL: *Am. J. Physiol.*,
40, 526 (1916).

[4] *J. Am. Chem. Soc.*, **43**, 2199 (1921).

[5] *Rec. trav. chim.*, **42**, 787 (1923).

[6] *Cf.* FISCHER and BOBERTAG: *Jahresber. schles. Ges. vaterl. Kultur*, **86**, 33
(1909). *Chem. Zentr.*, I, 262 (1909).

[7] *Biochem. J.*, **12**, 351 (1918); **14**, 91 (1920); **15**, 553 (1921).

[8] *Kolloid-Z.*, **23**, 11 (1918).

[9] *J. Russ. Phys.-Chem. Soc.*, **47**, 2163 (1915).

[10] *Chem. Met. Eng.*, **23**, 61 (1920); *J. Am. Chem. Soc.*, **44**, 1343 (1922).

threads of molecules. According to his view, the catenary threads are very short and but slightly swollen in the sol condition, but elongate and absorb a great deal of water as the temperature falls and the sol starts to gel. A solid jelly results when the relative volume occupied by the swollen molecular threads is so great that freedom of motion is lost and the adjacent, heavily swollen aggregates cohere.

Although it is possible for colloidal particles to possess the thread-like characteristics essential for forming an entangling mesh in which each particle is discrete, it seems more probable that in most cases the micelles actually become stuck together or orientated into loose aggregates which may take the form of chance granules, threads, or chains. Such a linking together of the particles to form an enmeshing network seems essential in some of the extremely dilute hydrous oxide jellies to which I shall refer later on. Laing and McBain[1] consider the gelatinization of soap to result from the linking up of colloidal particles to form a filamentous structure. "The colloidal particles in soap and gel are the same; but whereas in the former they are independent, in a fully formed gel they become linked up probably to form a filamentous structure." The formation of the soap curd is looked upon as a phenomenon analogous to crystallization that is distinct from the process of jelly formation.[2] The conception of micellar orientation in the process of gelation is supported by a number of observations mentioned by Laing and McBain, among which are the following: the identity in sol and gel of the electrical conductivity,[3] and the lowering of the vapor pressure; the intensifying of the molecular movement by heat which overcomes the forces holding the particles and causes melting of the gel; the transformation of certain jellies, such as nitrocotton into sol, by mechanical stirring which breaks down the orienting bonds between the particles;[4] the absence of Brownian movement in soap or gelatin jellies;[5] the dependence of the apparent viscosity of sols on their previous treatment and

---

[1] *J. Chem. Soc.*, **117**, 1506 (1920).

[2] *Cf.* PIPER and GRINDLEY: *Proc. Phys. Soc.* (*London*), **35**, 269; **36**, 31 (1923).

[3] *Cf.* ARRHENIUS: *Öefvers. Stockholm Akad.*, **6**, 121 (1887).

[4] *Cf.* ALEXANDER: "Glue and Gelatin," 75 (1923).

[5] BACHMANN: *Z. anorg. Chem.*, **73**, 125 (1912).

history which influence the degree of orientation of their particles;[1] the tendency of the jelly structure to shrink and exude liquid— synerize—as a result of the component of attraction in the orienting force between the particles; and the frequent occurrence of supersaturation and hysteresis with regard to gelation. To these should be added the observation of Walpole[2] that the refractive index of a gelatin-water system is a linear function of the concentration, and when plotted against the temperature, no break occurs at the point of gelation; and the findings of Bogue[3] that the viscosity-plasticity change in the sol-gel transformation is gradual and regular.

Barratt[4] observed in fibrin jellies a non-crystalline fibrillary structure which formed an enmeshing network. When the jelly was first formed by gelatinization of a fibrinogen sol, no fibrils could be detected, but later they became visible in the ultramicroscope. This growth of particles in jellies has been observed frequently and in some cases is unquestionably due to growth of crystals, notably with barium malonate and some of the arsenate jellies[5] and with the dyes, benzopurpurine and chrysophenene;[6] but in other cases, it is the result of the agglomeration of amorphous particles. In accord with this view Scherrer[7] showed that certain rigid jellies like hydrous silicon dioxide and hydrous stannic oxide showed well-defined crystalline interference figures as well as the characteristics of amorphous bodies, whereas gelatin jellies showed no signs of a crystalline structure. Harrison[8] obtained spherical coagulation forms of starch which resembled Bradford's spherites; but he does not regard them as crystalline.

In the course of their investigations, Zsigmondy and Bachmann observed ultramicroscopically the formation of gelatin,

[1] *Cf.* HATSCHEK: *Kolloid-Z.*, **13**, 881 (1913).

[2] *Kolloid-Z.*, **13**, 241 (1913).

[3] *J. Am. Chem. Soc.*, **44**, 1313 (1922).

[4] *Biochem. J.*, **14**, 189 (1920).

[5] DEISZ: *Kolloid-Z.*, **14**, 139 (1914).

[6] HARRISON: "The Physics and Chemistry of Colloids and Their Bearing on Industrial Questions," report of a general discussion held jointly by the Faraday Society and Physical Societies of London, Oct. 25, 57 (1920).

[7] *Nachr. Kgl. Ges. Wiss. Göttingen*, 96 (1918).

[8] *J. Soc. Dyers Colourists*, **32**, 40 (1916).

agar, and silica jellies by agglomeration into flaky groups of freely movable ultramicrons of unknown structure. It is thus implied that all jellies are not necessarily filamentous in structure. This is supported by recent ultramicroscopic observations carried out by Harrison[1] on gelatin and cellulose jellies which were found to consist of minute portions joined together in a somewhat irregular manner. Alexander[2] believes that the formation of chains or threads is not essential to gelation, although chain-like structures may form as a result of orientation of the polar molecules.

Whatever may be the exact structure of jellies, most of the experimental evidence supports the micellar or sponge theory rather than the cellular or honeycomb theory. The presence of definite threads or filaments leaves little room to doubt the existence of an interlacing network structure in certain jellies. It would, of course, be highly interesting, if jellies of widely different substances were all essentially identical in structure. Such a condition seems altogether unlikely; but investigators have apparently sought to establish such an identity. Studies on specific jellies have led some to conclude that all jellies are made up of a framework of amorphous threads; other that they are composed of crystalline threads; and still others who fail to find any threads or filaments at all but observe an irregular grouping of particles. Doubtless all are right in specific cases. Indeed, it is not unlikely that there are various arrangements of molecular aggregates in different jellies and perhaps in the same jelly. In a heterogeneous mixture of complex groups such as are found in gelatin sol or jelly, it is probable that the process of gelation and the jelly structure are more complex than in the inorganic jellies or in soap jellies. The orientation of the particles may result in fibrils in certain cases and in more or less irregular arrangements in others. In certain cases the fibrils may consist of definite crystals, while in others the crystalline characteristics may be entirely lacking. In all cases it seems probable that the particles are highly hydrous as a result of adsorption or absorption and that they are linked together, forming an irregular mesh or network in the interstices of which liquid is entrained.

[1] "The Physics and Chemistry of Colloids and Their Bearing on Industrial Problems," 57 (1920).
[2] "Glue and Gelatin," 84 (1923).

We may next inquire into the structure of gelatinous precipitates. Since a gelatinous precipitate differs from a jelly only in having undergone contraction with the consequent excretion of liquid, the two types of gels are generally considered to be quite similar in structure. Recent investigations of the physical character of bodies by means of x-rays confirm von Weimarn's contention that many gelatinous precipitates, such as hydrous alumina and ferric oxide, which we used to think were amorphous, are, in reality, made of myriads of tiny crystals. This naturally raises the question whether the submicroscopic crystals are themselves gelatinous and so impart the gelatinous property to the mass. Unfortunately, von Weimarn does not enlighten us on this point; but it is apparently possible to have gelatinous crystals. Thus Harrison[1] speaks of aqueous solutions of benzo-purpurine and chrysophenene setting to jellies containing gelatinous crystals, some of them so fine that they can pass unbroken through a filter paper. Similarly, cholic acid gives a blue precipitate with iodine which may form in clusters of needle crystals possessing rigidity. Under other conditions needle-shaped crystals are formed which are gelatinous and can be bent in all kinds of shapes by moving the cover glass on the microscope slide. Some of these so-called gelatinous crystals show remarkable vibrations due to the impact of the molecules and move about like the spiral bacteria present on the teeth. Harrison's observations seem to throw some light on the problem of what constitutes a gelatinous crystal or aggregate and hence on the related problem of what is a gelatinous precipitate.

Le Chatelier[2] succeeded in polishing metal with colloidal silicic acid and hence concluded that the gelatinous precipitate consists of anhydrous silica and water. Bancroft[3] considers this evidence inconclusive since anhydrous silica may have been formed as a result of pressure during polishing, and suggests that a better method of attack is to consider whether grains of sand mixed with water will give a gelatinous precipitate. Since this does not happen, as a rule, Bancroft concludes:

[1] "The Physics and Chemistry of Colloids and their Bearing on Industrial Problems," 58 (1920).
[2] "La Silice et les Silicates," 76 (1914).
[3] "Applied Colloid Chemistry," 236 (1921).

We must therefore assume one of two things. Either the sand grains are held together extraordinarily firmly by water when they are very fine, or there is some other factor comes in. The first explanation cannot be the right one because, if it were, one ought then to be able to get a gelatinous precipitate of any colloid at ordinary temperatures without much difficulty, which is not the case. We never get gelatinous gold, and while we can get gelatinous calcium carbonate, we have to do it in a very special way. Consequently, Le Chatelier's hypothesis cannot be accepted without modification.

As previously noted, Zsigmondy[1] explains the liquid character of gels rich in water by assuming the ultramicrons to be surrounded by water layers and to have a certain free path and motion. The objection to this view is that Zsigmondy does not show why it should be so. Harrison's observations on gelatinous crystals bear on this point. Gelatinous crystals are apparently extremely fine, needle-shaped masses so thin that they lack rigidity and so flexible that they can be bent and twisted into various shapes and may move under the bombardment of water molecules. A cluster or network of such needle-shaped, flexible crystals that adsorb water strongly would form a viscous or plastic mass, usually known as a gelatinous precipitate. If the crystals are compact and rigid rather than thin and flexible, they would not form a gelatinous precipitate unless they united into threads or strings possessing the flexibility and elasticity which characterizes a thin needle crystal. Obviously the particles need not be crystalline, and as a rule they probably are not. A gelatinous precipitate is apparently a network composed of extremely finely divided particles which have coalesced to form flexible filaments or chains and which adsorb water very strongly and so are highly hydrous. Where the particles do not adsorb water particularly strongly and where the tendency to coalesce into filaments or threads is not great, a high concentration of the finely divided particles is necessary, as in the case of calcium carbonate and barium sulfate. It is probable that neither tendency is very marked in the case of gold, which accounts for the fact that no one has prepared a gold jelly. I am not aware, however, that anyone has attempted to precipitate a fairly large amount

[1] ZSIGMONDY: "Chemistry of Colloids," translated by Spear 138 (1917).

of gold in a small volume, as von Weimarn does with barium sulfate. While a gelatinous precipitate of gold has not yet been prepared, this might be a fairly simple process if the metal were dispersed in some liquid, other than water, which is very strongly adsorbed by gold. Börjeson[1] working in Svedberg's laboratory, prepared a cadmium jelly by allowing a very dilute sol of cadmium in alcohol to stand for some time in a glass bottle. In this case the particles were only $5\mu\mu$ in radius and the concentration but 0.2 to 0.5 per cent. Barium sulfate is readily obtained in a gelatinous form by precipitation in selenium oxychloride.[2] The physical character of the precipitate is due to very strong adsorption of selenium oxychloride by the minute particles which form as a result of the extreme insolubility of the sulfate in the liquid medium.

PREPARATION

If we start out with the assumption that a gel consists of myriads of particles enmeshed into a network which entrains liquid, it follows that any substance should form a gel, provided a suitable amount of a highly dispersed substance is precipitated and provided the particles adsorb the dispersing medium very strongly. The amount of the dispersed phase that must be present to form a firm jelly by a precipitation method will depend on the size and nature of the orientation of the particles and the extent to which they adsorb the dispersing liquid. The methods of procedure which have been employed will be considered separately.

Cooling of Sol.—Certain substances such as gelatin and agar-agar swell in water at ordinary temperatures but are not peptized, forming a sol, until the temperature is raised. At the higher temperature, the liquid phase serves the double role of peptizing agent and dispersing medium. On cooling such a sol, a jelly is formed provided the concentration is suitable.

---

[1] "The Physics and Chemistry of Colloids and their Bearing on Industrial Problems," 55 (1920).

[2] LENHER and TAYLOR: *J. Phys. Chem.*, **28**, 962 (1924).

Thus a sol containing 1 per cent of pure gelatin does not gel until around 10°, and gelation does not take place at any concentration above ±35°.   According to Bachmann,[1] pure warm solutions of gelatin are almost homogeneous, but on cooling, a new phase appears, as evidenced by a heterogeneity that is amicroscopic or submicroscopic, depending on the concentration. This process is similar in certain respects to crystallization but differs from it in that microns, submicrons, ultramicrons, and amicrons are formed according to the concentration.   The appearance of visible particles is not dependent on the formation of a jelly, as these may be seen before the jelly sets and in dilute solutions that do not set.   When a jelly results on cooling a sol, the process apparently consists in the formation of highly hydrous molecular aggregates which are linked together to form a more or less rigid network.   Bogue believes that the aggregates not only grow but become more hydrous on cooling. This might be expected in view of the rapid increase in adsorption which usually results from lowering the temperature.   The sol-gel transformation in a given system does not occur at a definite transition point, but the transition is continuous and reversible over a somewhat indefinite period.[2]

Swelling. Non-aqueous Gels.—Practically all substances which form the so-called elastic gels show the capacity of swelling in a suitable liquid.   Thus dry gelatin, fibrin, and starch will swell in water at ordinary temperature, forming jellies that are peptized at higher temperatures giving sols.   Similarly, albumin swells in water but not in alcohol, benzene, ether, or turpentine.   Vulcanized india rubber swells in various organic solvents such as benzene, toluene, and xylene but not in water; and soaps swell in water and in many organic solvents.   Numerous theories[3] have been advanced to explain the phenomenon, but there is as yet no explanation to account for the fact that certain substances swell in only a limited number of liquids. The swelling of gelatin has been studied most extensively and has been found to depend on a number of factors, among which

[1] Z. anorg. Chem., **73**, 125 (1911).

[2] BOGUE: J. Am. Chem. Soc., **44**, 1313 (1922).

[3] These theories have been summarized and their limitations pointed out in a paper by BARTELL and SIMS: J. Am. Chem. Soc., **44**, 289 (1922).

may be mentioned the hydrogen ion concentration;[1] the addition of neutral salts;[2] the temperature; and the structure.[3]

The importance of the hydrogen ion concentration on the swelling phenomenon was suggested by Ostwald and has been emphasized particularly by Procter and Wilson and by Loeb, who have applied Donnan's theory of membrane equilibria in interpreting the mechanism of the swelling process. Before taking up the Procter-Wilson theory of swelling, the theory of membrane equilibria on which the former is based will be considered briefly.

Donnan's theory of membrane equilibria[4] deals with the equilibria resulting when a membrane separates two electrolytes containing 1 ion which cannot diffuse through the membrane. Starting with two completely ionized electrolytes, (1) NaCl and (2) NaR, separated by a membrane impermeable to the ion R', Donnan shows that equilibrium will be established only when the product of the concentration of sodium and chloride ions has the same value on both sides of the membranes, thus,

$$[Na^{\cdot}]_1 \times [Cl']_1 = [Na^{\cdot}]_2 \times [Cl']_2$$

the brackets signifying concentration in mols per liter, and the subscripts 1 and 2 referring to solution 1 and solution 2, respectively. This is the so-called equation of products based on the distribution law.

For the specific case cited above, the equation of products may take a somewhat different form. Thus, at the outset, the system of two solutions separated by a membrane may be represented as follows:

Solution 1	Solution 2
$[Na^{\cdot}][Cl']$	$[Na^{\cdot}][R']$

---

[1] CHIARI: *Biochem. Z.*, **33**, 167 (1911); PROCTER: *J. Chem. Soc.*, **105**, 313 (1914); LOEB: *J. Gen. Physiol.*, **1**, 41 (1918).

[2] HOFMEISTER: *Arch. exptl. Path. Pharmakol.*, **27**, 395 (1890); **28**, 210 (1891); PAULI: Pflüger's Arch., **67**, 219 (1897); **71**, 333 (1898); SPIRO: *Beiträge zur chem. Physiol.*, **5**, 276 (1904); WOLFGANG OSTWALD: *Pflüger's Arch.*, **108**, 563 (1905); FISCHER: *"Edema,"* New York (1910).

[3] PROCTER and BURTON: *J. Soc. Chem. Ind.*, **35**, 404 (1916); ARISZ: *Kolloidchem. Beihefte*, **7**, 42 (1915).

[4] *Z. Elektrochem.*, **17**, 572 (1911).

On allowing the system to stand, the diffusible sodium and chloride ions distribute themselves until equilibrium is established. At equilibrium in solution 1, let

$$x = [\text{Na}^{\cdot}] = [\text{Cl}']$$

and at equilibrium in solution 2 let

$$y = [\text{Cl}']$$

and $$z = [\text{R}']$$

hence, $$(y + z) = [\text{Na}^{\cdot}]$$

Thus we have

Solution 1	Solution 2
$x_{\text{Na}^{\cdot}} \cdot x_{\text{Cl}'}$	$(y + z)_{\text{Na}^{\cdot}} \cdot y_{\text{Cl}'} \cdot z_{\text{R}'}$

and the equation of products is

$$x^2 = y(y + z)$$

In solution 1, $x_{\text{Na}^{\cdot}} = x_{\text{Cl}'}$, while in solution 2, $y_{\text{Na}^{\cdot}} + z_{\text{Na}^{\cdot}} = y_{\text{Cl}'}$; but since the product of the concentrations in solution 1 is the same as the product of the concentrations in solution 2, it must follow that

$$x_{\text{Na}^{\cdot}} + x_{\text{Cl}'} < y_{\text{Na}^{\cdot}} + y_{\text{Cl}'} + z_{\text{Na}^{\cdot}}$$

or $$2x < 2y + z$$

In other words, at equilibrium, the concentration of diffusible ions in solution 2 is greater than in solution 1. Now, if we let

$$e = (2y + z) - 2x$$

then $$2y + z = e + 2x$$

and the equation of products becomes

$$x = y + \sqrt{ey}$$

which shows again that sodium chloride does not distribute itself equally, but the concentration of the ionized sodium chloride at equilibrium is greater in solution 1 than in solution 2. This gives rise to an osmotic-pressure difference as well as to a difference in potential across the membrane. The equation for this potential difference was derived by Donnan in the following way:

Let π_1 and π_2 be the potential for positive electricity in solution 1 and solution 2, respectively, in the above mentioned system;

and let the minute amount of positive electricity Fdn be transferred isothermally from solution 2 to solution 1. This process involves a change in free electrical energy represented by Fdn $(\pi_1 - \pi_2)$ and the simultaneous transfer of udn mols of Na· from solution 2 to solution 1 and of vdn mols of Cl′ from solution 1 to solution 2, where u and v are the transport numbers of the respective ions. The maximum osmotic work involved in the transfer of the ions is given by the expression

$$udn\ RT\ log_e\ \frac{[\text{Na}\cdot]_2}{[\text{Na}\cdot]_1} + vdn\ RT\ log_e\ \frac{[\text{Cl}′]_1}{[\text{Cl}′]_2}$$

Since the system is in equilibrium, the electrical work is equivalent to the osmotic work, or

$$Fdn\ (\pi_1 - \pi_2) = udn\ RT\ log_e\ \frac{[\text{Na}\cdot]_2}{[\text{Na}\cdot]_1} + vdn\ RT\ log_e\ \frac{[\text{Cl}′]_1}{[\text{Cl}′]_2}$$

But $\dfrac{[\text{Na}\cdot]_2}{[\text{Na}\cdot]_1} = \dfrac{[\text{Cl}′]_1}{[\text{Cl}′]_2} = \dfrac{x}{y}$ and $u + v = 1$

Hence, if $E = \pi_1 - \pi_2$

$$E = \frac{RT}{F}\ log\ \frac{x}{y}$$

It may be shown that this equation is valid even when other ions of any valence are added to the system. Donnan has tested the accuracy of the equation in the following cases: (1) Congo red and sodium chloride; (2) potassium chloride and potassium ferricyanide; (3) sodium arsenate and sodium chloride. In every instance there is fairly good agreement between the calculated and experimental values. Donnan has also applied the same general principles to such cases as NaA and KA, and NaA and CaA$_2$, in which the membrane is impermeable to the ion A′.

The Procter-Wilson Theory of Swelling.[1]—To account for the swelling of gelatin, Procter and Wilson assume that hydrochloric acid, say, combines with gelatin forming a readily soluble high-ionized salt, gelatin chloride, and that the resulting equilibrium is a special case of the Donnan membrane equilibria. To make the

---

[1] PROCTER: *J. Chem. Soc.,* **105**, 313 (1914); *Kolloidchem. Beihefte,* **2**, 243 (1911); PROCTER and WILSON: *J. Chem. Soc.,* **109**, 307 (1916); WILSON and WILSON: *J. Am. Chem. Soc.,* **40**, 886 (1918).

reasoning general, a protein G is supposed to react with an acid HA in accord with the following equation:

$$G + H^{\cdot} + A' = GH^{\cdot} + A'$$

Hence, if a millimol, say, of G is immersed in a solution of HA, the solution penetrates the jelly which combines with a part of the $H^{\cdot}$ ions giving $GH^{\cdot}$. In this way the concentration of $H^{\cdot}$ ions within the jelly is reduced below that of the A' ion; whereas in the solution surrounding the jelly, the concentrations of the two ions are necessarily equal. Thus the solution is separated into two phases, an external phase with the two diffusible ions $H^{\cdot}$ and A' and a jelly phase containing the diffusible ion A' and the ion $GH^{\cdot}$ which is a part of the elastic jelly structure and so cannot diffuse. This constraint imposes a restraint on the equal distribution of ions within and without the jelly. When equilibrium is established, in the external phase, let

$$x = [H^{\cdot}] = [A']$$

and in the jelly let

$$y = [H^{\cdot}]$$

and

$$z = [GH^{\cdot}]$$

From which

$$[A'] = y + z$$

Since the product $[H^{\cdot}] \times [A']$ will have the same value in both phases at equilibrium, it follows that

$$x^2 = y(y + z)$$

If, as before, we let

$$e = 2y + z - 2x$$

then

$$x = y + \sqrt{ey}$$

This shows x to be greater than y, which means that $[H^{\cdot}]$ is greater outside the jelly than in it. From this it follows that $[A']$ is greater in the jelly than in the external solution. For this reason the anions of the protein salt will tend to diffuse outward into the external phase. This exerts a pull on the cations $GH^{\cdot}$ forming part of the protein framework, and causes an increase in the volume of the jelly directly proportional to e, the excess of concentration of diffusible ions of the jelly over that of the external solution.

Procter and Wilson have tested this theory experimentally in the case of gelatin and hydrochloric acid, and have found good agreement between observed and calculated values. Moreover, Loeb and Kunitz[1] showed that all monobasic acids produce approximately the same degree of swelling at the same hydrogen ion concentration, as the theory predicts.

The addition to acid-swollen jellies of neutral salts, such as MA, neither of whose ions combine with the protein as hydrogen ion is supposed to do, increases the cation concentration y in the jelly but not the alleged gelatin cation concentration z. This decreases the excess of diffusible ions inside the jelly over that outside and so decreases the swelling, as observed experimentally.

The application of the Donnan theory of membrane equilibria to the swelling of gelatin is certainly a step forward in explaining the mechanism of the swelling process, although it is apparently inapplicable to such cases as the swelling of rubber in benzene or xylene, where the existence of a Donnan equilibrium is precluded by the absence of dissociation. Moreover, it is a serious mistake to conclude, as some have done, that prediction of results by means of a formula proves the assumptions on which the formula is based. Procter, Wilson, and Loeb assume a definite chemical combination between gelatin and hydrochloric acid with the formation of a highly ionized salt, gelatin chloride, which gives a non-diffusible cation $GH^{\cdot}$. The mathematical formulas deduced from this hypothesis do not prove its correctness, for one can get exactly the same formulas and make exactly the same predictions by making the more probable assumption that hydrogen ion is preferentially adsorbed on the surface of gelatin particles rather than entering into definite chemical combination with the particles. This is recognized clearly by Donnan:[2]

Very many interesting investigations based on this simple theory have been made by Jacques Loeb and his collaborators. In this work, among other things, the effects of acids, alkalies, and salts on the osmotic pressures and membrane potentials of the amphoteric proteins have been studied. Loeb has shown that the simple theory of membrane equilibria is capable of accounting fairly quantitatively for a great many of his experimental results, and regards this as a proof that the phenomena exhibited by the protein ampholytes are due to simple chemical reactions and not to the adsorption of ions by colloid aggre-

---

[1] *J. Gen. Physiol.*, **5**, 665, 693 (1923).
[2] *Chem. Reviews*, **1**, 87 (1924).

gates or micelles. While this view may be correct in many instances, it is necessary to remember that the theory of membrane equilibria depends simply on two assumptions: (*a*) the existence of equilibrium; (*b*) the existence of certain constraints which restrict the free diffusion of one or more electrically charged or ionized constituents; and that the equations which result from the theory will hold equally well whether we have to deal with "colloid units" which have acquired an ionic character (electrical charge) by adsorption of ions, or with simple molecules which have become ionized by the loss or gain of electrons. All that is necessary for the theory is that the simple ionized molecules of the ionic micelles be subjected to the same constraint, namely, inability to diffuse freely through the membrane. This constraint then imposes a restraint on the equal distribution on both sides of the membrane of otherwise freely diffusible ions, thus giving rise to the concentration, osmotic, and electrical effects with which the theory deals.

The investigations of Loeb led him to conclude that only the anions of neutral salts are taken up by gelatin on the acid side of the so-called isoelectric point of gelatin (pH $= 4.6$) and only cations on the alkaline side. This conclusion is hardly justified by Loeb's experiments since, throughout most of the range investigated, he was working with relatively low concentrations of salts and so detected no effect of cations other than hydrogen on the acid side and of anions other than hydroxyl on the basic side. At relatively high concentrations of neutral salts, the specific effect of cations other than hydrogen and of anions other than hydroxyl would doubtless appear. This inference is supported by work carried out in the author's laboratory on the adsorption of anions by hydrous chromic oxide on the alkaline side of the isoelectric point. If the concentration of the anion under consideration is very large relatively to that of hydroxyl, the effect of the latter is negligible, whereas if the hydroxyl ion concentration is appreciable, the adsorption of the other ion is cut down enormously or completely nullified.[1]

As noted above, the dehydration and swelling of a gelatin jelly is reversible over a considerable range. This is not the case with hydrous oxide jellies such as silica. Van Bemmelen[2]

---

[1] *Cf.* MICHAELIS: *Colloid Symposium Monograph*, **2**, 1 (1924); STIASNY: *Kolloid-Z.*, **35**, 353 (1924).

[2] "Die Absorption" (1910).

showed that a silica gel containing a great deal of water shrinks very much when the water is removed; and, while it will take up some water again, the volume change is not reversible. If the drying is carried sufficiently far, pores are developed that are filled with air, and these pores can then be filled with a liquid other than water; but there is no appreciable swelling. When gelatin is dried, such pores are not developed and a dry gel of natural gelatin will not adsorb benzene.

Although the porous mass formed by drying a non-elastic gel will not swell in organic liquids, Graham found that such liquids will replace the water in a jelly. Thus a silica gel containing 11 per cent SiO_2 was suspended repeatedly in alcohol, and an alcogel was formed having approximately the same volume as the original gel. In a similar way the water was replaced by inorganic and organic acids. Van Bemmelen substituted acetone for the water and Bachmann[1] put in benzene. Neuhausen and Patrick[2] found that the replacement of water was not quite so complete as Graham reported on repeated immersions of a silica jelly in anhydrous alcohol or benzol. Elastic jellies show a similar behavior. Thus Bütschli[3] found it comparatively easy to replace the water in a gelatin jelly with alcohol and this again by chloroform, turpentine, or xylene, even though dry gelatin does not swell in these liquids.

Concentrated Gels.—Many difficultly soluble salts that ordinarily precipitate in relatively large crystals can be thrown out in the form of a gelatinous precipitate or jelly from very concentrated solutions. This phenomenon was observed by Hartung,[4] Büchner,[5] Biedermann,[6] Neuberg,[7] and particularly by von Weimarn.[8] The latter[9] made a systematic study of the form in which substances precipitate from solution. He calls attention to a

[1] *Z. anorg. Chem.*, **73**, 125 (1912).

[2] *J. Am. Chem. Soc.*, **43**, 1844 (1921).

[3] "Uber den Bau quellbarer Körper," Göttingen, 22 (1896).

[4] "Recherches de morphologic synthétique sur la production artificielle de quelques formations calcaries organiques," Amsterdam (1872).

[5] *Chem. Ztg.*, **17**, 878 (1893).

[6] *Z. allgem. Physiol.*, **1**, 154 (1902).

[7] *Sitzb. Akad. Wiss. Berlin*, 820 (1907).

[8] "Zur Lehre von den Zuständen der Materie" (1914).

[9] Von Weimarn: "Grundzüge der Dispersoidchemie," 39 (1911).

number of very different factors on which precipitation depends: the solubility of the substance; the latent heat of precipitation; the concentration at which the precipitation takes place; the normal pressure at the surface of the solvent; and the molecular weights of the solvent and the solute. He points out the impossibility of taking all of these factors into account and simplifies the problem by considering, first, but two of the factors: the solubility of the precipitating substances, and the concentration at which precipitation begins. The effect of viscosity is discussed briefly in a later work.[1] The process of condensation (precipitation) is divided into two parts: the first stage, in which the molecules condense to invisible or ultramicroscopic crystals; and the second, which is concerned with the growth of the particles as a result of diffusion. The velocity at the important first moment of the first stage of the precipitation is formulated thus:

$$W = K \frac{\text{Condensation pressure}}{\text{Condensation resistance}} = K \frac{Q - L}{L} = K \frac{P}{L} = KU$$

where W is the initial rate of precipitation; Q the total concentration of the substance that is to precipitate; L the solubility of coarse crystals of the substance; $Q - L = P$ the amount of supersaturation. The ratio $\frac{P}{L} = U$ is the precentage supersaturation at the moment precipitation begins.

The velocity of the second stage is given by the Nernst-Noyes equation:

$$V = \frac{D}{S} \cdot O \cdot (C - l)$$

where D is the diffusion coefficient; S the thickness of the adherent film; O the surface; C the concentration of the surrounding solution; and l the solubility of the dispersed phase for a given degree of dispersity. $C - l$ may be termed the absolute supersaturation.

From these general formulations, von Weimarn arrives at the conclusion that jellies are obtained only when the ratio $\frac{P}{L}$, that is, the percentage supersaturation U, can be made enormous. It is pointed out that the nature of a precipitate is quite different,

[1] VON WEIMARN: *Kolloidchem. Beihefte*, **4**, 101 (1912).

depending on whether a given value of U is obtained by a large P or by a small L.   If a large U is obtained by a high value of P, a large amount of disperse phase is produced and a gel forms, while if P is small and L very small, a relatively small amount of disperse phase is produced and a sol is formed.   Von Weimarn has demonstrated the accuracy of his deductions in a large number of cases, using reacting solutions of high concentrations; and it is apparently true that any salt can be obtained in a gelatinous form if the concentration of the reacting solutions and so the velocity of precipitation is sufficiently high.   Thus, von Weimarn[1] prepared gelatinous precipitates of barium sulfate which usually comes down in the form of crystals, by mixing 1 to 3 N solutions of manganese sulfate and barium thiocyanate.   By using solutions of sufficiently high concentration (3 to $7N$) all the solute was enclosed, forming jellies.   These are not the conditions under which jellies are usually obtained, and their existence is temporary. By mixing very high concentrations of materials that react to form an insoluble precipitate, a very large number of relatively small particles are formed, because of the high degree of supersaturation.[2]   Each of these minute particles adsorbs a little water and as they are very close together, a semisolid mass results that entrains all the liquid phase, thus forming what has been termed a jelly.   These so-called jellies break down on standing, on account of growth of the particles and the consequent liberation of adsorbed water.   I do not believe that precipitates in which the ratio of mols of water to mols of salt is, say, 20:1 or 25:1 should be considered as jellies in the same sense as precipitates in which this ratio is two or three hundred times as great.   Very finely divided sand or fuller's earth may be matted in the bottom of a test tube, and this solid will take up a great deal of water before a supernatant water layer is observed; but I should not call such a preparation a jelly.   It seems to me that von Weimarn's barium sulfate jelly may be similar except that the particles are much smaller, and so a given amount will take up more water.   On the other hand, with true jellies where the amount of enclosed water may be relatively enormous, time must be allowed for

[1] "Zur Lehre von den Zuständen der Materie," 21 (1914).
[2] BANCROFT: *J. Phys. Chem.*, **24**, 100 (1920).

formation of a definite structure. As a matter of fact, von Weimarn[1] recognized a difference between a barium sulfate jelly prepared by his method and a jelly formed by uniform gelatinization of a liquid throughout its mass, as in the case of gelatin jelly. The former he terms a "coarsely cellular gel" and the latter a "reticulated gel."

Precipitation of Sol.—Since finely divided particles that adsorb water strongly are of primary importance for the formation of a hydrous jelly, it would seem that the most promising method of preparing dilute jellies would be to precipitate hydrous substances from colloidal solution. The von Weimarn theory would tell us, of course, that this precipitation would have to take place at a suitable rate under conditions that are not conducive to growth of the individual particles; but it does not enable us to predict the optimum rate of coagulation, the effect of salts on jelly formation, or the conditions that favor the formation of a jelly rather than a gelatinous precipitate. As a result of recent investigations in the author's laboratory on the formation of typical dilute inorganic jellies, the hydrous oxides particularly, it is possible to outline the general conditions of jelly formation and the effect on the process of various factors other than the percentage supersaturation "at the important first moment of the first stage of condensation" from molecules to invisible particles. Jellies would be expected to form from colloidal solution if a suitable amount is precipitated at a suitable rate without agitation in the absence of a medium that exerts an appreciable solvent or peptizing action. If the concentration of the colloid is too low, no jelly or only a very soft jelly can result. If the velocity of precipitation is too great, contraction is likely to occur with the formation of a gelatinous precipitate instead of a jelly. The effect of the presence of salts on jelly formation is, therefore, determined in large measure by the precipitating and stabilizing action of the ions in so far as these affect the rate of precipitation. In general, a slow rate of precipitation favors the formation of a jelly rather than a gelatinous precipitate if there is little or no tendency of the particles to grow as a result of the solvent action of the electrolyte. The favorable concentration for different electrolytes is in the immediate region of their

[1] *J. Russ. Phys.-Chem. Soc.*, **47**, 2163 (1915).

precipitation concentration. A little below this value, no precipitation or only a slight precipitation takes place; while above this value, coagulation is usually so rapid that a gelatinous precipitate is formed instead of a jelly. The reason is that time is not allowed for the uniform mixing of the colloid with coagulant, and the slow uniform precipitation necessary for the building of a uniform jelly structure is replaced by rapid uneven coagulation and the consequent contraction that distinguishes a gelatinous precipitate from a jelly.

The accuracy of these deductions has been demonstrated repeatedly, and frequent reference will be made to them in later chapters. In many cases, these jellies may be obtained in relatively low concentrations. A notable example is the case of hydrous chromic oxide which formed a firm jelly containing but 0.18 per cent Cr_2O_3 and a soft jelly containing 0.09 per cent Cr_2O_3. The formation of such dilute jellies can result only when the particles are very hydrous and when the conditions of precipitation allow time for the building up of an enmeshing network. In case the particles are but slightly hydrous and show but little tendency to link together into threads, extremely high concentrations must be present, as von Weimarn found.

Dialysis of Sols.—Prolonged dialysis of colloidal solutions frequently leads to the precipitation of a part of the suspended phase as a gelatinous precipitate. When this process was carried out in a suitable way on a colloidal solution of ferric arsenate peptized by ferric chloride, Grimaux[1] obtained a firm, transparent jelly. This observation has been confirmed and extended by Holmes and his pupils.[2] Similar observations have been made in the author's laboratory with hydrous oxides of chromium and aluminum, and the method is probably a general one. From the point of view outlined in the foregoing section, the formation of jellies by dialysis of a colloidal hydrous substance is readily understood. Dialysis merely removes the stabilizing ion slowly and uniformly below the critical value necessary for peptization; and precipitation results just as if the adsorption of the stabilizing

---

[1] *Compt. rend.*, **98**, 1540 (1884).

[2] HOLMES and RINDFUSZ: *J. Am. Chem. Soc.*, **38**, 1970 (1916); HOLMES and ARNOLD: *Ibid.*, **40**, 1014 (1918); HOLMES and FALL: *Ibid.*, **41**, 763 (1919).

ion were compensated for or neutralized by the addition of an electrolyte having a suitable precipitating ion. The accuracy of these deductions has been demonstrated conclusively in a series of investigations on the arsenates of iron and aluminum.[1]

Dilute Jellies by Metathesis.—According to the von Weimarn theory, mixing dilute solutions that interact at once may give a gelatinous precipitate but not a jelly, since the percentage supersaturation $\dfrac{P}{L} = U$ is too small because of the small value of P. As a matter of fact, however, jellies have been obtained under certain conditions by mixing very dilute solutions in which L is sufficiently large that precipitation is slow and quantitative precipitation impossible, so that $\dfrac{P}{L} = U$ is very small. Such cases are apparently not covered by the von Weimarn theory. It is quite possible to obtain a gelatinous precipitate by mixing dilute solutions of two salts which precipitate immediately (P small, but L very small); but a jelly will not form under these conditions. The reason is evident when we consider the impossibility of getting the instantaneous mixing of the solutions which is essential for uniform precipitation throughout the mixture. One part is precipitated before another is mixed with the precipitant, and the uniformity characteristic of a jelly is lost. Moreover, the mixing itself will tend to destroy the jelly structure. The results are, therefore, not unlike those obtained when a colloid capable of forming a jelly by slow precipitation is coagulated too rapidly by the addition of excess electrolyte. To obtain a jelly from a colloidal solution, it is necessary to add such an amount of electrolyte that thorough mixing is possible before appreciable coagulation takes place. From these considerations, it follows that precipitation of a hydrous substance as a result of double decomposition might form a jelly instead of a gelatinous precipitate in case the thorough mixing of the solutions could be effected before precipitation begins and in case the precipitation, once started, proceeds at a suitable rate. Such conditions do not obtain as a rule; but they are entirely possible theoretically. Thus the precipitation

---

[1] Weiser and Bloxsom: *J. Phys. Chem.*, **28**, 26 (1924).

may be the result of a stepwise process, one step of which proceeds at a suitably slow rate. It is further possible to have a reaction that goes very slowly at low temperatures but with marked velocity at higher temperatures. This would not only allow of mixing without precipitation but would enable one to control the subsequent rate of reaction by a suitable regulation of the temperature. Such a favorable combination of circumstances apparently obtains when a manganese salt of a strong acid and KH_2AsO_4 are mixed. The latter salt ionizes thus: $KH_2AsO \leftrightarrows K^{\cdot} + H_2AsO_4{}'$; but on account of the solubility of $Mn(H_2AsO_4)_2$, no $Mn^{\cdot\cdot}$ ions are removed from solution by interaction with $H_2AsO_4{}'$. The latter ion, however, undergoes secondary ionization to a slight degree as follows: $H_2AsO_4{}' \leftrightarrows H^{\cdot} + HAsO_4{}''$; and insoluble $MnHAsO_4$ is formed in accord with the reaction: $Mn^{\cdot\cdot} + HAsO_4{}'' = MnHASO_4$.[1]

Since the precipitation of $MnHAsO_4$ is accompanied by the formation of an equivalent amount of free hydrogen ion in solution, an equilibrium is set up which prevents the complete precipitation of the manganese. However, the amount of $MnHAsO_4$ formed and the rate of formation by the above process are influenced to a marked degree by the temperature, so that it is possible to obtain good jellies by mixing dilute solutions of the necessary salts in the cold and allowing the mixture to stand at room temperature or warming to a suitable temperature. This has been demonstrated with the arsenates of manganese, cobalt, iron, cadmium, and zinc.[2] When the precipitated particles are very highly hydrous and when the tendency to crystallize is slight, very dilute jellies may be prepared by this method. Thus a firm jelly is formed with 0.5 per cent and soft jelly with but 0.25 per cent $MnHAsO_4$. A microscopic examination of this jelly shows that it consists of filaments or fibrils. Here again, the time factor is important for the formation of an enmeshing network of hydrous filaments.

Favorable conditions for the precipitation of a jelly may be realized by the slow hydrolysis of a suitable salt. Thus if a solution of aluminum sulfate is poured on a few iron turnings,

[1] Deisz: *Kolloid-Z.*, **14**, 139 (1914).
[2] Weiser: *J. Phys. Chem.*, **28**, 26 (1924).

slow hydrolysis takes place, with the ultimate formation of a firm hydrous aluminum oxide jelly.[1]

VAPOR-PRESSURE RELATIONS

Freshly precipitated gelatinous oxides, such as the hydrous oxides of iron, chromium, aluminum, tin, and silicon, have a vapor pressure almost the same as water and maintain it until the water content of the gels is lowered quite appreciably. Van Bemmelen[2] has examined a large number of such oxides and has found the loss of water in dry air to be continuous, the vapor-pressure curve showing no breaks such as would be expected if definite chemical compounds—hydrates—were formed. Formulas for definite hydrates of precipitated oxides are frequently given in the literature, but in the vast majority of cases, the composition indicated by these formulas is purely accidental, depending as it does on so many factors, such as the conditions of formation, the method of drying, and the age.[3] In general, it may be said that the metallic oxides precipitated in a highly gelatinous form are never hydrates, so that they should be looked upon as hydrous oxides rather than hydrous hydrated oxides. This does not mean that there are no hydrates of the metallic oxides, for there are a few, among which may be mentioned $Fe_2O_3 \cdot H_2O$ and $Al_2O_3 \cdot 3H_2O$; but, as a rule, these must be prepared in a special way.

Four general types of vapor-pressure-composition curves may be distinguished.[4] These are represented diagramatically in Fig. 1. Curve I is typical of the crystalline hydrates of which $MoO_3 \cdot 2H_2O$ is an example. Curve II likewise indicates the formation of a hydrate, although the steps in the curve are not so sharp as in curve I. The absence of sharp breaks even when definite hydrates are formed is accounted for by assuming that a part of the hydrate water is held definitely in place in the crystal lattice while a part may move about in the crystal lattice with

---

[1] CUSHMANN and COGGESHALL: *Trans. Am. Electrochem. Soc.*, **39,** 81 (1921).

[2] "Die Absorption" (1910).

[3] WEISER: *J. Phys. Chem.*, **24,** 277, 505 (1920); **26,** 401, 654 (1922); **27,** 501 (1923).

[4] *Cf.* HÜTTIG: *Kolloid-Z.*, **35,** 337 (1924).

more or less freedom.[1] Yellow tungsten trioxide $WO_3 \cdot H_2O$ behaves in this way. Curve III is an adsorption curve typical of such hydrous oxides as ferric oxide and chromic oxide in which the water is not held in any definite proportion. Curve IV is likewise an adsorption curve in which there is a break, owing to change in the size of the pores in the hydrous gel such as is observed with silica.

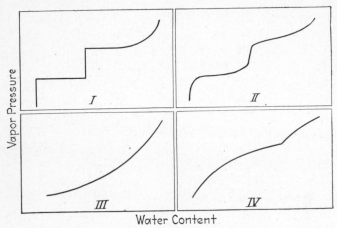

Fig. 1.—Types of vapor-pressure curves.

An elastic jelly, such as gelatin, loses water continuously in dry air, just as does a gelatinous oxide;[2] but, unlike the latter, the process is very much more nearly reversible, a dry plate taking up moisture and swelling again in moist air. As already pointed out, pores are not developed by the dehydration, as in the case of silica gel. A still more striking difference between the non-elastic gels is that the former will take up a great deal more water when dipped in the liquid than when suspended in the vapor at the same temperature. Von Schröder[3] studied the behavior of gelatin in liquid water and in water vapor, and was led to conclude that the vapor pressure of water in gelatin must be higher than that of pure water because water distills from the gelatin

[1] Hüttig: *Fortsch. Chem., Physik, physik. Chem.*, **18**, 5 (1924).
[2] Katz: *Z. Elektrochem.*, **17**, 800 (1911).
[3] *Z. physik. Chem.*, **45**, 109 (1903).

to the vapor phase. Bancroft[1] explains von Schröder's results by postulating a cellular structure for gelatin. The walls of the cell will adsorb a certain amount of water from the saturated vapor, but the microscopic cells or pockets will not be filled unless the gelatin is immersed in water. On lifting the swollen jelly into the vapor phase, water will distill from the curved microscopic droplets to the plane surface of water in the containing vessel, because of the higher vapor pressure of the former. As Bancroft points out, the objection to this explanation is that it postulates a cellular structure for gelatin, which seems more and more improbable in the light of recent investigations. Wolff and Büchner[2] claim that water does not distill from a fully distended gelatin jelly into the vapor phase and that von Schröder's conclusions are the result of experimental error. Washburn[3] finds that moistened clays will dry in a closed vessel above water, a result that supports von Schröder's observations; but he believes this to be due to the action of gravity. There seems no way of settling the question definitely except by a careful repetition of von Schröder's experiments.

Whenever a dry gel takes up moisture, heat is evolved[4] and a contraction in volume[5] takes place, particularly in the earlier stages. Although the volume of the system, water + dry gel, is greater than that of the swollen gel, the gel itself increases in volume and so may exert a very high pressure. In some experiments on dried seaweeds, Reinke[6] found that water was taken up against a pressure of 41 atmospheres, the volume increase amounting to 16 per cent. Similarly, Rodewald[7] found that starch swells against a pressure of 2500 atmospheres. Posnjak[8] made some observations on the amount of water with which gelatin is in equilibrium at various pressures and on the cor-

---

[1] "Applied Colloid Chemistry," 75 (1921).

[2] *Koninklijke Akad. Wetenschappen Amsterdam*, **17**, May 30 (1914); *Z. physik. Chem.*, **89**, 271 (1915).

[3] *J. Am. Ceram. Soc.*, **1**, 25 (1918).

[4] WIEDEMANN and LÜDEKING: *Wied. Ann.*, **25**, 145 (1885); RODEWALD: *Z. physik. Chem.*, **24**, 193 (1897).

[5] LÜDEKING: *Wied. Ann.*, **35**, 552 (1888).

[6] *Hanstein's botan. Abhandl.*, **4**, 1 (1879).

[7] *Z. physik. Chem.*, **24**, 193 (1897).

[8] *Kolloidchem. Beihefte*, **3**, 417 (1912).

responding behavior of raw rubber in different organic solvents. In all experiments the amount of liquid taken up decreases with increasing pressure. The data do not enable us to determine what pressure would be necessary to prevent any swelling or to remove all the adsorbed liquid from a swollen jelly; these values would probably be very high in every case. Some idea of the magnitude of the swelling pressure of gelatin may be obtained by coating a glass plate with gelatin which has absorbed the maximum amount of water and observing the degree to which the glass plate is bent by the drying film of gelatin.[1] The strain is frequently sufficient to break the plate or to pull pieces of glass off the surface.

Having outlined the general properties of gels and their general methods of formation, we may proceed to a detailed consideration of the colloid chemistry of the hydrous oxides. It seems advisable to start off with hydrous ferric oxide, one of the most common members of this class of compounds.

[1] GRAHAM: *J. Chem. Soc.*, **17**, 320 (1864).

CHAPTER II

THE HYDROUS OXIDES OF IRON ·

Hydrous Ferric Oxide

Composition.—Hydrous ferric oxide, frequently misnamed ferric hydroxide, is thrown down as a highly gelatinous precipitate when an alkali is added to a solution of ferric salt that is not too dilute. This might be expected, since the percentage supersaturation preceding precipitation is relatively enormous, a condition favorable to the formation of extremely minute particles. The orientation of these particles into an enmeshing network that entrains water constitutes the gelatinous precipitate. The bulky mass loses water gradually on standing and becomes more compact and granular. Since a small integral ratio between oxide and water may be realized by drying the precipitated oxide under suitable conditions, many hydrates have been described from time to time.[1] Tommasi[2] recognized two series of such hydrated oxides, yellow and red or brown, that were believed to bear an isomeric relation to each other. The members of the red series, obtained by precipitating a ferric salt with alkali, were very bulky, were soluble in dilute acids, and were dehydrated even by boiling water.[3] The members of the yellow series, prepared by oxidation of hydrous ferrous oxide[4] or ferrous carbonate, were denser than the red, were but sparingly soluble in concentrated acids, required a higher temperature for

---

[1] Lefort: *J. prakt. Chem.*, **54**, 305 (1851); Péan de St. Gilles: *Ann. chim. phys.*, (3) **46**, 47 (1856); Davies: *J. Chem. Soc.*, **19**, 69 (1866); Wittstein: *Chem. Zentr.*, (1) **24**, 367 (1853); Schaffner: *Liebig's Ann. Chem.*, **51**, 177 (1844); Brescius: *J. prakt. Chem.*, (2) **3**, 272 (1871); Ramsay: *J. Chem. Soc.*, **32**, 395 (1877).

[2] *Bull. soc. chim.*, (2) **38**, 152 (1882).

[3] Davies: *J. Chem. Soc.*, **19**, 71 (1866).

[4] *Cf.* Phillips: "Graham-Otto Lehrbuch," 3rd ed., II, **2**, 725 (1853).

dehydration, and retained a molecule of water even on prolonged boiling with water.[1]

Since the brown precipitated oxide can be dehydrated by prolonged heating under water, it seems unlikely that it should form a definite hydrate. As a matter of fact van Bemmelen[2] demonstrated conclusively that the ratio of oxide to water in the red-brown compound depends entirely on the method of treatment; and that all the various formulas corresponding to definite hydrates are the accidental result of the method of drying used by the different investigators. Van Bemmelen attributed all the differences between the yellow and the brown oxide to differences in physical structure; but there are some grounds for believing that the much greater tenacity with which the yellow compound holds onto water between certain temperatures is due to the formation of a yellow hydrate. The evidence for this view comes chiefly from attempts to establish the composition of minerals.

In addition to the anhydrous ferric oxide, hematite, mineralogists distinguish at least five hydrates of ferric oxide: turgite, $Fe_2O_3 \cdot 0.5H_2O$; gothite and lepidocrocite, $Fe_2O_3 \cdot H_2O$; limonite, $Fe_2O_3 \cdot 1.5H_2O$; xanthosiderite, $Fe_2O_3 \cdot 2H_2O$; and limnite, $Fe_2O_3 \cdot 3H_2O$. Hematite is sometimes found in nature as a well-crystallized substance; but the monohydrate alone of all the others occurs in a definite crystalline form. Ruff[3] attempted to produce hydrates synthetically by heating the red-brown gelatinous precipitate under pressure of 5000 atmospheres. Between 30 and 42.5°, he claimed to get a yellow hydrate corresponding to limonite; between 52.5 and 62.5°, a yellow-red hydrate corresponding to gothite; and at higher temperatures, brick-red turgite. His synthetic preparations, however, did not agree with the corresponding minerals in stability; and it is improbable that they were identical either in physical structure or in the amount of water they contained. By hydrolysis of a solution of ferric chloride, Fischer[4] obtained an oxide whose

[1] *Cf.* Muck: *Z. für Chemie*, 41 (1868).

[2] *Rec. trav. chim.*, **7**, 106 (1888); *Z. anorg. Chem.*, **20**, 185 (1899); "Die Absorption," **70**, 370 (1910).

[3] *Ber.*, **34**, 3417 (1901).

[4] *Z. anorg. Chem.*, **66**, 37 (1910).

dehydration curve was very similar to that of a natural limonite. The composition of a synthetic compound, prepared in a similar way by Posnjak and Merwin,[1] approached that of a monohydrate at 165°; and above this critical temperature it went over rapidly to red anhydrous oxide, analogous to hematite. However, the existence of a definite temperature of inversion of limonite to red hematite has not been established.[2]

Some years ago Posnjak and Merwin[1] in the Geophysical Laboratory made a systematic analytical, optical, crystallographic, and thermal study of ferric oxides, which proved conclusively that, even in the case of minerals, no series of hydrated ferric oxides exists. The only hydrate whose existence has been established satisfactorily is the monohydrate. This occurs in nature in two crystalline forms, gothite and lepidocrocite; and in an indefinite amorphous condition with a considerable excess of adsorbed water, known under the name limonite. The other minerals, previously considered hydrates, are either hydrous ferric oxide monohydrate or solid solutions of hydrous monohydrate and hydrous ferric oxide. By heating the system Fe_2O_3-SO_3-H_2O below 130°, a synthetic yellow crystalline monohydrate is formed which is identical microscopically with certain natural gothites.[3] This appears to be the first crystalline hydrate to be synthesized although, more than 30 years ago, van Bemmelen[4] claimed to have prepared a crystalline monohydrate by the action of water on sodium ferrite at 15°. Van Bemmelen's so-called hydrate crystals possessed the same transparency and shape as the crystals from which they were derived, strongly suggesting that they were pseudomorphs after sodium ferrite rather than crystals of a definite monohydrate. Moreover, they decomposed and lost water below 100°, whereas the natural and synthetic monohydrates are prefectly stable at this temperature.

Since, with but one exception, there is no definite ratio of ferric oxide to water, the water must be retained by the hydrous

[1] *Am. J. Sci.*, (4) **47,** 311 (1919).
[2] *Bureau Soils, Bull.* **79,** 18 (1911).
[3] POSNJAK and MERWIN: *J. Am. Chem. Soc.*, **44,** 1965 (1922).
[4] VAN BEMMELEN and KLOBBIE: *J. prakt. Chem.*, (2) **46,** 497 (1892).

oxides either by adsorption, as van Bemmelen supposed, or in solid solution, or both. Foote and Saxton[1] attempted to determine the manner in which water was held, by observing the volume changes on freezing the precipitated oxide. They came to the conclusion that the water which freezes gradually with falling temperature is held in capillaries; while water which cannot be frozen is in the "combined" state. The "combined" water is given up slowly on heating the precipitate with water, with no tendency toward simple ratios between ferric oxide and water; and when once dehydrated, the material does not take up water to form hydrates. It was assumed, therefore, that the ferric oxide and water "combine" in indefinite proportions, which is essentially a case of solid solution rather than of adsorption. The failure of gel water to freeze at a certain temperature is no criterion for determining whether water is dissolved or adsorbed. Therefore, there appears to be no justification for assuming the existence of a solid solution, unless it is proved that the gelatinous oxide is always crystalline, and that some of the water forms an integral part of the crystal lattice. Some recent observations of Simon and Schmidt[2] bear on this point:

Samples of hydrous ferric oxide of different degrees of fineness were prepared as follows: (1) by precipitation of a ferric nitrate solution with ammonia at 40°; (2) by precipitation of a cold ferric chloride solution with ammonia; and (3) by dialysis of a solution of ferric nitrate until the gel precipitated and the dialysate was free from nitrate. Sample 1 was relatively coarse, sample 3 very fine, and sample 2 of intermediate fineness. The temperature-composition curve for each preparation was obtained with a special tensi-eudiometer.[3] As shown in Fig. 2, all the curves are continuous and give no indication whatsoever of the formation of definite hydrates containing one, two, or more molecules of water. It was demonstrated by x-ray spectography that oxide 1 was completely amorphous when dried in the air, but showed amicroscopic crystals of Fe_2O_3 when heated to a temperature sufficiently high to drive off all the water. The air-dried oxide 3, prepared by slow hydrolysis of a ferric salt, gave a weak interference pat-

[1] *J. Am. Chem. Soc.*, **38**, 588 (1916); **39**, 1103 (1917).
[2] *Kolloid-Z.* (*Zsigmondy Festschrift*), **36**, 65 (1925).
[3] HÜTTIG: *Z. anorg. Chem.*, **114**, 161 (1920).

tern[1] which appeared somewhat different from the x-radiogram of anhydrous ferric oxide. This suggests that certain gelatinous preparations may contain some water in solid solution between the oriented Fe_2O_3 molecules in the lattice. As Posnjak and Merwin have shown, under certain special conditions the water

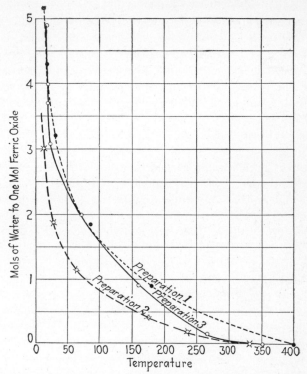

Fig. 2.—Temperature-composition curves of hydrous ferric oxides.

molecules in the Fe_2O_3 lattice may assume fixed positions in the stoichiometrical relation represented by the definite compound, $Fe_2O_3 \cdot H_2O$.

FERRIC OXIDE SOLS

The Péan de St. Gilles Sol.—Péan de St. Gilles[2] prepared colloidal ferric oxide by continued boiling of a solution of ferric

---

[1] *Cf.*, however, Böhm: *Z. anorg. Chem.*, **149**, 203 (1925).
[2] *Compt. rend.*, **40**, 568, 1243 (1855).

acetate. The red-brown color which is characteristic of the acetate becomes brick red as the boiling continues, and the peculiar taste of ferric salts gives place to that of acetic acid. The colloid is distinctly turbid in reflected light, but is perfectly clear in transmitted light. The red-brown deposit, formed by coagulation with dilute sulfuric acid, is relatively insoluble in even the more concentrated acids. When the colloid is poured into hydrochloric acid, there is formed a finely divided granular brick-red precipitate which shows no resemblance to ordinary hydrous ferric oxide. Giolitti[1] extended the experiments of Péan de St. Gilles and confirmed the important observation that the physical character of the precipitated colloid varies with different precipitating agents. The addition of a small quantity of sulfurous, sulfuric, selenious, iodic, periodic, boric, or phosphoric acid produces a gelatinous precipitate which is not repeptized by water, while adding a small amount of hydrochloric, hydrobromic, hydriodic, nitric, perchloric, or perbromic acid causes slight precipitation of a finely divided brick-red powder not easily removed by filtration. A larger amount of one of the latter group of acids precipitates completely a powder that is readily peptized by water, as Péan de St. Gilles observed.[2]

An investigation[3] of the anomalous behavior of the Péan de St. Gilles colloid with different electrolytes showed that the formation of a gelatinous precipitate is independent of the valence of the precipitating ion; and that the most voluminous precipitate is obtained when there is immediate agglomeration throughout the entire solution and when the precipitating agent has no solvent action on the particles. The conclusions accord with the view that a gelatinous precipitate will result whenever finely divided hydrous particles are thrown down under conditions favoring the formation of an enmeshing network enclosing liquid. It is well known that slow precipitation from a supersaturated solution is conducive to the building up of large crystals; whereas rapid precipitation results in very small crystals which may give rise to a gelatinous mass. In a Péan de St. Gilles sol, we have the very finely divided particles essential to the formation of gelati-

[1] *Gazz. chim. ital.*, **35**, II, 181 (1905).
[2] *Cf.* WEISER: *J. Phys. Chem.*, **24**, 312 (1920).
[3] WEISER: *Ibid.*, **24**, 298 (1920).

nous ferric oxide; but if the sol agglomerates too slowly, the primary particles may orient themselves into more or less granular masses that will entangle relatively little water. On the other hand, if the sol agglomerates rapidly, there is no time for the orientation of the primary particles, and a network may form that will enclose relatively large amounts of water and hence will be relatively voluminous. On this account, a gelatinous precipitate is always obtained when the precipitating anion is polyvalent, since low concentrations of such ions cause rapid agglomeration.

Although substances containing anions of high precipitating power cause rapid agglomeration to gelatinous precipitates, this property is obviously not confined to electrolytes with strongly adsorbed anions. Thus, potassium chloride produces a very voluminous precipitate although chloride ion is not usually adsorbed strongly; whereas hydrochloric acid causes the precipitate to come down granular. With these two electrolytes the different character of precipitate is due to the rate of agglomeration and the solvent action of the precipitant. Potassium chloride possesses no solvent action, and the stabilizing influence of potassium ion is relatively slight; hence, when the precipitation value is exceeded, rapid agglomeration takes place. On account of the stabilizing influence of hydrogen ion, the precipitation value of hydrochloric acid is greater than that of its potassium salt, and the rate of precipitation is slower.

Contrary to the usual statement, hydrochloric acid has an appreciable solvent action on the Péan de St. Gilles ferric oxide, particularly while the oxide is in the colloidal state. Accordingly, the slower the sol is agglomerated by an acid, the greater will be the amount of oxide dissolved. Although the Péan de St. Gilles colloid is fairly uniform, there is unquestionably considerable variation in the size of the individual particles, such as Zsigmondy and others have observed with colloids generally; and it is the smallest particles that are the most readily attacked. Hence, the solvent action will, to a greater or lesser extent, prevent the formation of an enmeshing network of particles, thus cutting down the amount of water that can be enclosed and carried down; and so decreasing the volume of the precipitate.

From what has been said, it follows that the addition of sufficient hydrochloric acid to cause rapid agglomeration, before the solvent action of the acid has had time to manifest itself appreciably, should yield a more voluminous precipitate than is obtained in the region of the precipitation value. Furthermore, a less gelatinous precipitate should be obtained with a concentrated solution of sulfuric acid than with the very weak solution necessary to cause precipitation. Finally, if the stabilizing influence of the cation tends to cut down the rate of agglomeration, then salts with polyvalent cations and univalent anions should produce a granular precipitate under certain conditions. All these conclusions are readily verified experimentally.

Scheurer-Kestner[1] obtained the Péan de St. Gilles colloid by heating a dilute solution of ferric nitrate; while Krecke[2] used

TABLE I.—HYDROLYSIS OF FERRIC ACETATE

Solution boiled		Old solutions		New solutions	
Ferric acetate 0.7 M	Water	Color of sol	Color of precipitate	Color of sol	Color of precipitate
50.0	0.0	Reddish orange	Yellow	Very dark red	Dark red
25.0	25.0	Orange	Yellow	Dark red	Dark red
12.5	37.5	Light orange	Yellow	Red	Dark red
6.3	43.7	Yellow	Yellow	Light red	Dark red
3.2	46.8	Canary	Yellow	Orange red	Dark red

ferric chloride. A pure sol may be prepared[3] in a relatively short time by boiling a colloidal solution of ferric oxide peptized by the minimum amount of acetic acid. The Péan de St. Gilles colloid is always described as brick red, but the color varies with the conditions of preparation, a yellow sol being formed if the ferric acetate solution is allowed to stand for some time at room temperature before subjecting it to the boiling temperature. This is shown by the results recorded in Table I: A solution of ferric acetate approximately 3 M with respect to iron but con-

[1] *Ann. chim. phys.*, (3) **57**, 23 (1850).

[2] *J. prakt. Chem.*, (2) **3**, 286 (1871); *cf.* DEBRAY: *Compt. rend.*, **68**, 913 (1869).

[3] WEISER; *J. Phys. Chem.*, **24**, 299 (1920).

taining excess ferric oxide was allowed to stand 10 days, after which a 20-cubic-centimeter portion was diluted to 100 cubic centimeters and from it were prepared 50-cubic-centimeter portions of other solutions of various concentrations, as given in the table. In a similar way, a series of solutions was made up from a freshly prepared solution of ferric acetate. Both sets of solutions were boiled vigorously on an electric hot plate for 15 hours, the water being replaced as it evaporated. A difference in the color of the two series of sols was soon noted and became quite pronounced as the boiling continued; the colloids from the old ferric acetate were yellow, and from the new red. After discontinuing the boiling, samples of each sol were precipitated with potassium sulfate and the color of the precipitate noted.

Neidle[1] obtained a yellow colloid by dialysis of a ferric chloride solution in the hot; but only the sols prepared from very dilute solutions were stable.

The Graham Sol.—Graham[2] prepared a sol differing in certain respects from the Péan de St. Gilles sol, by the dialysis of a ferric acetate solution in the cold; or more usually, by peptizing gelatinous ferric oxide in ferric chloride solution and then removing the excess ferric chloride by dialysis. Unlike the Péan de St. Gilles sol, Graham's preparation is colored deep reddish brown and is clear. Moreover, the coagulum obtained on adding electrolytes is highly gelatinous and is readily soluble in dilute acids.

The Graham sol has been widely used in investigations of colloidal behavior and various methods have been employed in its preparation. Krecke[3] hydrolyzed ferric chloride solutions without dialysis. Biltz[4] hydrolyzed dilute solutions of ferric nitrate; while van Bemmelen[5] used ferric chloride, and Freundlich,[6] iron carbonyl. Grimaux[7] prepared a similar product by pouring an alcoholic solution of ferric ethylate into water.

[1] *J. Am. Chem. Soc.*, **39**, 76 (1917).

[2] *J. Chem. Soc.*, **15**, 250 (1862).

[3] *J. prakt. Chem.*, (2) **3**, 286 (1871); *cf.* WRIGHT: *J. Chem. Soc.*, **43**, 156 (1883).

[4] *Ber.*, **35**, 4431 (1902).

[5] *Z. anorg. Chem.*, **36**, 380 (1903).

[6] FREUNDLICH and WOSNESSENSKY: *Kolloid-Z.*, **33**, 222 (1923).

[7] *Compt. rend.*, **98**, 105, 1434 (1884).

Gaurilow[1] oxidized ferrous carbonate with hydrogen peroxide; and Neidle and Crombie[2] oxidized ferrous chloride with potassium permanganate in the cold and dialyzed. Neidle also oxidized ferrous chloride with hydrogen peroxide[3] and dialyzed in the hot.[4] The latter method is particularly satisfactory for the rapid preparation of colloidal ferric oxide free from metals other than iron. A similar sol was formed by hot dialysis of a solution of ferric chloride to which was added sufficient ammonium hydroxide to react with 60 per cent of the salt.[5] Tribot and Chrétien[6] used electrodialysis to obtain a pure sol fairly rapidly. The cathode was placed in the colloid and the anode in the water which surrounds the membrane of the dialyzer.

Giolitti[7] reports that the Graham sol approaches more nearly to the properties of the Péan de St. Gilles sol the longer the time of standing and the higher the temperature of preparation. Browne,[8] on the other hand, failed to find any appreciable difference between old and fresh Graham sols or between cold and hot dialyzed sols provided the hot dialysis was not begun until the first large excess of electrolyte had been removed. A 4-year-old sol containing 40 equivalents of iron to 1 of chlorine had the same conductivity and stability toward electrolytes as a fresh sol of the same concentration and purity.

In the preparation of the Péan de St. Gilles sol by the author's method, particular care was taken to wash the hydrous oxide by a centrifugal process until it started to go into colloidal solution, before peptizing with acetic acid. The process of washing out the precipitating agent constitutes one of the general dispersion methods of making sols; but its application to the preparation of colloidal solutions of the hydrous oxides we owe to Bradfield[9] who worked out a centrifugal method which appears

[1] *Kolloid-Z.*, **37**, 46 (1925).
[2] *J. Am. Chem. Soc.*, **38**, 2607 (1916).
[3] *J. Am. Chem. Soc.*, **39**, 2334 (1917).
[4] *J. Am. Chem. Soc.*, **38**, 1270 (1916).
[5] NEIDLE and BARAB: *J. Am. Chem. Soc.*, **39**, 79 (1917).
[6] *Compt. rend.*, **140**, 144 (1905).
[7] GIOLITTI: *Gazz. chim. ital.*, **38**, II, 252 (1908); *cf. Ibid.*, **35**, II, 181 (1905); **36**, II, 157 (1906).
[8] Private communication.
[9] *J. Am. Chem. Soc.*, **44**, 965 (1922).

particularly useful for preparing a pure sol in the minimum time: Ammonium hydroxide was added to a concentrated solution of ferric chloride with constant stirring until minute floccules of hydrous oxide were barely visible. The more granular precipitate, formed by adding an excess of ammonium hydroxide, was less reversible. The precipitate was allowed to settle and was washed by decantation until it commenced to become colloidal. This solution was then passed through a Sharples Laboratory Supercentrifuge making 32,500 revolutions per minute, at the rate of about 3 liters per hour. At the end of the run the sleeve was coated with an extremely finely divided layer of a reddish-brown hydrous oxide. This material was removed, mixed to a uniform paste with water, using a mortar and pestle; and was then poured into a large bulk of water for the next washing. After repeating the process four times, the contents of the bowl could be divided into two distinct parts: (1) a yellowish-brown fairly stiff deposit on the lowest 5 centimeters of the sleeve which graded slowly into (2), a dark-red highly hydrous deposit that was barely stiff enough to adhere to the sleeve. The two fractions were separated, shaken with a small amount of water, and analyzed. From these stock solutions, stable sols of any desired concentration could be prepared. The liquid discharged after the third washing was a beautiful cherry-red sol, containing but a minute trace of chloride.

The Negative Sol.—A century ago, Rose[1] observed that glycerin, mannite, sucrose, and glucose will prevent the precipitation of hydrous ferric oxide on adding alkali or ammonia to a solution of ferric salt. This observation was confirmed by Grimaux,[2] who attributed the solubility of the hydrous oxide to the formation of a negative sol stabilized by preferential adsorption of hydroxyl ion.[3] Invert sugar is seven times as effective as cane sugar in preventing the precipitation.[4] In this connection, it is of interest to note that a small amount of hydrous ferric oxide inhibits the crystallization of cane sugar to such an extent that a high percentage of molasses is obtained in plant work if

[1] *Ann. chim.*, **24**, 27 (1827).
[2] GRIMAUX: *Compt. rend.*, **98**, 1485 (1884).
[3] *Cf.* CHATTERJI and DHAR: *Chem. News*, **121**, 253 (1921).
[4] RIFFARD: *Compt. rend.*, **77**, 1103 (1874).

the raw sugar is kept in iron vessels or the clearing "char" contains iron.[1]

Robin[2] added ammonia to a mixture containing glycerin, peptone, and ferric chloride. He claimed to get a clear solution of ferric peptonate; but what he had was a negative ferric oxide sol in which both peptone and glycerin functioned as protective colloids. Fischer[3] used glycerin as a protector in preparing a negative sol to use for intravenous injection in arsenic poisoning. The ordinary positive sol cannot be employed, as it precipitates the negatively charged serum. A negative sol containing excess of both alkali and glycerin does not precipitate serum and is not immediately toxic to rabbits, but it met with limited success in intravenous injections.[4] Dozzie[5] reports considerable success in the treatment of anæmia by injection of colloidal hydrous ferric oxide.

Powis[6] prepared a stable negative sol without a protective colloid by allowing 100 cubic centimeters of $0.01N$ ferric chloride to run slowly, with constant shaking, into 150 cubic centimeters of $0.01N$ sodium hydroxide. The sol was of clear brownish-yellow color and showed no sign of precipitation after standing 3 weeks, although a trace of barium chloride caused immediate coagulation.[7]

A ferric oxide sol prepared by electrical disintegration of iron electrodes under water[8] is usually positively charged; but it becomes less positive, neutral, and finally negative by repeated filtration through such substances as filter paper, glass wool, cotton, or sand, which are negatively charged in the presence of water. According to Malarski,[9] the reversal of charge on the particles is brought about by contact with the negative filtering media. While this explanation seems plausible, the experiments should be repeated to determine to what extent the properties of

[1] THORPE: "Dictionary of Applied Chemistry," **3**, 176 (1912).

[2] *Compt. rend.*, **101**, 321 (1885).

[3] *Biochem. Z.*, **27**, 223, 238 (1910).

[4] FISCHER and KUZNITZKY: *Biochem. Z.*, **27**, 311 (1910).

[5] *Gazz. ospedali clin.*, **41**, 182 (1920).

[6] *J. Chem. Soc.*, **107**, 818 (1915).

[7] *Cf.* KELLER: *Kolloid-Z.*, **26**, 173 (1920).

[8] BREDIG: *Z. Elektrochem.*, **4**, 514 (1898); *Z. physik. Chem.*, **34**, 258 (1899).

[9] *Kolloid-Z.*, **23**, 113 (1918).

the sol are altered by adsorption of stabilizing ions during repeated filtration.

Composition of Ferric Oxide Sol.—Since but one precipitated hydrate of ferric oxide exists—the yellow monohydrate—it seems altogether improbable that the red colloidal solutions of Péan de St. Gilles or Graham contain definite hydrates. The variation in properties between the Graham sol and the red and yellow Péan de St. Gilles sol is not due to chemical structure or the existence of hydrates, but is the result of differences in the size-distribution curve of the primary colloidal particles. For the Graham sol, the maximum is in the region of exceedingly small particle size, the position of the maximum shifting toward larger size particles as we pass to the red and the yellow Péan de St. Gilles sols.[1] The conditions under which the sols are formed favor this view. Thus the percentage supersaturation of ferric oxide is highest for the conditions which give the Graham sol and lowest for those which give the yellow Péan de St. Gilles sol. Differences in hydration of the ferric oxide sols are due to differences in specific surface, the Graham sols possessing the greatest specific surface and, therefore, the greatest amount of adsorbed water. If the Graham sol is impure and dilute, there is a gradual growth of primary particles accompanied by a decrease in the amount of adsorbed water. The absence of chemical combination between water and ferric oxide in sols prepared by hot dialysis was confirmed recently by means of freezing-point determinations carried out by Browne.[2] Although the colloid contains ferric oxide in a highly hydrous condition, the effect of dextrose on the freezing point of the sol showed that the water associated with the oxide was adsorbed, as all the water present in the sol acted as solvent for dextrose or for any other soluble substance.

While the particles of the red sol are hydrous oxides, it is possible that the yellow Péan de St. Gilles sol may contain particles of monohydrate or of hydrous monohydrate.

Colloidal ferric oxides can be prepared fairly free from electrolytes but it has been demonstrated repeatedly that at least some

---

[1] ZSIGMONDY: "Chemistry of Colloids," translated by Spear, 163 (1917).
[2] *J. Am. Chem. Soc.*, **45**, 297 (1923).

electrolyte must be present in such sols to ensure their stability.[1] Thus the Graham sol, peptized by ferric chloride or hydrochloric acid, always contains traces of chlorides, however long the dialysis may be continued.[2] On this account, a number of investigators consider the various dialyzed colloids to be chlorides of condensed ferric hydroxides like $Fe_2(OH)_6\frac{1}{5}{}_0Fe_2Cl_6$ or as oxychlorides of variable composition.[3] This conception of the nature of colloidal solutions meets with serious objection at the outset, since Fischer[4] and others[5] have shown that definite chemical oxychlorides of iron do not exist at ordinary temperatures. Naturally, investigators who assume the existence of such definite compounds in ferric oxide sols are unable to agree on their composition. Thus, Nicolardot claims that the sols are made up of mixtures of two compounds in which the ratios of iron to chlorine in equivalents are 6 and 125, respectively. Neidle showed these ratios to be purely accidental; but believes there is a compound in which the ratio is 21. Recently Thomas and Frieden have arrived at the conclusion that 1 mol of ferric chloride is necessary to keep 21 mols of ferric oxide (ratio of iron to chlorine in equiv-

---

[1] KASTNER: *Ann. chim. phys.*, (3) **57**, 231 (1859); DEBRAY: *Compt. rend.*, **59**, 174 (1864); MAGNIER DE LA SOURCE: *Ibid.*, **90**, 1352 (1880); HANTZSCH and DESCH: *Liebig's Ann. Chem.*, **323**, 28 (1903); LINDER and PICTON: *J. Chem. Soc.*, **87**, 1920 (1905); WYROUBOFF: *Ann. chim. phys.*, **7**, 449 (1905); RUER: *Z. anorg. Chem.*, **43**, 85 (1905); NEIDLE: *J. Am. Chem. Soc.*, **39**, 2334 (1917).

[2] *Cf.* UFER: "Uber kolloides Eisenoxyd.," Dissertation, Dresden (1915).

[3] WYROUBOFF and VERNEUIL: *Bull. soc. chim.*, (3) **21**, 137 (1899); JORDIS: *Z. anorg. Chem.*, **35**, 16 (1903); *Z. Elektrochem.*, **10**, 509 (1904); DUCLAUX: *Compt. rend.*, **138**, 144, 809 (1904); **140**, 1468, 1544 (1905); **143**, 296, 344 (1906); *J. chim. phys.*, **5**, 29 (1907); LINDER and PICTON: *J. Chem. Soc.*, **87**, 1919 (1905); NICOLARDOT: *Ann. chim. phys.*, **6**, 334 (1905); MALFITANO: *Compt. rend.*, **139**, 1221 (1904); **140**, 1245 (1905); **141**, 660, 680 (1905); **143**, 172, 1141 (1906); *Z. physik. Chem.*, **68**, 232 (1910); MALFITANO and MICHEL: *Compt. rend.*, **145**, 185, 1275 (1907); MICHEL: *Compt. rend.*, **147**, 1052, 1288 (1908); DUMANSKI: *Kolloid-Z.*, **8**, 232 (1911); NEIDLE: *J. Am. Chem. Soc.*, **39**, 2334 (1917); MATULA: *Kolloid-Z.*, **21**, 49 (1917); THOMAS and FRIEDEN: *J. Am. Chem. Soc.*, **45**, 2522 (1923); PAULI and ROGAN: *Kolloid-Z.*, **35**, 131 (1924); PAULI and WALTER: *Kolloidchem. Beihefte*, **17**, 256 (1923); KÜHNL and PAULI: *Ibid.*, **20**, 319 (1925).

[4] *Z. anorg. Chem.*, **66**, 38 (1910).

[5] CAMERON and ROBINSON: *J. Phys. Chem.*, **11**, 690 (1907); GIOLITTI: *Gazz. chim. ital.*, **36**, 1157 (1906); SMITH and GIESY: *J. Am. Pharm. Assoc.*, **12**, 855 (1923).

alents = 42) dispersed in the colloidal condition, irrespective of the concentration of the sol. These observations and conclusions are not in accord with Neidle, who showed that the maximum purity obtainable before precipitation sets in increases appreciably with decreasing iron content. Neidle prepared a sol, approximately 0.05 N with respect to iron, in which the ratio equivalents Fe$\cdots$: equivalents Cl' was 84; while the maximum purity obtained by Thomas and Frieden at this concentration was only about half as great. Bradfield[1] prepared a ferric oxide sol by washing by the use of the centrifuge, in which the ratio was 396. In the purest sol Ufer[2] was able to prepare by dialysis, the ratio was approximately 2700.

In the light of the wide variation in the iron: chlorine ratio obtained by different investigators, there seems no room to doubt but that, within reasonable limits, the composition of a dialyzed colloid depends upon the condition of formation. Everybody knows that precipitation of a colloid will take place if the dialysis is carried too far; and that consistent results can be obtained only by a very careful control of the experimental conditions. Since the method of procedure followed by different investigators is likely to vary widely, we might expect the wide variation in the results which the records show. Some people require very little evidence to convince them of the existence of chemical compounds and these assign definite formulas to the dialyzed sol. Others who have observed the passing of many cherished and time-honored "compounds" content themselves with postulating the formation of a series of "indefinite" compounds in order to explain their observations. This course is of questionable value because of the complexity and variability of the systems that are encountered and the consequent complexity of the hypothetical compounds that must be assumed to exist.

Recently, attempts have been made to determine the number of molecules in a single collodial particle per unit of electrical charge, from electrical conductivity and transport measurements on the sols themselves and on the ultrafiltrates from the

---

[1] *J. Am. Chem. Soc.*, **44**, 965 (1920).

[2] "Uber kolloides Eisenoxyd.," Dissertation, Dresden (1915); *cf.* FREUND-LICH: "Kapillarchemie," 511 (1922).

sols.[1] According to Duclaux[2] the specific conductance K_m of the colloidal particles or micelles of a sol is given by the expression

$$K_m = K_s - K_f$$

where K_s and K_f are the specific conductances of the sol and the ultrafiltrate from the sol, respectively. If a quantity of electricity E_s is passed through the sol, the part carried by the micelles E_m will be

$$E_m = \frac{K_m}{K_s} \cdot E_s \tag{1}$$

If one knows the mass of the micelle ions m transferred by a quantity of electricity E_s, together with the mobility of the micelle ion U_c and of accompanying anion U_a, one can calculate the charge on the mass Ae corresponding to the electrochemical equivalent, from the equation,

$$Ae = \frac{F}{E_m} \cdot m \cdot \frac{U_c + U_a}{U_c} \tag{2}$$

where F is 1 faraday. Substituting for E_m its value from Eq. (1), Eq. (2) becomes

$$Ae = \frac{FK_s}{E_s K_m} \cdot m \cdot \frac{U_c + U_a}{U_c} \tag{3}$$

If E_s is made identical with F, then m becomes S, the mass of the micelle ions in mols of dispersed substance, Fe_2O_3. Ae thus becomes A_F and since

$$\frac{U_c + U_a}{U_c} = \frac{u + v}{w} = \frac{\Delta}{u}$$

Eq. (3) may be written

$$A_F = \frac{SK_s\Delta}{K_m u} \tag{4}$$

Representing the sum of the mobilities of the cation and anion from conductivity measurements in the usual way by $u + v$;

[1] WINTGEN: *Z. physik. Chem.*, **103**, 250 (1922); WINTGEN and BILTZ: *Ibid.*, **107**, 403 (1923); WINTGEN and LÖWENTHAL: *Ibid.*, **109**, 378 (1924); *cf.* PUIGGARI: "First American Congress of Chemistry" (1924); *Chem. Abstracts*, **19**, 1518 (1925).
[2] *Compt. rend.*, **140**, 1468, 1544 (1905).

the molecular weight of the colloidal component, Fe_2O_3, by M; and the weight in grams of Fe_2O_3 in a liter of sol by g, then Ae, which becomes A_L, is

$$A_L = \frac{g}{M} \cdot \frac{u + v}{1000_m} \qquad (5)$$

Wintgen has developed this formula from Kohlrausch's law of the independent migration of the ions, in the following way: For a ferric oxide sol prepared by dialysis of ferric chloride, let $M =$ molecular weight of Fe_2O_3; $g =$ concentration in grams of Fe_2O_3 per liter; $Z =$ number of elementary charges carried by 1 micelle; and $n =$ number of Fe_2O_3 molecules in 1 micelle. The electrochemical equivalent weight W of the micelle is given by

$$W = \frac{nM}{Z} \qquad (6)$$

which corresponds to the electrochemical equivalent weight of an ordinary ion; and so gives the weight in grams of Fe_2O_3 which carries 1 faraday. The value

$$Ae = \frac{W}{M} = \frac{n}{Z} \qquad (7)$$

gives the number of mols of Fe_2O_3 in a micelle ion carrying 1 faraday. The equivalent concentration C_{Ae} of the micelles is then

$$C_{Ae} = \frac{g}{W} \qquad (8)$$

If u and v are the mobilities of the micelle ion and chloride ion, respectively, from conductivity measurements, then

$$1000K_m = (u + v)C_{Ae} = (u + v)\frac{g}{W} \qquad (9)$$

from which

$$W = \frac{g(u + v)}{1000_m} \qquad (10)$$

Substituting for W its value MAe from Eq. (7), Eq. (10) becomes

$$A_L = Ae = \frac{g}{M} \cdot \frac{u + v}{1000K_m}$$

The value Ae is spoken of as the "equivalent aggregate" or as the electrochemical equivalent of the micelle. If, in a liter of sol, there are m_1 mols of Fe_2O_3 and m_2 gram atoms of chlorine (ionized and combined); and if the concentration of chlorine in the intermicellar liquid (that is, in the ultrafiltrate) is $[Cl_1]$, then the gram atoms of chlorine corresponding to Ae mols of Fe_2O_3 are

$$\frac{m_2 - [Cl_1]}{m_1} \cdot Ae$$

Of this, unit amount is split off from the micelle and the remainder E is a part of the micelle; therefore

$$E = \frac{m_2 - [Cl_1]}{m_1} \cdot Ae - 1$$

Using these formulas, Wintgen[1] calculated the composition of the micelles of a number of sols. For example, assuming the micelles of an aged iron oxide sol (containing 1.601 grams Fe_2O_3 and 0.06014 gram Cl in 100 grams of sol) to be all the same size, the average composition of the micelles is represented by the formula

$$(\boxed{75.35Fe_2O_3 ; 7.86HCl ; xH_2O}\ FeO^{\cdot})_{10,230} + 10{,}230Cl'$$

Lottermoser[2] found the hydrogen ion concentration of the ultra-filtrates from an aged sol to be the same as that of the sol. The micelles are believed to contain neutral chloride as well as chloride ion. Since the positive charge on the particles is probably due to stronger adsorption of hydrogen ion than of chloride ion, their composition may be represented by the general formula

$$(\boxed{xFe_2O_3 \cdot yHCl \cdot zH_2O}\ H^{\cdot})_n \cdot (n - q)Cl'$$

where qCl' represents the chloride ion corresponding to the excess of adsorbed hydrogen ion to which the particle owes its free charge. Lottermoser[3] found the specific conductance of the sol to be higher than that of the ultrafiltrates, the difference being regarded as the true conductivity of the micelles. If

---

[1] Wintgen and Löwenthal: *Z. physik. Chem.*, **109**, 378 (1924).

[2] *Z. Elektrochem.*, **30**, 391 (1924).

[3] *Cf.* Kopaczewski: *Compt. rend.*, **179**, 628 (1924).

the micelles P are considered to be complex electrolytes, the equivalent conductivity at infinite dilution may be calculated from the equation

$$\Delta_{P\,\infty} = \frac{1000K_P}{K_{Cl}}$$

The mobility of the micelle was found to rise abnormally with increasing dilution in purified sols containing but small amounts of chlorine. This fact necessitates the assumption that the micelles are adsorption complexes, the abnormality being due to the displacing of the adsorption and hydrolysis equilibria by dilution. The value $\Delta_{P\,\infty}$ approaches a constant value only in sols rich in chlorine. From this, it would appear that nothing is gained by looking upon ferric oxide sols as electrolytes with complex cations. But if one insists on regarding them in this light, there is no particular objection provided one recognizes clearly that there is a fundamental difference between sols and non-colloidal, complex electrolytes. In the latter, there exists a simple, stoichiometric ratio between the neutral component and the complex-forming ion; while in sols, the ratio of neutral constitutent to what Lottermoser calls sol-forming ions is indefinite and changes continuously.

A simpler and probably quite as exact an interpretation of the variable properties and composition of the sols may be given from the point of view of specific adsorption: Any number of hydrous ferric oxides are possible, differing among themselves in the size of the particles, and hence in the amount of salt or ion adsorption. The colloid prepared by the Graham method is formed in the presence of ferric chloride, hydrochloric acid, ferric ions, hydrogen ions, and chloride ions.[1] Accordingly, we might expect the colloidal particles to adsorb some ferric chloride and hydrochloric acid, and they will always adsorb ferric, hydrogen, and chloride ions in amounts depending on the nature of the colloid, the specific adsorbability, and the concentration.[2] Now it is well known that a substance always shows a strong tendency to adsorb its own ions, and hydrogen ion is usually very strongly adsorbed; on the other hand, chloride ion is not usually adsorbed so

[1] BROWNE: *J. Am. Chem. Soc.*, **45**, 297 (1923).
[2] *Cf.* MAFFIA: *Kolloidchem. Beihefte*, **3**, 85 (1911).

strongly, and this preferential adsorption results in a stable positive colloid. Since there is an equilibrium between the amount of a substance adsorbed and the amount in solution, prolonged dialysis will result in the loss of part of the adsorbed cations (together with an equivalent amount of anions) and this will decrease the stability of the sol. Adsorbed chloride, either as salt or as ion, will not give a test with silver nitrate; and small amounts of unadsorbed chloride in the presence of colloidal ıron oxide cannot be detected by precipitation with silver nitrate, since the protecting action of the hydrous oxide does not allow the particles of silver chloride to become large enough to cause turbidity.[1] Moreover, adsorbed chloride will have a negligible effect on a chlorine electrode and will not be detected potentiometrically; hence it is not surprising to learn that the amount of chlorine as ion is less than the total chlorine content of the sol.[2] From this point of view, it is obviously unnecessary to postulate the existence of oxychlorides of varying composition to account for the observation that only a part of the chlorine present appears to exist as ion.[3]

Since colloidal solutions, in general, are instable in the absence of some soluble substance that is strongly adsorbed by the colloidal particles, it follows that a colloidal solution will show a slight osmotic pressure and freezing-point lowering. This has been observed by a number of investigators with Graham's colloidal ferric oxide. Duclaux[4] found that the osmotic pressure increases with the concentration of sol but is not proportional to it. He demonstrated also that the osmotic pressure falls off slightly with rise in temperature, a result that was confirmed by Zsigmondy.[5] Both Duclaux and Malfitano[6] observed that the osmotic pressure of ferric oxide sols does not vary directly with their conductivity, the latter decreasing more rapidly than the former with dilution of the sol. It has been customary to interpret these results qualitatively by postulating the presence

[1] RUER: *Z. anorg. Chem.*, **43,** 85 (1905).

[2] PAULI and MATULA: *Kolloid-Z.*, **21,** 49 (1917)

[3] See DUMANSKI: *Kolloid-Z.*, **8,** 232 (1911).

[4] *Compt. rend.*, **140,** 1544 (1905).

[5] "Chemistry of Colloids," translated by Spear, 167 (1917).

[6] *Compt. rend.*, **139,** 1221 (1904).

in the sol of complex oxy-salts having all the necessary properties;[1] but such an explanation is not particularly helpful.

If we have a suspension that is altogether insoluble and contains no impurities, it will give rise to no osmotic pressure. The osmotic pressure of a well-dialyzed Graham sol is due partly to the colloidal particles which have adsorbed ions; but chiefly to the ions of ferric chloride and hydrochloric acid. Since the behavior of an adsorbed ion will depend on the size and nature of the adsorbing particle, it follows that any factor affecting the physical character of the particles or the adsorption of ions by them will influence the osmotic pressure of the sol. Moreover, since the osmotic pressure and freezing-point lowering in a well-purified sol are necessarily small, molecular weights deduced therefrom may be absurdly large.[2] In the nature of things, it is wrong to attribute the observed osmotic pressure and freezing-point lowering of any sol to the insoluble suspended material, and molecular weights deduced from such data are meaningless. The experiments of Duclaux and Malfitano should be repeated, and observations made of the effect of dilution and temperature on the number, physical character, adsorbability, and mobility of the colloidal particles of hydrous oxide.

Optical Properties.—Majorana[3] made the interesting observation that a sol exhibits pronounced double refraction when placed in the field of a powerful electromagnet and traversed by a light ray at right angles to the lines of force. This property is undoubtedly due to orientation of the particles of sol by the electric field;[4] for this orientation and the concomitant double refraction can be observed directly by working with a sol containing particles large enough to see with an ordinary microscope. Moreover, a gel formed by coagulation of a sol in an electric field exhibits permanent double refraction, whereas coagulation under ordinary conditions gives an optically inactive gel. Large

---

[1] MALFITANO: *Compt. rend.*, **139**, 1221 (1904); DUCLAUX: *J. chim. phys.*, **7**, 405 (1919).

[2] LINDER and PICTON: *J. Chem. Soc.*, **87**, 1920 (1905); DUMANSKI: *Kolloid-Z.*, **8**, 232 (1911).

[3] *Atti accad. Lincei*, **11**, (1) 374, 463, 531; **12**, (1) 90, 139 (1902).

[4] SCHMAUSS: *Drude's Ann.*, **12**, 186 (1903); COTTON and MOUTON: *Compt. rend.*, **141**, 317, 349 (1905); "Les Ultramicroscopes," Paris, Chap. VIII (1906).

particles cause a greater effect than small ultramicrons since the Brownian movement of the latter prevents sufficient orientation to cause pronounced double refraction. Cotton and Mouton attribute the optical phenomenon to the particles themselves and not to their position alone. This is in accord with Freundlich's[1] observation that colloidal solutions of ferric oxide and vanadium pentoxide[2] showing the Majorana phenomenon exhibit double refraction when stirred mechanically[3] or when a current of electricity is passed through the sols. These observations lend support to Nägeli's[4] view that the particles of certain sols consist of anisotropic ultramicrons having a resemblance to tiny crystals.

THE PRECIPITATION OF SOLS BY ELECTROLYTES

Investigations on the precipitation of ferric oxide sols by electrolytes have been confined pretty largely to Graham's sol. Duclaux, working with a colloid of this type containing 203 $\times$ 10^{-6} equivalents of iron and 16.6 $\times$ 10^{-6} equivalents of chlorine per 10 cubic centimeters, found the critical coagulation concentration of sodium sulfate, citrate, chromate, carbonate, phosphate, hydroxide, and ferrocyanide to vary from 13 $\times 10^{-6}$ in the case of ferrocyanide to 19 $\times 10^{-6}$ equivalents in the case of phosphate. These observations were believed to show that equivalent amounts of the various ions cause the same effect, and furthermore, that the amount necessary for precipitation is the same as the chloride content of the colloid, within the limits of the experimental errors. He thus came to regard the precipitation process as a definite stoichiometric chemical action, a double decomposition of the ordinary type. A marked variation from the equivalence rule was observed with sodium chloride and sodium nitrate which required 2000 $\times$ 10^{-6} and 1880 $\times$ 10^{-6} gram equivalents, respectively, to precipitate the same amount of colloid as the seven salts above referred to. Freundlich[5] found a wide

---

[1] *Z. Elektrochem.*, **22**, 27 (1916).

[2] See p. 266.

[3] *Cf.* QUINCKE: *Drude's Ann.*, (4) **15**, 28 (1904); TIERI: *Atti accad. Lincei*, (5) **19**, 470 (1910).

[4] "Theorie der Gärung," München, 121 (1879).

[5] "Kapillarchemie," 352, 358 (1909).

variation from equivalence in the precipitation concentration of various salts, which he attributed to a difference in the adsorbability of the precipitating anions. From Freundlich's observations the order of precipitating power of the anions is: dichromate > sulfate > hydroxide > salicylate > benzoate > c h l o r i d e > nitrate > bromide > iodide.

The results of some experiments[1] on the precipitation of a Péan de St. Gilles sol (1.54 grams Fe_2O_3 per liter) with various potassium salts give the following series, beginning with ferrocyanide which has the greatest precipitating power: ferrocyanide > ferricyanide > dichromate > t a r t r a t e > s u l f a t e > o x a l a t e > chromate > iodate > bromate > thiocyanate > chloride > chlorate > nitrate > bromide > iodide. As one should expect, the order of ions is identical with that deduced from Freundlich's data for the ions common to both series. Owing to differences in nature and purity[2] of the Péan de St. Gilles sol and Duclaux's sol, the precipitation concentrations of electrolytes were higher for the former than for the latter; but the magnitude of the variation is relatively unimportant compared with the fact that the precipitation values are not the same, as Duclaux believed. The Graham sol is stabilized by preferential adsorption of hydrogen ion and probably some ferric ion. The unadsorbed chloride ion present in an extremely pure sol is a measure of the excess cationic adsorption which gives the colloid particles their charge and the colloid its stability. Different concentrations of electrolytes are necessary to neutralize the adsorbed ions and precipitate the sol. The concentration of anion necessary to effect neutralization will approximate the chloride ion concentration only in so far as its adsorption tendency approaches that of the adsorbed cations. The precipitation concentrations of acids are uniformly higher than those of potassium salts since the stabilizing hydrogen ion is more strongly adsorbed than potassium ion. The order of precipitating power of electrolytes changes but little with variation in the hydrogen ion concentration of the sol.[3]

[1] WEISER and MIDDLETON: *J. Phys. Chem.*, **24**, 641 (1920).

[2] See p. 91 for a discussion of the influence of purity of sols on the precipitation values.

[3] RONA and LIPMANN: *Biochem. Z.*, **147**, 163 (1924).

The change in dispersity of ferric oxide during coagulation does not involve a measurable heat effect. The precise investigations of Mathews and Browne[1] show that the heat effects during precipitations of sols of low purity, are due to dilution of the ferric chloride and hydrochloric acid in the sols; to mixing of these electrolytes with the coagulating electrolyte; and to changes in the adsorption equilibria. The absence of heat effect on coagulation indicates either (1) a very low interfacial tension between hydrous ferric oxide and water, or (2) no appreciable change in specific surface during coagulation. In support of the latter viewpoint Bradfield[2] showed that so-called "irreversible" coagula could be repeptized by thorough washing in the centrifuge. Apparently, coagulation by electrolytes is not accompanied by a growth of the primary colloidal particles, but the latter merely agglomerate into loose clumps without occasioning any marked decrease in the specific surface.

Effect of Concentration of Sol.—The early observations of Freundlich[3] on the precipitation of colloidal arsenious sulfide led him to the erroneous conclusion that the precipitation values of electrolytes for colloids of different concentrations bear a constant ratio to each other. Thus Kruyt and van der Spek[4] found that the precipitation value of potassium chloride for colloidal arsenious sulfide increases, and of aluminum chloride falls off, with decreasing concentration of colloid; while the precipitation value of barium chloride does not change appreciably with the dilution. Similar results obtained by Burton and Bishop[5] with colloidal arsenious sulfide and mastic[6] led to the formulation of the following rule: The precipitating action of univalent ions increases, that of divalent ions remains unchanged, and that of trivalent ions decreases with diminishing concentra-

---

[1] *J. Am. Chem. Soc.*, **43**, 2336 (1921); BROWNE: *Ibid.*, **45**, 297 (1923).

[2] *J. Am. Chem. Soc.*, **44**, 965 (1922).

[3] *Z. physik. Chem.*, **44**, 129 (1903).

[4] *Kolloid-Z.*, **25**, 3 (1919); *cf.* MUKHOPADHYAYA: *J. Am. Chem. Soc.*, **37**, 2024 (1915).

[5] *J. Phys. Chem.*, **24**, 701 (1920); BURTON and MACINNES: *Ibid.*, **25**, 517 (1921).

[6] *Cf.* NEISSER and FRIEDEMANN: *Münch. med. Wochenschr.*, **51**, 827 (1904); *cf.* BECHHOLD: *Z. physik. Chem.*, **48**, 385 (1904); BACH: *J. chim. phys.*, **18**, 52 (1920).

tion of sol.   Some investigations[1] were carried out in the author's laboratory using colloidal chromic oxide, Prussian blue, Péan de St. Gilles ferric oxide, and arsenious sulfide.   The results of a

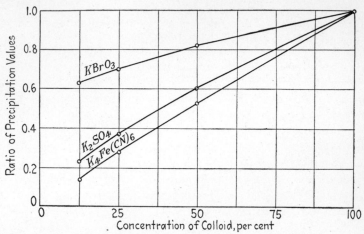

FIG. 3.—Precipitation of colloidal hydrous ferric oxides.

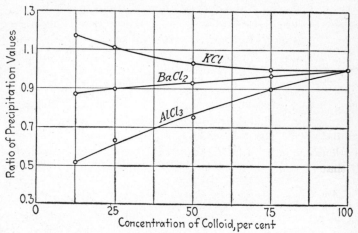

FIG. 4.—Precipitation of colloidal arsenious sulfide sols.

series of experiments on colloidal ferric oxide and arsenious sulfide are given in Table II and shown graphically in Figs. 3 and 4.   The concentrations of the sols are expressed in per

[1] WEISER and NICHOLAS: *J. Phys. Chem.*, **25**, 742 (1921).

cent, taking the most concentrated as 100 per cent. The curves in the figures were obtained by plotting concentration against ratio of each precipitation value for a given electrolyte to that of the strongest sol. In the case of ferric oxide sol, the effect of dilution on the precipitation value of electrolytes is clearly not in accord with Burton and Bishop's rule.[1]

TABLE II

Precipitation of Ferric Oxide Sols

Concentration of colloid, per cent	Precipitation values of		
	$KBrO_3$	K_2SO_4	$K_4Fe(CN)_6$
100 (1.7 grams per liter)	40.1	0.68	0.57
50	34.4	0.41	0.30
25	28.0	0.25	0.16
12.5	25.0	0.16	0.08

Precipitation of Arsenious Sulfide Sols

Concentration of colloid, per cent	Precipitation values of		
	KCl	$BaCl_2$	$AlCl_3$
100 (6.24 grams per liter)	68.3	1.940	0.513
75	68.3	1.877	0.473
50	70.0	1.800	0.380
25	76.7	1.733	0.333
10	80.0	1.683	0.260

Similarly with colloidal Prussian blue[2] and chromic oxide, the precipitation value of all electrolytes diminishes as the concentration of the colloid falls off irrespective of the valence of the precipitating ion. In the case of colloidal arsenious sulfide, the precipitation value of potassium ion increases and of aluminum ion decreases with dilution of the sol, in accord with Burton and

[1] BURTON and BISHOP: *J. Phys. Chem.*, **24**, 701 (1920).
[2] *Cf.*, however, GHOSH and DHAR: *J. Phys. Chem.*, **29**, 663 (1925).

Bishop's rule. However, from the slope of the curve in Fig. 2, it is obviously incorrect to say that the precipitating action of divalent barium ion is independent of the concentration of the colloid; this is no more true of barium ion than of potassium ion.

According to Kruyt and van der Spek, two factors determine the effect of dilution of a colloid on the precipitation value of electrolytes: First, the smaller number of particles requires *less* electrolyte to lower the charge on the particles to the point of agglomeration; and, second, the greater distance between particles making collision less probable, a further reduction in particle charge must be effected through the addition of *more* electrolyte. Since these two factors have opposite effects on the precipitation value, it is only necessary to assume the predominating influence of one or the other in order to account for the results in a given case. Thus, Kruyt and van der Spek assume that the predominating influence in the precipitation of arsenious sulfide with potassium ion is the changing chance of collision, while the more important factor in the precipitation of ferric oxide with chloride ion is the alteration in the required amount to be adsorbed. The difference in behavior with precipitating ions of the same valence is attributed to the lyophile properties of hydrous ferric oxide.

Although both of the factors recognized by Kruyt and van der Spek unquestionably have an influence in determining the effect on the precipitation value of changing the concentration of sol, it would seem that these factors alone are inadequate to account for all the experimental results. The explanation suggested for the difference in behavior of colloidal arsenious sulfide and hydrous ferric oxide with univalent precipitating ions is of doubtful value, particularly since mastic emulsion[1] behaves much like colloidal arsenious sulfide although certainly possessing more lyophile properties than Péan de St. Gilles' ferric oxide. Furthermore, if the decreased chance of collision is the predominating factor in preventing a weaker arsenious sulfide sol from coagulating in a given time in the presence of enough potassium chloride to coagulate a stronger sol, it would seem that

[1] Neisser and Friedemann: *Münch. med. Wochenschr.* **51**, 827 (1904); Burton and Bishop: *J. Phys. Chem.*, **24**, 701 (1920).

complete coagulation of the weaker sol should result if sufficient time were allowed. As a matter of fact, however, enough potassium chloride to precipitate in 2 hours a colloid containing 5 grams per liter will not precipitate a colloid one-fourth as strong in several weeks. Other observations indicate that Kruyt and van der Spek attach too much importance to the decreased chance of collision of the particles resulting from dilution of sols. Thus, everyone finds that the precipitation concentration varies almost directly with the concentration of sol in case the precipitating ion is of high valence.

That the theory of Kruyt and van der Spek should be inadequate in certain respects might be expected, since these investigators concerned themselves only with the precipitating ions of electrolytes, disregarding entirely the effect of adsorption of the stabilizing ions having the same charge as the colloid. If there is no adsorption of the stabilizing ion and if the adsorption of the precipitating ion is very great, there will be a tendency for the precipitation concentration to vary directly with the concentration of the sol. On the other hand, if the stabilizing ion is adsorbed, a greater concentration of precipitating ion will be required to produce coagulation. This effect will be more pronounced the greater the dilution of the sol since the decreased chance both of collision and of coalescence will combine to render the sol proportionately more stable, so that correspondingly more of the precipitating ion must be added for complete precipitation. These conclusions are in accord with experimental results.

With electrolytes having multivalent precipitating ions, the influence of the stabilizing ion is frequently very small, since the adsorption is so slight at the very low precipitation concentration. Under these conditions, the precipitation value diminishes to a greater or lesser extent as the concentration of the colloid decreases. As might be expected, the greater the valence of the precipitating ion and hence the lower the precipitation value, the more nearly we find the latter varying directly with the concentration of the sol.

With electrolytes having univalent precipitating ions, the precipitation value is usually quite large. Although this is generally attributed to weak adsorption of the precipitating ion, at the high concentration necessary for coagulation, the adsorption of the stabilizing ion cannot be disregarded. In fact, if the adsorption of the two ions is of the same order of magnitude, both may be taken up fairly strongly and a high precipitation value will result. Considerable experimental evidence[1] indicates that potassium ion and lithium ion are fairly strongly adsorbed by arsenious sulfide, the high percipitation value of potassium chloride or lithium chloride for this colloid arising from appreciable adsorption of chloride ion. On the other hand, the high precipitation value of potassium chloride for colloidal hydrous ferric oxide is due to relatively weak adsorption of the precipitating ion, the stabilizing ion having much less effect than with colloidal arsenious sulfide.[2] In general, it may be said that the adsorption of the stabilizing ion varies widely but is never negligible for electrolytes which precipitate only in the high concentration characteristic of uni-univalent electrolytes. This adsorption of the ion having the same charge as the sol renders the latter more stable, and proportionately more of the precipitating ion is required for coagulation than in those cases where the influence of the stabilizing ion is negligible. Under these conditions we may expect the precipitation value to fall off much less sharply or even to increase as the colloid concentration is reduced, the increase being greater the higher the valence of the stabilizing ion.

Mutual Precipitation of Sols.—Biltz[3] investigated the precipitation of positive sols, including hydrous ferric oxide by negative colloids, such as platinum, selenium, silica, stannic oxide, molybdenum blue, Mo_3O_8, tungsten blue, W_2O_3, and the sulfides of arsenic, antimony, and cadmium. Complete precipitation occurs when a sol of one sign is neutralized by adsorption of an amount of colloid carrying an equivalent quantity of ion of opposite sign. The amount of various colloids necessary to effect mutual precipitation will depend on their nature. Thus a certain colloidal ferric oxide is more effective than cerium oxide and less effective than thorium oxide in precipitating colloidal gold; while both thorium oxide and cerium oxide are more effec-

[1] WEISER: *J. Phys. Chem.*, **25**, 665 (1921); *Ibid.*, **28**, 232 (1924).
[2] WEISER: *Loc. cit.; cf.* FREUNDLICH: *Z. physik. Chem.*, **44**, 157 (1903).
[3] *Ber.*, **37**, 1095 (1904).

tive than ferric oxide in precipitating colloidal antimony sulfide and arsenious sulfide. Similarly, a red colloidal gold, prepared by reduction of gold chloride with formaldehyde, requires for complete precipitation considerably less of a given ferric oxide sol than a blue-gold sol prepared with phosphorus as reducing agent.[1] Recently, Freundlich and Nathanson[2] found colloidal arsenious sulfide sol and Oden's sulfur sol to be instable in the presence of each other. Since both sols are negatively charged, this instability cannot be due to neutralization by adsorption, but was found to result from interaction between the stabilizing agents of the two sols, hydrogen sulfide and pentathionic acid. This observation led Thomas and Johnson[3] to attribute the mutual precipitation of sols of opposite sign to chemical inter-action of the stabilizing electrolytes in the sols. Thus, the precipitation of Graham's colloidal ferric oxide, stabilized by hydrogen ion, and colloidal stannic oxide, stabilized by hydroxyl ion, was attributed to chemical neutralization. This view was supported by the observation that mutual precipitation was effected over a limited range of purity of sols, when the hydro-chloric acid and sodium hydroxide concentrations in the sols were approximately equivalent. The variation from equivalence was quite marked in case the sols were fairly pure. Thus a silica sol containing 16 SiO_2 to 1 $NaOH$ was precipitated at various dilutions with a sol containing 13 Fe_2O_3 to 1 $FeCl_3$. At the highest dilution possible for obtaining accurate data, mutual precipitation was observed when an amount of colloidal silica was added corresponding to but 50 per cent of the hydrochloric acid. This variation was attributed to the metastability of pure sols, which causes them to precipitate with a subnormal disturbance. This does not seem quite convincing since, in the absence of contamination other than that mentioned, the purity of the sols would scarcely be great enough to make them abnor-mally sensitive. Erratic results were also obtained when the amount of peptizing agent was too large, say three times as much as in the case referred to above. Thus, to obtain data to support a purely chemical mechanism involving the stabilizing agents,

[1] GALECKI and KASTOVSKI: *Kolloid-Z.*, **13**, 143 (1913).
[2] *Kolloid-Z.*, **28**, 258 (1921); **29**, 16 (1921).
[3] *J. Am. Chem. Soc.*, **45**, 2532 (1923).

it seems necessary to choose the experimental conditions to fit
the case.   While everyone will agree that the peptizing agents of
two sols may interact under certain conditions, thus affecting
the stability of each, such an interpretation of the mechanism of
the mutual precipitation process would not account for the
repeated observation of mutual precipitation of sols where interaction between the peptizing agents is impossible or improbable.
A sol peptized by hydrogen ion will be precipitated by a base or
by a salt of a weak acid.   From such observations alone, we
might conclude that the precipitation of the sol was a result of
chemical neutralization of the stabilizing agent.   But the same
sol will, in general, be precipitated with a small amount of an
acid having a multivalent ion where chemical neutralization of
hydrogen ion is impossible.

If there are no disturbing influences, such as interaction between
peptizing agents, Wintgen and Löwenthal[1] found the reciprocal
precipitation of oppositely charged sols to be a maximum when
the concentrations of the sols, expressed in "equivalent aggregates," are the same; that is, when equal numbers of charges of
opposite sign are mixed.   This rule does not hold in certain
cases where a highly dispersed sol of one sign is mixed with a
coarser sol of opposite sign, possibly because the smaller particles
penetrate the larger ones and are precipitated by the electrolyte
contained in the latter.

Billitzer[2] found that gelatin in acid or neutral solution is a
positive sol and so precipitates negative sols, but not positive
ones such as hydrous ferric oxide; whereas gelatin in ammoniacal
solution is a negative sol and precipitates hydrous ferric oxide.
No precipitate is thrown down, however, if gelatin is first added
to colloidal ferric oxide, followed by the addition of ammonia.
In the latter case, we get a stable mixture of positive sols changed
simultaneously to a stable mixture of negative sols by the addition of hydroxyl ions.

Brossa and Freundlich[3] studied the precipitation and repeptization of colloidal albumin by means of colloidal ferric oxide in
the presence of electrolytes.   The amount of albumin thrown

---

[1] *Z. physik. Chem.*, **109**, 391 (1924).

[2] *Z. physik. Chem.*, **51**, 148 (1905).

[3] *Z. physik. Chem.*, **89**, 306 (1915).

down by the ferric oxide sol decreases with decreasing concentration of electrolytes until eventually only a slight turbidity results, which disappears on adding a sufficient amount of ferric oxide sol. Obviously, the colloidal ferric oxide adsorbs, and so keeps the colloidal albumin in solution. The ferric oxide-albumin sol formed in this way is positively charged but is much more sensitive than the original sol. The sensitivity is at its maximum when the ferric oxide has adsorbed all the negative albumin sol that it can hold, without precipitation taking place. With increasing concentrations of ferric oxide sol, the sensitivity falls off, approaching that of the pure positive sol. If instead of adding an electrolyte to a ferric oxide-albumin sol, an albumin sol containing an electrolyte is precipitated with ferric oxide sol, the relationships are identical in many respects, particularly in the amount of albumin adsorbed by the ferric oxide. The presence of non-electrolytes such as urethane, camphor, and thymol have likewise been shown to increase the sensitivity of ferric oxide sol toward electrolytes.[1] Freundlich attributes this to a lowering of the surface charge on the particles as a result of adsorption of a substance having a lower dielectric constant than water; but Michaelis[2] failed to detect any adsorption of non-electrolytes by hydrous ferric oxide or any effect of their presence on the adsorption of electrolytes. This failure to confirm Freundlich's hypothesis may be due to the limitations of the experimental method in the systems investigated. The author[3] has observed a marked antagonistic action of phenol and isoamyl alcohol on the adsorption of barium ion by colloidal arsenious sulfide.

Ferric Oxide Jellies.—Although hydrous ferric oxide is usually thrown down as a gelatinous precipitate, jellies may be prepared by coagulation of a sol under suitable conditions. Thus, Grimaux[4] added to an excess of water an alcoholic solution of ferric ethylate which hydrolyzed very rapidly, forming a colloidal ferric oxide. The sol was similar to Graham's, but the

---

[1] Freundlich and Rona: *Biochem. Z.*, **81**, 87 (1915); *cf.* Matsuno: *Biochem. Z.*, **150**, 139 (1924).

[2] Michaelis and Rona: *Biochem. Z.*, **102**, 268 (1920).

[3] Weiser: *J. Phys. Chem.*, **28**, 1253 (1924).

[4] *Compt. rend.*, **98**, 105, 1434 (1884).

particles were probably much smaller on account of the more rapid rate of hydrolysis.[1] The sol coagulated spontaneously on standing for some time at room temperature; and more rapidly on heating or by the addition of electrolytes such as carbonic, sulfuric, and tartaric acids; the nitrate, chloride, and bromide of potassium; the chlorides of sodium and barium, etc. The coagulum formed in every case was a transparent jelly, provided the sol was not agitated during the process of coagulation. Even with quite dilute sols, the jelly was firm; but contraction took place, very slowly in the cold and more rapidly at high temperature.

With colloidal ferric oxide as with a number of other sols, slow uniform precipitation throughout the entire solution produces a jelly, while rapid uneven precipitation results in contraction and the consequent formation of a gelatinous precipitate. As compared with the usual Graham sol, Grimaux's colloid is much more easily thrown down in the form of a jelly. This is accounted for by the fact that a sol formed by rapid hydrolysis in the cold will contain finer and more hydrous particles than one formed by prolonged dialysis in the cold or shorter dialysis in the hot. For the same reason, the coagulum from the Graham sol is much more hydrous and bulky than that obtained from a Péan de St. Gilles sol. The usual Graham sol can be precipitated as a jelly, provided the concentration is sufficiently high. Schalek and Szegvary[2] added electrolytes in amounts below their precipitation values to colloidal solutions containing 6 to 10 per cent of ferric oxide and allowed the sols to stand quietly. After a time, the mixture set to a jelly that was no more cloudy than the original sol. This jelly solidified slowly after shaking up. The logarithm of the time required for solidification after shaking was found to be inversely proportional to the temperature and to the concentration of coagulating electrolyte. Ultramicroscopic observation of the liquefaction process showed no change in the average distance between the particles and no formation of secondary particles. I am inclined to attribute the reversible sol-gel transformation in such a system to the breaking

[1] *Cf.* WAGNER: *Kolloid-Z.*, **14**, 150 (1914).

[2] *Kolloid-Z.*, **32**, 318 (1923); **33**, 326 (1923); FREUNDLICH and ROSENTHAL: *Ibid.*, **37**, 129 (1925).

up and subsequent realignment of the orienting forces among the particles.

Ferric oxide jellies may be prepared also, by slow removal of the peptizing agent by dialysis. Thus Grimaux[1] obtained a firm jelly by dialysis of a negative sol prepared by peptization of the hydrous oxide with alkali in the presence of glycerin. If ammonia were used instead of alkali, and the sol exposed to the air, the slow loss of peptizing agent by evaporation resulted in the precipitation of a jelly. Grimaux's observations were confirmed by Fischer,[2] who prepared a firm jelly on prolonged dialysis of a sol containing but 1 per cent of iron. Unlike the more concentrated jellies of Schalek and Szegvary, this preparation broke down into a gelatinous precipitate when it was warmed, stirred, or frozen, Browne[3] obtained a jelly simply by allowing part of the water to evaporate slowly from a concentrated Graham sol of high purity.

ADSORPTION BY HYDROUS FERRIC OXIDE

Hydrous ferric oxide as a technical adsorbent finds its most important use as a mordant in the dye industry and in the purification of municipal water supplies. These applications are considered in Chaps. XVI and XVII, respectively.

Adsorption of Arsenious Acid.—Ninety years ago Bunsen[4] made the important discovery that freshly precipitated hydrous ferric oxide is an antidote for arsenic poisoning. As might be expected, this action was attributed by Bunsen to stoichiometric chemical union of ferric oxide and arsenious acid. While some people[5] still maintain that iron arsenites of varying degrees of complexity[6] are formed when hydrous ferric oxide and arsenious acid are brought together under varying conditions, the investigations of Biltz[7] show the apparent interaction to be an adsorption

[1] *Compt. rend.*, **98**, 1485 (1884).

[2] *Biochem. Z.*, **27**, 223 (1910).

[3] Private communication.

[4] BUNSEN and BERTHOLD: "Hydrated Ferric Oxide, an Antidote for Arsenious Acid," Göttingen (1834); *cf.* GUIBOURT: *Arch. Pharm.*, (2) **23**, 69 (1840).

[5] REYCHLER: *J. chim. phys.*, **7**, 362 (1909); **8**, 10 (1910).

[6] ORYNG: *Kolloid-Z.*, **22**, 149 (1918).

[7] *Ber.*, **37**, 3138 (1904); *cf. Kolloid-Z.*, **26**, 179 (1920).

process in which the arsenic content of the hydrous oxide varies continuously with the concentration of arsenious acid in contact with it, giving a typical adsorption isotherm without a break or an evidence of discontinuity.

Lockemann and Paucke[1] made a quantitative study of the adsorption of arsenious acid by charcoal, aluminum oxide, ferric oxide, and albumin. With ferric oxide, they find most complete adsorption when the iron is precipitated with stoichiometric quantities of ammonia; excess of ammonia or precipitation by potassium or sodium hydroxide decreases the adsorbability. This accords with Bradfield's[2] observation that the most finely divided and most readily peptized particles of hydrous ferric oxide are formed by precipitation with but a very slight excess of ammonia. The amount of hydrous oxide necessary to adsorb a given amount of arsenic can be calculated by means of the formula $E = \beta A p$ where $E =$ milligrams ferric oxide, $A =$ milligrams arsenic, and β and p are constants which vary with the temperature;[3] but it should be pointed out that this equation serves only as a simple approximation to the course of the adsorption.[4]

Fischer and Juznitzky[5] injected colloidal ferric oxide simultaneously with arsenious acid, under the skins of mice, and obtained partial protection from a fatal dose of arsenic. The negative colloidal hydrous oxide formed by peptizing ferric oxide with dilute alkali and glycerin was more effective than a positive Graham sol. Since it was thought improbable that a negative colloid would adsorb a negative ion, Fischer advanced the more improbable hypothesis that the antidotal effect was due to the formation of an iron-arsenic complex of some sort. These observations should be confirmed and a plausible explanation formulated.

Catalytic Action.—Slightly hydrous or anhydous ferric oxide seems to have a relatively high adsorption capacity for gases

---

[1] *Kolloid-Z.*, **8**, 273 (1911).

[2] *J. Am. Chem. Soc.*, **44**, 965 (1922).

[3] Cf. LOCKEMANN and LUCIUS: *Z. physik. Chem.*, **83**, 735 (1913).

[4] BOSWELL and DICKSON: *J. Am. Chem. Soc.*, **40**, 1793 (1918); *cf.* MECK-LENBURG: *Z. physik. Chem.*, **83**, 609 (1913).

[5] *Biochem. Z.*, **27**, 311 (1911).

even at elevated temperatures since it is used as a catalyst in such industrial operations as the burning of hydrogen sulfide in the Chance-Claus process for recovering sulfur from alkali waste;[1] in the Hargreaves and Robinson process for making salt cake;[2] and in the manufacture of sulfuric acid by the contact process.[3] In the latter process the conversion of sulfur dioxide to trioxide is 98 per cent using platinum as catalyst at 425°, dropping to 91 per cent at 500° owing to dissociation of the trioxide. The velocity with which sulfur dioxide and oxygen combine is less in the presence of ferric oxide so that it is necessary to work at a higher temperature when this catalyst is employed. On this account, the efficiency does not rise much over 60 per cent. It ought to be possible to make a ferric oxide catalyst that would work at as low a temperature as platinum if adsorption were the sole criterion of catalytic efficiency. Unfortunately this does not appear to be the case, as evidenced by such cases as charcoal which has a high adsorptive capacity but relatively poor catalytic properties. A good catalyst is a good adsorbent but the converse is not necessarily true.

Adsorption during Precipitation of Sol. "Acclimatization."— When a positive colloidal solution of hydrous ferric oxide is agglomerated by the addition of electrolytes, there is considerable adsorption of the negative precipitating ion.[4] From precipitation and adsorption experiments, the order of precipitating power of the anions, deduced on the assumption that the most readily adsorbed anion precipitates at lowest concentration, was found to be different from the order obtained directly from adsorption data. The explanation of the discrepancy is that the adsorption measured is not ion adsorption only, but is ion adsorption plus adsorption of neutral salt during agglomeration. On account of

[1] THORPE: "Dictionary of Applied Chemistry," **5**, 294 (1917); JOBLING: "Catalysis and Industrial Applications," **33**, (1916); RIDEAL and TAYLOR: "Catalysis in Theory and Practice," 112 (1919).

[2] THORPE: *Loc. cit.*, **5**, 25 (1913); JOBLING: *Loc. cit.*, **32**, (1916); RIDEAL and TAYLOR: *Loc. cit.*, 89 (1919).

[3] LUNGE and REINHARDT: *Z. angew. Chem.*, **17**, 1041 (1904); KEPPELER, D'ANS, SUNDELL, and KAISER: *Ibid.*, **21**, 532, 577 (1908); KEPPELER and D'ANS: *Z. physik. Chem.*, **62**, 89 (1908); WÖHLER, PLUDDEMANN, and WÖHLER: *Ibid.*, **62**, 653 (1908).

[4] WEISER and MIDDLETON: *J. Phys. Chem.*, **24**, 30 (1920).

the variation of the latter with the nature of the salt, the true order of adsorbability of the ion is masked.

Since adsorption by neutralized colloidal particles during agglomeration is not negligible in any case and may rise to large proportions,[1] it is not surprising that such colloids as hydrous ferric oxide,[2] arsenious sulfide,[2] and albumin[3] require less electrolyte to cause precipitation when added all at once than when added stepwise through a long interval of time, particularly when the slow addition produces fractional precipitation of the sol. This phenomenon is known as "acclimatization," the connotation being that the colloid becomes acclimatized to its surrounding when the electrolyte is added slowly and so more is required to produce a given result. It would appear, however, that the necessity for using more electrolyte to effect complete precipitation on slow addition arises not so much from the adaptability of the colloid to the presence of electrolytes, as from fractional precipitation, which not only removes ions owing to adsorption by neutralized particles but alters the stability of the sol by decreasing its concentration. From this point of view, the factors which determine the excess required for a given slow rate of addition are: the extent to which the colloid undergoes fractional precipitation; the adsorbing power of the precipitated colloid; the adsorption of the precipitating ions; and the effect of dilution of the sol on the precipitation concentration of electrolytes.[4]

THE COLOR OF HYDROUS FERRIC OXIDE

That hydrous ferric oxide exists in many different colors, varying from yellow to violet red, is evident from the colors of the minerals. Thus, anhydrous hematite is black when crystalline and red when powdered; turgite is a deep brown; limonite varies from a light brown to yellow; and limnite is a full yellow.[5] It is now known that hematite was the red ceramic pigment used by the prehistoric Indians of the Southwest. Their black

[1] FREUNDLICH: *Z. physik. Chem.*, **44,** 151 (1903); WEISER: *J. Phys. Chem.*, **25,** 405 (1921); **30,** 22 (1926).

[2] FREUNDLICH: *Z. physik. Chem.*, **44,** 143 (1903).

[3] HÖBER and GORDON: *Beitr. chem. Physiol. Path.*, **5,** 436 (1904).

[4] WEISER: *J. Phys. Chem.*, **25,** 413 (1921); **30,** 20 (1926).

[5] DAMMER: "Handbuch anorg. Chem.," **3,** 304 (1893).

pigment was the magnetic oxide of iron commonly called magnetite.[1]

The variations in color of the anhydrous oxide appear to be due to the size of the particles. Thus Andersen[2] found plates of hematite as thin as 0.1μ to be yellow by transmitted light, the color varying with increasing thickness through reddish brown to deep brown·red or blood red; similarly, Wöhler and Condrea[3] prepared anhydrous oxides that vary in color from yellow to red by simply varying the size of the particles, the red being the largest. Keane[4] attributes the yellow color of the so-called Mars pigments to finely divided ferric oxide which is kept from agglomerating by the presence of aluminum oxide; and the yellow color which iron imparts to bricks, to sufficiently finely divided anhydrous ferric oxide; when the particles are too large, the color is red rather than yellow.[5] Mott[6] obtained anhydrous red and yellow ferric oxide by volatilization in the electric arc; the yellow particles were the smaller.

The hydrous oxide can be prepared in a variety of colors so similar to those of the anhydrous oxide that it seems reasonable to attribute the difference in color to the same cause—a difference in the size of the hydrous particles. As a matter of fact, the variation in color from brown through yellow to red was shown by Malfitano and by Fischer to be associated with an increase in the size of the particles although they did not recognize the possible connection between the two. That there is a definite connection between particle size and color was shown by a series of experiments[7] on the hydrolysis of ferric chloride solutions. The very finely divided brown particles may be transformed either into the larger yellow or the still larger brick red, by heating under suitable conditions.

Since a very dilute solution of ferric chloride is colorless at the outset, changing spontaneously to yellow and then to reddish

[1] GERMANN: *Science,* **30,** 20 (1926).
[2] *Am. J. Sci.,* (4) **40,** 370 (1913).
[3] *Z. angew. Chem.,* **21,** 481 (1908).
[4] *J. Phys. Chem.,* **20,** 734 (1916).
[5] *Cf.* SCHEETZ: *J. Phys. Chem.,* **21,** 576 (1917); YOE: *Ibid.,* **25,** 196 (1921).
[6] *Trans. Am. Electrochem. Soc.,* **34,** 292 (1918).
[7] *J. Phys. Chem.,* **23,** 313 (1920).

brown,[1] it would appear that yellow hydrous particles are smaller than brown. This conclusion is unwarranted, since the color of a dilute colloidal solution is not necessarily determined by the color of the particles. Thus colloidal solutions of gold have been obtained which are red, violet, or blue by transmitted light;[2] but this does not tell us the color of light reflected from the particles in the respective sols. As a matter of fact, massive gold reflects yellow when compact and brown to black when porous. Small particles of gold which do not resonate are yellow to brown by reflected light and transmit blue. The surface color of gold is red by multiple reflection and very thin films are green by transmitted light.[3] Colloidal solutions with very fine particles of gold reflect green and transmit red. Hence, we conclude that the particles in the blue sol are yellow to brown, and in the red sol they are green.[4] A deep-red Graham colloid from which can be thrown down a red-brown gelatinous precipitate appears distinctly yellow when diluted sufficiently. A 5-year-old brick-red Péan de St. Gilles sol appears yellower on dilution, although the reddish color persists. It is possible that the reddish-brown particles in a red Graham colloid transmit more yellow than red when sufficiently highly dispersed. At any rate, there seems no reason for believing the yellow colloid formed by hydrolysis of ferric chloride to be other than a highly diluted Graham sol. The color of such a solution becomes redder with age, owing to the formation of more red-brown colloidal hydrous oxide. A thousandth normal solution which Goodwin found to be completely hydrolyzed in a few hours, is very much redder than a fiftieth normal or hundredth normal solution after 24 hours.

It appears that a colloidal solution of hydrous ferric oxide contains varying amounts of small highly hydrous red-brown particles and larger less hydrous yellowish-brown particles, both of which may be converted into still larger and less hydrous brick-red particles by heating at 100°. If the conditions are such that the red particles remain in colloidal solution, we have the

---

[1] ANTONY and GIGLIO: *Gazz. chim. ital.*, **25**, 1 (1895); GOODWIN: *Z. physik. Chem.*, **21**, 1 (1896); *cf.* WAGNER: *Kolloid-Z.*, **14**, 150 (1914).

[2] FARADAY: *Phil. Trans.*, **147**, 145 (1857).

[3] BEILBY: *Proc. Roy. Soc.*, **72**, 226 (1913).

[4] *Cf.* BANCROFT: "Applied Colloid Chemistry," 004 (1921).

.rick-red Péan de St. Gilles colloid. Bradfield[1] demonstrated conclusively that the reddish-brown precipitate formed by adding ammonia to ferric chloride solution until minute floccules are barely visible, contains both very small highly hydrous dark-brown particles and larger less hydrous yellowish-brown particles which can be separated rather sharply from each other by centrifuging the suspended precipitate. Both the reddish and yellowish particles in a sol formed by heating a 1 per cent solution of ferric chloride from room temperature to the boiling point appear to be transformed to larger less hydrous bright-red particles by heating at 100°. The granular ocher-yellow particles formed by heating a more concentrated solution slowly are not converted into the red at this temperature. This difference might be ascribed to the dense granular character of the particles which precipitate on heating the more concentrated solutions; but it will be recalled that a yellow Péan de St. Gilles colloid formed by slow hydrolysis of ferric acetate is not changed to red by prolonged boiling of the sol. The yellow particles formed under certain conditions lose water much less readily at 100° than the reddish brown; and this seems to account for the difference in behavior. As previously pointed out, Keane and Scheetz have shown the yellow color of bricks to be due to finely divided anhydrous ferric oxide which is kept from agglomerating by alumina and probably by certain other substances as well. This requires a rather high percentage of alumina. In the so-called Mars pigments which are yellow, the ferric oxide is in the hydrous state; and in this condition it agglomerates less readily to the red oxide, and less alumina is required to prevent the transformation. Since the yellow oxide retains its water more tenaciously than the brown, it is natural to inquire into the cause of the increased stability. In view of the synthesis of a yellow monohydrate of ferric oxide by the slow hydrolysis of ferric sulfate,[2] it would appear reasonable to conclude that the yellow oxide which does not lose water and become red at 100° is ferric oxide monohydrate. The yellow oxide that apparently loses water and agglomerates to red at 100° may be regarded as hydrous ferric oxide in which the particles are somewhat larger and less hydrous

---

[1] *J. Am. Chem. Soc.*, **44**, 965 (1922).
[2] Posnjak and Merwin: *J. Am. Chem. Soc.*, **44**, 1965 (1922).

than the brown. But as I am aware of no case in which yellow
hydrous particles free from brown appear to be transformed into
red by heating at 100°, it is open to anyone to assume that the
yellow particles are really never transformed into red; but that
the bright-red color formed by agglomeration of the brown oxide
masks the yellow monohydrate.

If one objects to the assumption that the yellow colloid is a
hydrous monohydrate, another alternative is to attribute its
stability at 100° to adsorption of some salt. Bancroft[1] suggested
that the yellow color of the oxide is due to the presence of
adsorbed ferric salt. This suggestion was based on Fischer's
observation that the brown colloid goes over into red in the presence of hydrochloric acid; on Malfitano's experiment, that the
brown colloid is transformed into the yellow by boiling with
ferric chloride; and on Phillips' method of preparing the yellow
oxide by oxidation of ferrous carbonate. Malfitano's observation is inconclusive, since boiling a ferric chloride solution alone
will give a yellow colloid. Moreover, the author precipitated
the hydrous oxide in a gelatinous form in the presence of a large
excess of ferric chloride, a condition favorable to adsorption of
ferric salt; and yet the oxide was distinctly red. Hence, there
seems no reason for attributing the color of the yellow colloid
to adsorbed iron salt. Bancroft's hypothesis was the outgrowth
of the observation that the yellow colloid is formed when the
adsorption of an iron salt is a possibility. The converse appears
not to be the case, namely, that the adsorption of an iron salt
always results in the formation of a yellow hydrous oxide.
Although the adsorption of an iron salt does not impart a yellow
color to a hydrous ferric oxide, it is possible that the yellow oxide
which is not converted to red by heating at 100° is stabilized by
adsorbed iron salt.

LOWER OXIDES OF IRON

Hydrous Ferrous Oxide.—On account of its relatively low
solubility, hydrous ferrous oxide comes down in a highly gelatinous form when a solution of ferrous salt is treated with potassium or sodium hydroxide.[2] The gel is white when absolutely

---

[1] *J. Phys. Chem.*, **19**, 232 (1916).
[2] SCHMIDT: *Liebig's Ann. Chem.*, **36**, 101 (1840).

pure; but owing to the difficulty in excluding all air during pre-cipitating and washing, it is usually obtained as a green hydrous mass. Even when dried, the gel oxidizes so readily in the air that the whole mass sometimes becomes incandescent.

As ordinarily prepared, the gel is hydrous FeO; but de Schulten[1] obtained the monohydrate or hydroxide by crystallization from solution in strong caustic soda. The crystals were small green prisms which oxidized very rapidly in the air even after they were washed with alcohol and ether, and dried in hydrogen. Owing to its strong affinity for oxygen, the oxide is a powerful reducing agent, converting nitrites and nitrates to ammonia, a reaction that may be used for the quantitative estimation of the substances.[2]

Whitman, Russell, and Davis[3] find that the rate of corrosion of iron in salt solutions parallels the solubility of ferrous hydroxide in these solutions. It is suggested that this is due to changes in film protectivity with the solubility of the ferrous salt.

Hydrous Ferro-ferric Oxide.—The gel of ferro-ferric oxide is obtained by adding alkali to a solution containing equivalent amounts of ferrous and ferric salts. If washed and dried out of contact with air, it is a magnetic brownish-black mass containing an indefinite amount of water.[4]

---

[1] *Compt. rend.*, **109**, 266 (1889).

[2] MIYAMOTO: *J. Chem. Soc. Japan*, **43**, 397 (1922).

[3] *J. Am. Chem. Soc.*, **47**, 70 (1925); *cf.* FRIEND: *J. Chem. Soc.*, **119**, 932 (1921).

[4] WÖHLER: *Liebig's Ann. Chem.*, **22**, 56 (1838); LEFORT: *Compt. rend.*, **69**, 179 (1869).

CHAPTER III

HYDROUS CHROMIC OXIDE

Composition.—The addition of ammonia or an alkali to a solution of chromic salt precipitates chromic oxide as a highly hydrous gel, the composition and properties of which depend on the conditions of precipitation and the subsequent treatment. The gel is frequently designated chromic hydroxide and assigned the formula $Cr(OH)_3$ or $Cr_2O_3 \cdot 3H_2O$, although 35 years ago van Bemmelen[1] determined the isotherm for chromic oxide and water between 15 and 280° and found no evidence of any definite hydrate. As van Bemmelen's observations have been confirmed by von Baikow,[2] it is altogether likely that the various so-called hydrates described from time to time[3] were merely hydrous chromic oxides dried to a composition expressible by a Dalton formula.

Férée[4] claims to have obtained the compound $Cr_2O_3 \cdot H_2O$ by electrolysis of a neutral solution of chromium chloride with a platinum cathode. The brownish-black amorphous powder loses water on heating to 80°; but it is questionable whether this is a definite inversion temperature at which all the water is lost. It is also claimed by some that a green hydrate, Guignet's green,[5] is formed by fusing 1 part of bichromate of sodium, potassium, or ammonium with 3 parts of boric acid; but there is a

[1] *Rec. trav. chim.*, **7**, 37 (1888).

[2] *J. Russ. Phys.-Chem. Soc.*, **39**, 660 (1907).

[3] SCHAFFNER: *Liebig's Ann. Chem.*, **51**, 169 (1844); SIEWERT: *Jahresber.*, 242 (1861); LOEWEL: *J. Pharm.*, (3) **7**, 323, 401, 424 (1845); FREMY: *Compt. rend.*, **27**, 269; **30**, 415 (1847); **47**, 883 (1858); LEFORT: *J. Pharm.*, (3) **18**, 27 (1850); VINCENT: *Phil. Mag.*, (4) **13**, 191 (1850).

[4] *Bull. soc. chim.*, (3) **25**, 620 (1901); *cf.* BUNSEN: *Pogg. Ann.*, **91**, 619 (1854); GEUTHER: *Liebig's Ann. Chem.*, **118**, 66 (1861).

[5] GUIGNET: *Jahresber.*, 761 (1859).

difference of opinion as to the formula.[1] Wöhler and Becker[2] obtained a similar green pigment by heating the ordinary oxide in an autoclave at 180 to 250°. It retains its color when dried at 80° but darkens gradually and loses water above this temperature. The oxide was taken to be a definite hydrate, since its composition on drying at 80° may be represented by the formula $2Cr_2O_3 \cdot 3H_2O$. The green pigment prepared in any way is amorphous in character and, like the ordinary precipitated oxide, loses water continuously as the temperature is raised. Of course, it is entirely possible to dry the pigment under such conditions that the percentage composition may be expressed by a simple formula, but that does not prove that a true hydrate is formed.

Ageing.—Hydrous chromic oxide, freshly precipitated from a cold chromic salt solution with an alkali or ammonia, is readily soluble in acids giving the corresponding salts and is peptized by alkali hydroxides with the formation of a colloidal solution. On standing, the oxide undergoes a change in physical character accompanied by a marked decrease in solubility and reactivity. This process called "ageing" is probably due to the growth and agglomeration of primary colloidal particles, since the velocity of change increases rapidly with rising temperature and is hastened in a medium possessing a slight solvent action. Recoura[3] followed the change by determining the molar heat of solution in hydrochloric acid of the oxide precipitated with acid from the colloidal solution in alkali, after definite intervals of time. From his results given in Table III, it will be noted that the change in the heat of solution is quite marked during the first few minutes. This change is accompanied by a similar decrease in solubility. Since the ageing is more rapid at higher temperatures, the oxide precipitated at 100° is much less soluble than that thrown down at room temperature.

[1] SALVÉTÄT: *Compt. rend.*, **48**, 295 (1859); SCHEURER-KESTNER: *Dinglers polytech. J.*, **176**, 386 (1865); EBNER and HUE: *Farbeztg.*, **15**, 2106, 2157, 2213, 2268, 2319 (1910).

[2] *Z. angew. Chem.*, **21**, 1600 (1908); **24**, 484 (1911).

[3] *Compt. rend.*, **120**, 1335 (1895); *cf.* FRICKE and WINDHAUSEN: *Z. physik. Chem.*, **113**, 248 (1924); *Z. anorg. Chem.*, **132**, 273 (1924).

TABLE III.—MOLAR HEAT OF SOLUTION OF HYDROUS CHROMIC OXIDES
PRECIPITATED FROM SOLUTION IN ALKALI

Time	Molar heat of solution, calories	Time	Molar heat of solution, calories
0	20.70	7 hours	2.40
10 minutes	7.90	1 day	1.75
1 hour	5.80	7 days	1.20
2 hours	3.90	30 days	0.75
4 hours	2.85	60 days	0.50

Solutions of hydrous chromic oxide in alkali were found by Bourion and Senechal[1] to lose their reducing power toward hydrogen peroxide on standing. The reaction (loss of reducing power) with a solution containing 0.938 gram chromic oxide and 58 grams sodium hydroxide per liter appeared to be approximately tetramolecular for the first 8 hours. The results were attributed to the transformation of the original oxide into complexes of decreasing chemical activity, the tetramolecular order being only apparent. Bourion and Senechal evidently believe that hydrous chromic oxide dissolves in alkali with the formation of chromite; but in reality it is held in colloidal solution, for the most part. The decreased activity on standing is due to a gradual change in the physical character of the particles, a change that is sufficiently marked with a concentrated sol to cause partial precipitation in a short time. This transformation from a very soluble to a less soluble and less reactive form of hydrous chromic oxide has very naturally been attributed to the existence of definite allotropic or isomeric modifications. This is very unlikely, particularly since there is no inversion point for a soluble and an insoluble modification. Between these two extremes of solubility, it is possible to prepare an indefinite number of hydrous oxides, each differing slightly from the others in water content, in size of particles, in structure of the mass, and consequently, in reactivity with acids and alkalies.[2]

The Glow Phenomenon.—When hydrous chromic oxide is heated at a suitable rate to temperatures around 500°, it evolves

[1] *Compt. rend.*, **168**, 59, 89 (1919).
[2] FRICKE and WINDHAUSEN: *Z. anorg. Chem.*, **132**, 273 (1924).

enough heat to cause it to become incandescent. The temperature at which the glowing takes place varies with the sample and with the method of heating. Berzelius, Wöhler,[1] and Endell and Rieke[2] give approximately 500° for the glow temperature; Le Chatelier[3] gives 900°, and Rothaug[4] finds it to vary between 420 and 680°, depending on whether the precipitate is in a powdery or granular form. The glow is regarded by some[5] as an accompaniment of the transformation of one allotropic modification of the oxide to another; but this seems unlikely, since the glowing depends on the rate of heating[6] and since the glow temperature varies with the size of the particles. Moreover, the phenomenon is observed with a number[7] of hydrous oxides as well as other substances; and it is improbable that all of them should exist in two forms. Wöhler found that the glowing is increased by all conditions which favor hydrosol formation in the preparation of the oxide, for example, the use of dilute solutions of reagents, the use of chloride rather than sulfate, and of potassium hydroxide rather than ammonium hydroxide. Moreover, the glow was found to be greater, the greater the adsorption capacity of the precipitate, indicating that the phenomenon is connected closely with the surface area. Under the same conditions of heating, the heat evolved by 1 gram of oxide was sufficient to raise its temperature anywhere from 50 to 100°, depending altogether on the extent of surface.

In the light of Wöhler's observations, there is little doubt but that the glow is due to a very sudden decrease in the large surface of the oxides prepared by precipitation. The oxides thrown down under different conditions vary in the size of the particles and the amount of enclosed water and hence in the extent of surface. The maximum glow and heat evolution are obtained when the sample, made up of finest particles, is heated rapidly

[1] *Kolloid-Z.*, **11**, 241 (1913).

[2] *Zentr. Min. Geol.*, 246 (1914).

[3] *Bull. soc. chim.*, (2) **47**, 303 (1887).

[4] *Z. anorg. Chem.*, **84**, 165 (1913).

[5] MOISSAN: *Bull. soc. chim.*, (2) **34**, 70 (1880); *Ann. chim. phys.*, (5) **21**, 199 (1880); LE CHATELIER: *Bull. soc. chim.*, (2) **47**, 303 (1887); MIXER: *Am. J. Sci.*, (4) **26**, 125 (1908); **39**, 295 (1915).

[6] SIEWERT: *Jahresber.*, 243 (1861); *cf.* MIXER: *Loc. cit.*

[7] WÖHLER: *Kolloid-Z.*, **11**, 241 (1913); ENDELL and RIEKE: *Loc. cit.*

to the glow temperature, which is in the neighborhood of 500.° If a fine-grained precipitate is heated very slowly or kept for some time below the glow temperature, there is a gradual, instead of a sudden, diminution of surface, which is not accompanied by incandescence. Thus, glowing at elevated temperatures is the visible manifestation of the coalescence of primary colloidal particles into larger masses, involving a marked decrease in specific surface. Similarly, at ordinary temperature the gradual change in solubility, in reactivity, and in molal heat of solution in hydrochloric acid is due to coalescence of the small primary particles into larger primary particles with the concomitant diminution in specific surface. This change is a truly irreversible process differing from ordinary coagulation in which the primary particles merely form secondary aggregates with very little change in specific surface.[1]

Color.—Hydrous chromic oxide can be obtained in various shades from a clear gray blue to a dark green. Certain of these colors, such as chrome green and Guignet's green, constitute the most permanent green pigments. The color of the oxide freshly precipitated in the cold is variously described by different people as bluish, violet blue, clear blue, clear gray blue, and gray violet. The shade differs somewhat, depending on whether it is precipitated from a green or violet chromic salt. On drying the precipitate, the color changes to a distinct green, and the dry amorphous oxide is described as vivid green. Mention has been made of the transformation of the ordinary precipitated oxide into Guignet's green by ageing in an autoclave at 180 to 250°. The rate of precipitation seems to have a marked effect on the color. Thus, Casthelez and Leune[2] claim to have prepared an oxide with a richer and purer color than Guignet's green, simply by slow precipitation at ordinary temperatures of a green solution of a chromic salt with aluminum hydroxide, zinc carbonate, zinc sulfide, or zinc. This observation was confirmed[3] by adding mossy zinc to a solution of green chromic chloride and allowing to stand at 25° for several days. The clear dark-green oxide which formed was much more granular than the gray-blue

---

[1] See p. 57.

[2] *Bull. soc. chim.*, (2) **10,** 170 (1868).

[3] WEISER: *J. Phys. Chem.*, **26,** 410 (1922).

gelatinous oxide obtained by rapid precipitation; moreover, it was quite insoluble in normal sulfuric acid.

Berzelius[1] believed the oxides precipitated from violet and green solutions to be isomers, since they redissolve in acids giving solutions with the original colors. This, however, seems to depend altogether on the method of procedure. Thus Recoura[2] added alkali to a green solution until a precipitate was formed which was dissolved at once in hydrochloric acid giving a violet solution; while the hydrous oxide precipitated from what Recoura claimed to be Cr_2OCl_4 gave a green solution. It would appear, therefore, that the hydrous oxides from different-colored solutions are the same in chemical structure, the individual variation in color and solubility arising from the difference in the physical character of the hydrous particles[3] and the structure of the mass.

The wide difference in color between the gray-blue precipitated oxide and Guignet's green causes Wöhler and Becker to regard the two substances as hydrate isomers bearing a relation to each other similar to the relationship between blue and green chromic chloride. In support of this view, they show that two preparations with the same water content have a different vapor pressure; and that the ordinary oxide can be convered into Guignet's green by heating in an autoclave. These evidences are altogether inconclusive. In the first place, the vapor pressure of a hydrous oxide is determined not only by the amount of water it contains but by its structure;[4] and since the conditions of forming Guignet's green and the ordinary oxide are so different, it is not surprising to find variation in the size of the particles and the structure of the masses of each, as is evidenced not only by difference in vapor pressure but by difference in color. In the second place, Wöhler and Becker were unable to find an inversion temperature of gray-blue oxide to Guignet's green, and the following experiments[5] indicate that a definite transition point does not exist: 20-cubic-centimeter portions of a solution con-

---

[1] "Lehrbuch," 5th ed., **2**, 315 (1848).

[2] *Compt. rend.*, **104**, 1227 (1887); *Ann. chim. phys.*, (6) **10**, 1 (1887); *cf.* OLIE: *Z. anorg. Chem.*, **52**, 48 (1907).

[3] *Cf.*, however, RECOURA: *Loc. cit.*; LOEWEL: *J. Pharm.*, (3) **7**, 323, 401, 424 (1845); FREMY: *Ann. chim. phys.*, (3) **23**, 388 (1848).

[4] VAN BEMMELEN: "Die Absorption," 239 *et seq.* (1910).

[5] WEISER: *J. Phys. Chem.*, **26**, 409 (1922).

taining 0.2 gram of chromium chloride were treated with just enough sodium hydroxide solution to cause complete precipitation at the various temperatures shown in Table IV; and the precipitates were kept at this temperature for a definite length of time. For temperatures above 100° the precipitations were carried out in an autoclave. The color varies continuously from

TABLE IV.—EFFECT OF TEMPERATURE OF PRECIPITATION ON THE COLOR OF HYDROUS CHROMIC OXIDE

Temperature, degrees	Time of heating	Color of precipitate
0	30 minutes	Gray blue
50	30 minutes	Greenish blue
100	30 minutes	Bluish green
150	30 minutes	Green with faint tinge of blue
200	30 minutes	Clear green
200–225	15 hours	Bright green

gray glue to clear green with increasing temperature of precipitation. This indicates that the various colors are not due to isomers but to a difference in the size of the particles, the structure of the mass, and the amount of water enclosed under the different conditions of formation. As the color changes from blue to clear green with increasing temperature of precipitation, the oxide becomes less gelatinous, less soluble in acids, and less readily peptized by alkalies.

CHROMIC OXIDE SOLS

The Positive Sol Formed by Peptization Methods.—Graham[1] prepared colloidal hydrous chromic oxide by peptizing the freshly precipitated oxide with chromic chloride and dialyzing to remove excess electrolyte. The colloidal solution is dark green, and can be diluted with water or heated; but is very instable in the presence of salts.

Neidle and Barab[2] investigated the dialysis of a colloidal solution prepared by the Graham method. The sol was placed

[1] *Phil. Trans.*, **151**, (1), 183 (1861).
  J. Am. Chem. Soc., **38**, 1961 (1916).

in a parchment membrane surrounded by water. In one series of experiments the water was changed at intervals; while in a second series, a continuous flow of water through the dialyzer was maintained. Colloidal particles diffused through the membrane in both cases. In the intermittent dialysis, the sol continued to diffuse until but little remained within the membrane; whereas in the continuous process, the passage of the sol ceased after a time, and 75 per cent remained within the membrane. The growth of the colloidal particles during dialysis was influenced by two factors: agglomeration following removal of peptizing agent, and growth of nuclei by hydrolysis of adsorbed chloride by adsorbed water. In the intermittent process, the removal of peptizing agent was not rapid enough to cause sufficient agglomeration to prevent the passage of the colloid through the particular membrane; while in the continuous process, a gradual growth of the particles resulted finally in their retention by the membrane. By continuous dialysis at a high temperature,[1] the time required to get a colloidal solution containing a minimum amount of peptizing agent may be shortened by weeks.

Bjerrum[2] obtained small amounts of basic chlorides having the formulas $Cr(OH)Cl_2$ and $Cr(OH)_2Cl$ on adding alkali to chromic chloride,[3] and Recoura[4] claimed to get Cr_2OCl_4 by the oxidation of $CrCl_2$ in the air;[5] but it is unlikely that any quantity of basic salt is present in the well-dialyzed solution of hydrous chromic oxide in chromic chloride. Neidle and Barab dialyzed such a colloidal solution in the hot until the ratio, equivalents Cr: equivalents Cl, was above 1500. It seems absurd to regard such a solution as a basic salt; on the other hand, it does not preclude the possible presence of a trace of basic salt in a highly purified sol. For the most part, however, the sol consists of hydrous chromic oxide peptized by preferential adsorption of chromium and hydrogen ions.

[1] *J. Am. Chem. Soc.*, **39**, 71 (1917).

[2] *Z. physik. Chem.*, **73**, 724 (1910); *cf.* also DENHAM: *J. Chem. Soc.*, **93**, 41 (1908).

[3] *Cf.* FISCHER: *Z. anorg. Chem.*, **40**, 39 (1904).

[4] *Ann. chim. phys.*, (6) **10**, 1 (1887).

[5] See also MOBERG: *J. prakt. Chem.*, **29**, 175 (1843); LOEWEL: *J. Pharm.*, **4**, 424 (1843); PÉLIGOT: *Compt. rend.*, **21**, 24 (1845); ORDWAY: *Am. J. Sci.*, (2) **26**, 202 (1858); OLIE: *Z. anorg. Chem.*, **52**, 62 (1906).

If it were possible to dialyze the sol until all the chromic chloride were hydrolyzed and practically all of the hydrogen were adsorbed either as hydrogen chloride or as hydrogen ion, the composition of the sol might be represented by the general formula

$$[(\boxed{x\mathrm{Cr_2O_3} \cdot y\mathrm{HCl} \cdot z\mathrm{H_2O}}\ \mathrm{H^{\cdot}})_n \cdot (n - q)\mathrm{Cl'}] + q\mathrm{Cl'}$$

where q represents the excess of adsorbed hydrogen ions over adsorbed chloride ion, that is, the charge on the colloidal particles. Actually, the solution as well as the sol particles will contain hydrogen ions and may contain chromium ions; and the particles may contain adsorbed chromium. If hydrochloric acid is placed on one side and a well-dialyzed sol on the other side of a membrane permeable to hydrogen and chloride ions but not to the colloidal particles holding an excess of adsorbed hydrogen ion, a Donnan equilibrium will be set up with the attending concentration, osmotic, and electrical effects.[1] Bjerrum[2] placed a chromic oxide sol in a collodion bag and surrounded it by solutions of hydrochloric acid of varying concentration. The outside solution was renewed daily until equilibrium was established, and the osmotic pressure and membrane potential were measured in a special apparatus. Some observations are recorded in Table V. The concentration c_2 of HCl in the outer solution and the concentration $[\mathrm{Cr_2O_3}]$ of the sol are expressed in mols per liter. The

TABLE V.—OSMOTIC PRESSURE AND MEMBRANE POTENTIAL OF A CHROMIC OXIDE SOL AT 18°. THE "EQUIVALENT AGGREGATE" OF THE SOL

HCl c_2	$[\mathrm{Cr_2O_3}]$	P_1	E_m	$m = \infty$	$m = 1000$		$m = 500$		$m = 250$	
				Ae	P_1	Ae	P_1	Ae	P_1	Ae
0.010	0.042	7.6	....	12	1.0	13	2.1	14	4.1	18
0.010	0.038	6.0	6.4	12	0.9	13	1.9	15	3.7	20
0.005	0.038	9.7	10.5	14	0.9	14	1.9	15	3.7	17
0.005	0.027	5.0	....	14	0.6	14	1.4	16	2.7	20
0.005	0.027	4.8	9.2	14	0.6	14	1.4	16	2.6	20
0.005	0.026	4.4	9.1	14	0.6	15	1.3	16	2.5	21
0.0025	0.026	7.5	16.1	14	0.6	15	1.3	16	2.5	18
0.001	0.026	17.8	28.2	14	0.6	14	1.3	14	2.5	15
0.005	0.025	4.2	7.4	14	0.6	14	1.3	16	2.4	20
0.010	0.025	2.5	5.2	12	0.6	14	1.3	18	2.4	100

[1] *Cf.* p. 17.
[2] *Z. physik. Chem.*, **110**, 656 (1924).

osmotic pressure P_1 is given in centimeters of water and the membrane potential E_m in millivolts.

The measured osmotic pressured P is the sum of the pressure P_1, of the colloidal particles and the pressure P_2, caused by the difference in the number of dialyzed particles within and without the membrane, that is,

$$P = P_1 + P_2 \tag{1}$$

According to Avogadro

$$P_1 = RT \cdot \frac{[Cr_2O_3]}{m} \tag{2}$$

and according to Avogadro and Donnan,

$$P_2 = RT \cdot \frac{[Cr_2O_3]^2}{4Ae^2c_2} \tag{3}$$

where RT is 24,700 at 18°; m is the number of Cr_2O_3 molecules in a colloidal particle, and Ae the equivalent aggregate, that is, the number of Cr_2O_3 molecules carrying one electrical charge.[1] P is determined directly for the different values of c_2 and $[Cr_2O_3]$ as given in the table. Corresponding values of P_1 are calculated from (2) for various assumed values of m; and from these P_1 values, P_2 values can be gotten from (1) and Ae values from (3). Bjerrum took the values of m which give the most constant values of Ae as the correct m; and the average value of Ae as the correct Ae. One would conclude from the table that m is greater than 250; but the true value is quite indefinite. Bjerrum says m is approximately 500 and Ae approximately 15;[2] in other words, the colloidal particle contains something like 1,000 chromium atoms and carries 30 free positive charges.

From the osmotic-pressure measurements, Bjerrum also calculates the amount of free chloride ion in the sol. Subtracting this from the total chloride concentration is said to give the adsorbed chloride ion. From such considerations, the conclusion is reached that the colloidal particle contains 1,000 chromium atoms, carrying a total of 240 positive charges, 210 of which are neutralized by adsorbed chloride ion. This is prob-

---

[1] *Cf.* ZsIGMONDY: "Kolloidchemie," 206 (1925).

[2] *Cf.*, however, WINTGEN and LÖWENTHAL: *Z. physik. Chem.*, **109**, 378 (1924).

ably incorrect, as a part of the chlorine is doubtless adsorbed as chloride and not as ion.

It is of interest to compare the value $m = 500$ for a Cr_2O_3 sol, aged by prolonged boiling, with $m = 750,000$ for an aged Fe_2O_3 sol, as reported by Wintgen and Biltz.[1] I doubt very much whether there are 1500 times as many molecules in an aged iron sol as in an aged chromium sol. It is more likely that the limits of the experimental methods employed by both Bjerrum and Wintgen render the values for both sols of doubtful accuracy.

Richards and Bonnet[2] digested hydrous chromic oxide with chromium sulfate on the steam bath for several hours, obtaining a green solution which appeared to them to be a basic salt, $Cr(OH)SO_4$. A violet solution shaken for several days with hydrous chromic oxide changed to green which had a composition that could be expressed by the formula $Cr_3(OH)_7(SO_4)_4$. While these observations prove nothing one way or the other, they indicate that chromic sulfate solution peptizes rather than reacts with hydrous chromic oxide. Seymour-Jones[3] reduced a solution of sodium bichromate with sulfur dioxide, obtaining a solution which dialyzed completely through collodion membranes and passed unchanged through a hardened ultrafilter. Such a solution should have a basicity equivalent to $Cr(OH)SO_4$, but according to Basset[4] it contains a mixture of 95 to 96 per cent chromic sulfate and 4 to 5 per cent chromium dithionate. Hence, the existence of a basic salt of the formula $Cr(OH)SO_4$ has not been established. If such a basic salt were present in Seymour-Jones' solution, it was readily dialyzable, a circumstance that would argue against the presence of any basic chloride, $Cr(OH)Cl_2$, in the well-dialyzed Graham sol. Werner[5] isolated a crystalline basic sulfate of the formula $[Cr(OH)_2 \cdot (H_2O)_4]_2SO_4$; but this was done in a special way.

The nature of the basic solutions of chromic sulfate is of interest in connection with chrome tanning and chrome mordanting, which will be taken up in detail in Chaps. XV and XVI, respectively.

[1] *Z. physik. Chem.*, **107**, 414 (1923).
[2] *Z. physik. Chem.*, **47**, 29 (1904).
[3] *J. Ind. Eng. Chem.*, **15**, 77 (1923).
[4] *J. Chem. Soc.*, **83**, 692 (1903).
[5] *Ber.*, **41**, 3447 (1909).

Paal[1] prepared a colloidal solution of hydrous chromic oxide by reduction of a solution of ammonium chromate with colloidal platinum in the presence of the sodium salt of protalbinic acid which acts as a protective colloid. The preparation contained colloidal hydrous oxide, colloidal platinum, unchanged ammonium chromate, and sodium protalbinate. It may be purified to some extent by dialysis.

The Positive Sol Formed by Hydrolysis Methods.—If a solution of a ferric or aluminum salt is boiled with sodium acetate, there is formed the acetate of the trivalent metal which hydrolyzes, precipitating the respective hydrous oxides. By working at low concentrations, colloidal solutions of the hydrous oxides of iron and aluminum may be prepared by hydrolysis of the acetates;[2] but chromic acetate behaves differently.[3] Reinitzer[4] boiled solutions of chromic chloride and sulfate with sodium acetate for a short time, obtaining a violet solution but no precipitate. This solution was not precipitated in the cold with sodium or potassium hydroxide, ammonia, ammonium hydrosulfide, ammonium carbonate, sodium phosphate, barium hydroxide, or barium carbonate; but was thrown down in the hot by all the above reagents except sodium phosphate. A similar solution which gave no test for chromic ion was obtained by allowing the solution of chromic salt and sodium acetate to stand in the cold for a sufficient length of time. A slow action in the cold in the presence of alkalies is evidenced by a change in color of the solution and the formation of a jelly on standing quietly.

Although some colloidal hydrous chromic oxide may be formed by boiling a chromic salt solution with sodium acetate, it is altogether probable that this process results chiefly in the formation of one or more of the complex chromic acetates, a number of which have been isolated in a definite crystalline form by Werner,[5] and by Weinland and his pupils.[6] Solutions of these salts do not give the usual reactions for chromic ion since the chromium is a

---

[1] *Ber.*, **47**, 2211 (1914).

[2] *Cf.* WEISER: *J. Phys. Chem.*, **24**, 277, 505 (1920).

[3] SCHIFF: *Liebig's Ann. Chem.*, **124**, 168 (1862).

[4] *Monatshefte für Chemie*, **3**, 257 (1882).

[5] *Ber.*, **41**, 3447 (1908).

[6] *Ber.*, **41**, 3236 (1908); **42**, 2997, 3881 (1909); *Z. anorg. Chem.*, **67**, 167 (1910); **69**, 158, 217 (1910); **75**, 293 (1912); **82**, 426 (1913).

constituent of a complex ion. It is interesting that, in the presence of excess violet chromic acetate, iron and aluminum acetates cannot be detected either by heating to the boiling point or by adding caustic alkalies or ammonia. As will be pointed out later, hydrous chromic oxide peptized by hydroxyl ion adsorbs and so carries into colloidal solution a number of hydrous oxides not peptized by alkalies. This suggests that hydrous ferric oxide formed by hydrolysis of ferric acetate is kept from precipitating, owing to adsorption by colloidal hydrous chromic oxide. This suggestion does not seem to be in accord with the facts. In the first place, hydrous chromic oxide does not appear to be the primary product of the hydrolysis of chromic acetate; and in the second place, Reinitzer[1] showed that green chromic acetate formed by boiling and so hydrolyzing the violet salt does not prevent the precipitation of hydrous ferric oxide. This behavior of mixtures of ferric and violet chromic acetates is most likely due to the formation of one or more iron-chromic acetate complexes such as have been prepared by Weinland and Guzzmann.[2]

Reinitzer[3] and Woudstra[4] claim to have made colloidal hydrous chromic oxide by dialysis of chromic acetate, but the extraordinary stability of the preparations in the presence of salts points to their being chromic acetate chiefly. This view is supported by the more recent attempt of Neidle and Barab[5] to dialyze a chromic acetate solution into which superheated steam was passed. Although such a procedure would favor the growth of any particles of colloid, all the chromium passed through the membrane.

It is not possible to prepare a chromic oxide sol by dialysis of pure chromic chloride in the cold;[6] but the commercial salt yields a dilute sol. The difference in behavior is probably due to acceleration of hydrolysis of the commercial chloride by the presence of a little colloid as impurity.[7] Since the temperature

[1] *J. Chem. Soc.*, **42,** 825 (1882).

[2] *Ber.*, **42,** 3881 (1909).

[3] *Monatshefte für Chemie*, **3,** 249 (1883).

[4] *Kolloid-Z.*, **5,** 33 (1909).

[5] *J. Am. Chem. Soc.*, **38,** 1961 (1916).

[6] Neidle and Barab: *J. Am. Chem. Soc.*, **39,** 71 (1917).

[7] Goodwin and Grover: *Phys. Rev.*, **11,** 193 (1900).

coefficient of hydrolysis of chromic chloride is considerable,[1] very much higher yields are obtained by dialysis at 75 to 80°. The colloids are clear, deep green, and perfectly mobile when first prepared; but they gel on standing if the dialysis is carried too far.

Since nitrate ion usually has a smaller precipitating action on positive sols than chloride ion, Biltz[2] attempted to prepare a number of colloids by dialysis of nitrate solutions. This met with little success in the case of chromium nitrate, on account of · the relatively small hydrolysis constant of the salt.[3]

The Negative Sol.—If an excess of alkali hydroxide is added in the cold to a chromic salt solution, the precipitate first formed is peptized completely, giving a clear green colloidal solution. In this respect, hydrous chromic oxide differs from hydrous aluminum oxide which dissolves in alkali hydroxides, giving aluminate.[4] The sol formed in this way precipitates spontaneously on standing,[5] particularly if the ratio of oxide to hydroxyl ion is too large. This is due to ageing of the hydrous oxide. For the same reason, a precipitated and washed oxide is not peptized by alkalies.[6] The sol migrates to the anode under electrical stress,[7] is precipitated by low concentration of salts having strongly adsorbed cations,[8] and the oxide particles can be removed by an ultrafilter.[9]

Further evidence of the colloidal nature of an alkaline solution of hydrous chromic oxide is given by its action with other hydrous oxides. Thus Northcote and Church[10] observed that complete

[1] BJERRUM: *Z. physik. Chem.*, **59**, 343 (1907).

[2] *Ber.*, **35**, 4431 (1902).

[3] WOUDSTRA: *Kolloid-Z.*, **5**, 33 (1909).

[4] HILDEBRAND: *J. Am. Chem. Soc.*, **35**, 864 (1913).

[5] FISCHER and HEY: *Z. anorg. Chem.*, **31**, 352 (1902); HERZ: *Ibid.*, **28**, 344 (1901); **32**, 357 (1902).

[6] HANTZSCH: *Z. anorg. Chem.*, **30**, 338 (1902); *cf.*, however, HERZ: *Z. anorg. Chem.*, **28**, 344 (1901).

[7] KREMANN: *Z. anorg. Chem.*, **33**, 87 (1903).

[8] FISCHER: *Z. anorg. Chem.*, **40**, 39 (1904); *cf.*, however, KREMANN: *Ibid.*, **33**, 87 (1903).

[9] NAGEL: *J. Phys. Chem.*, **19**, 331, 569 (1915); BANCROFT: *Chem. News*, **113**, 113 (1916); *Trans. Am. Electrochem. Soc.*, **28**, 351 (1915); CHATTERJI and DHAR: *Chem. News*, **121**, 253 (1920).

[10] *J. Chem. Soc.*, **6**, 54 (1853).

solution takes place when chromic oxide is associated with 40 per cent of ferric oxide, 12.5 per cent of manganous oxide, and 20 per cent of either cobalt or nickel oxide; and that complete precipitation takes place when chromic oxide is associated with 80 per cent of ferric oxide, 60 per cent of manganous oxide and with 50 per cent of either cobalt or nickel oxide. Similar observations were made by Prud'homme[1] and by Kreps.[2] This anomalous behavior is readily explained in view of the colloidal nature of alkaline solutions of chromic oxide. The colloidal oxide adsorbs to a limited degree and so carries into colloidal solution the hydrous oxides of iron, manganese, cobalt, nickel, copper, and magnesium, thus preventing their precipitation. The latter oxides likewise adsorb chromic oxide and so tend to take it out of colloidal solution in alkali. Accordingly, if they are present in sufficient amount, they will carry down and so decolorize practically completely the green colloidal solution of chromic oxide.[3] As previously noted, the behavior of ferric acetate in the presence of violet chromic acetate cannot be accounted for in this way.

Wood and Black[4] treated precipitated chromic oxide with alkali of varying concentrations. After 2 months some chromate was found in solution, suggesting that chromic oxide dissolves in alkali with the formation of chromite. Since one should expect this action to be more marked if the oxide were in the colloidal state, the author added a large excess of alkali to a chromic chloride solution and allowed the mixture to stand 2 months. Most of the colloid precipitated in this time, leaving a greenish-yellow supernatant liquid, the yellow color being due to a small amount of chromate formed by oxidation of chromite in the air. While these observations show the oxide to possess a slightly acidic character,[5] they do not mean that the solution of hydrous chromic oxide in alkali is all chromite which subsequently decomposes, as Wood and Black imply. On the contrary, it is extremely doubtful whether any chromite at all is formed

[1] *Bull. soc. chim.*, (2) **17**, 253 (1872).
[2] Thesis, Berlin (1893).
[3] NAGEL: *J. Phys. Chem.*, **19**, 331 (1915).
[4] *J. Chem. Soc.*, **109**, 164 (1916).
[5] *Cf.* also MÜLLER: *Z. physik. Chem.*, **110**, 363 (1924).

within a reasonable time in the presence of slightly more than enough alkali to cause complete solution.[1]

PRECIPITATION AND ADSORPTION

A well-dialyzed chromic oxide sol prepared by the Graham method is very sensitive to the presence of electrolytes, particularly if they contain multivalent cations.[2] The precipitation values of a number of potassium salts for a sol containing 3.65 grams Cr_2O_3 per liter are given in Table VI. It will be noted that iodate behaves like a multivalent ion in having a very high precipitating power. It is not known why this should be, since a dilute solution of iodic acid acts like a monobasic acid.[3] It is

TABLE VI.—PRECIPITATION VALUES OF SALTS

Potassium salt	Precipitation value, milli-equivalents per liter	Nature of precipitate	Potassium salt	Precipitation value, milli-equivalents per liter	Nature of precipitate
Ferricyanide...	0.485	Firm jelly	Bromate......	19.0	Jelly
Chromate......	0.525	Firm jelly	Chloride......	30.0	Jelly
Dichromate....	0.535	Firm jelly	Bromide......	33.0	Jelly
Sulfate.........	0.550	Firm jelly	Chlorate......	33.8	Jelly
Oxalate........	0.570	Firm jelly	Iodide........	37.5	Jelly
Iodate.........	0.635	Firm jelly			

particularly interesting that the conditions at the precipitation concentration are favorable to the formation of a jelly. This point will be considered in a later section. The jellies can be broken up by shaking, yielding gelatinous precipitates.

Influence of Hydrogen Ion Concentration.—Everett E. Porter has recently made some precise precipitation and adsorption studies on a chromic oxide sol at varying hydrogen ion concentrations.[4] As an illustration, some precipitation experiments with oxalate are given in detail in Table VII; and some adsorption data for the same ion are recorded in Table VIII and shown

[1] *Cf.* WEISER: *J. Phys. Chem.*, **28**, 428 (1922).
[2] *Cf.* BJERRUM: *Z. physik. Chem.*, **110**, 678 (1924).
[3] MIOLATI and MASCETTI: *Gazz. chim. ital.*, **31**, I, 93 (1901); *Atti accad. Lincei*, (5) **14**, I, 217 (1905).
[4] Unpublished results.

TABLE VII.—PRECIPITATION OF CHROMIC OXIDE SOL AT VARYING pH
VALUES

Cubic centimeters solution mixed with 5 cubic centimeters sol, total volume 20 cubic centimeters		Precipitation value, milliequivalents per liter	pH values	
$N/50$ $H_2C_2O_4$	$N/50$ $K_2C_2O_4$		Before mixing	After mixing
3.35	0.0	3.35	3.05	3.19
3.15	0.2	3.35	3.11	3.32
2.80	0.4	3.20		
2.60	0.5	3.10	3.17	3.40
2.20	0.7	2.90		
2.00	0.8	2.80	3.38	3.51
1.60	0.9	2.50		
0.00	1.0	1.00	9.40	5.79

TABLE VIII.—ADSORPTION OF OXALATE BY HYDROUS CHROMIC OXIDE AT
VARYING pH VALUES

Cubic centimeters solution mixed with 50 cubic centimeters sol, total volume 200 cubic centimeters			Adsorption values, milliequivalents per gram Cr_2O_3	pH values	
$N/50$ $H_2C_2O_4$	$N/50$ $K_2C_2O_4$	$N/50$ KOH		Before mixing	After mixing
50	0	0	4.88	2.73	2.89
40	10	0	4.77	2.87	3.16
30	20	0	4.47	3.16	3.78
20	30	0	4.17	3.81	4.56
10	40	0	3.48	4.45	7.54
0	50	0	2.06	9.40	8.73
0	50	5	1.32	10.58	8.99
0	50	10	0.65	10.67	9.20
0	50	20	0.00	11.12	9.48
0	50	30	0.06	11.23	9.99

graphically in Fig. 5. The sol prepared by Graham's method was dialyzed until the hydrogen ion concentration was but little greater than that of water. The precipitation values at varying pH values for a preparation containing 2.5 grams Cr_2O_3 per liter, were determined by mixing 5 cubic centimeters of sol with 15 cubic centimeters of solutions containing salt and acid. The pH values "after mixing" were made on the supernatant liquid after precipitation. A like solution diluted with water instead

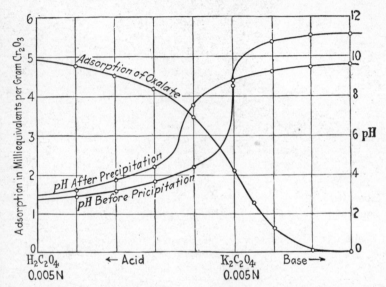

Fig. 5.—Influence of pH on adsorption of oxalate by hydrous chromic oxide.

of with the colloid was used to get the pH values "before mixing." The two determinations are, of course, not strictly comparable. The adsorption values were obtained by mixing 50-cubic-centimeter portions of sol with 150-cubic-centimeter portions of the several solutions and analyzing the supernatant liquid after precipitation. A rapid increase in precipitation value occurs between pH = 6 and pH = 3.5 in the solution after mixing. Above pH = 2.5, the adsorption of oxalate decreases quite rapidly with increasing pH value and becomes zero when the pH value after mixing is approximately 9.5. It is obvious, therefore, that both hydroxyl ion and oxalate ion are adsorbed

on the alkaline side of the isoelectric point, the carrying down of
oxalate being completely nullified only in the presence of a
relatively high concentration of hydroxide ion.

Precipitating Action of Mixtures of Electrolytes.—Thirty
years ago Linder and Picton[1] made the interesting observation
that the precipitating action of mixtures of pairs of electrolytes
for colloidal arsenious sulfide was not additive in case the electrolytes have widely varying precipitating power.[2]   Since this
so-called ionic antagonism was not observed with gold sol and
with von Weimarn's[3] sulfur sol which are anhydrous, but was
observed with Odén's[4] sulfur sol which is hydrous, Freundlich
and Scholz[5] conclude that the hydration of the colloid and of
the precipitating ions is of primary importance in producing
ionic antagonism and so in determining whether the precipitating
action of mixtures shall be additive or above the additive values.
This leads to the deduction that arsenious sulfide sol is a hydrophile, although it is not usually so considered; and to the suggestion that the behavior of colloids with mixtures is a suitable
means of determining to what extent the stability is influenced
by hydration.   These conclusions are not in accord with some
observations[6] on colloidal chromic oxide, a few of which are
recorded in Table IX and shown graphically in Fig. 6.

TABLE IX.—PRECIPITATION OF COLLOIDAL CHROMIC OXIDE BY MIXTURES
OF ELECTROLYTES

(Precipitation values in milliequivalents per liter)

KCl	+	K_2SO_4	KCl	+	$K_2C_2O_4$	K_2SO_4	+	$K_2C_2O_4$
00.0		0.675	0.00		0.700	0.000		0.700
12.5		0.425	12.5		0.460	0.250		0.430
25.0		0.300	25.0		0.325	0.338		0.350
37.5		0.185	37.5		0.200	0.500		0.175
50.0		0.065	50.0		0.070	0.675		0.000
56.8		0.000	56.8		0 000			

[1] *J. Chem. Soc.*, **67**, 67 (1895).
[2] *Cf.* WEISER: *J. Phys. Chem.*, **25**, 665 (1921).
[3] VON WEIMARN and MALYSCHEW: *Kolloid-Z.*, **8**, 214 (1911).
[4] "Der kolloide Schwefel" (1912).
[5] *Kolloidchem. Beihefte*, **16**, 267 (1922).
[6] WEISER: *J. Phys. Chem.*, **28**, 232 (1924); **25**, 665 (1921).

Although the sol is very highly hydrous, mixtures of electrolytes having widely different precipitating power, such as potassium chloride and potassium sulfate, do not give values considerably above the additive value, such as Freundlich and Scholz would predict. On the contrary, the values for such mixtures are actually *less* than additive by a quite appreciable amount. This is not unexpected in view of the fact that adsorp-

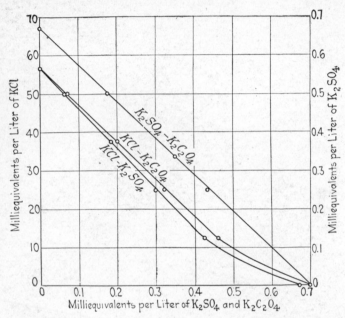

FIG. 6.—Precipitation of colloidal hydrous chromic oxide with mixtures of electrolytes

tion is relatively greater at lower concentrations. The adsorption of chloride ion is proportionately greater at concentrations below its precipitation value so that relatively less sulfate or oxalate is necessary to bring the combined adsorption above the critical value necessary for neutralization and coagulation. Such a result would follow, however, only in case there is little or no antagonistic action between chloride ion and sulfate or oxalate ion in the sense that the presence of each decreases the adsorption of the other at concentrations below the precipitation value.

This is evident from the experiments recorded in Table X. Below the precipitation concentration, a relatively large amount of chloride has no effect on the adsorption of oxalate; and above this concentration, the adsorption of oxalate is cut down but 4 per cent by 50 times its concentration of chloride and less than

TABLE X.—ADSORPTION BY HYDROUS CHROMIC OXIDE OF OXALATE IN THE PRESENCE OF CHLORIDE

Mixtures added to 30 cubic centimeters colloid containing 0.06 gram Cr_2O_3			Oxalate adsorbed	
$N/2$ KCl	$N/100$ $K_2C_2O_4$	H_2O	Cubic centimeters of $N/100$	Grams per mol Cr_2O_3
4.50	1.35	24.15	1.35	1.505
3.00	1.95	25.05	1.95	2.174
1.50	2.85	25.65	2.85	3.177
0.00	4.20[a]	25.80	4.20	4.682
0.00	8.50	21.50	7.34	8.182
21.50	8.50	0.00	6.66	7.424
0.00	12.00	18.00	9.42	10.500
18.00	12.00	0.00	8.83	9.842
0.00	15.00	15.00	11.10	12.373
15.00	15.00	0.00	10.68	11.905
0.00	20.00	10.00	12.46	13.889
10.00	20.00	0.00	12.35	13.667

[a] Precipitation value.

1 per cent by 25 times its concentration of chloride. It would appear, therefore, that the high precipitation value of potassium chloride is due to relatively weak adsorption of chloride ion associated with but slight adsorption of the stabilizing potassium ion. Similar behavior was noted with negative colloidal stannic oxide using mixtures of lithium chloride and either barium chloride or magnesium chloride.

For the sake of comparison, some results[1] on the precipitation of arsenious sulfide sol by mixtures are given in Table XI and represented graphically in Fig. 7.

TABLE XI.—PRECIPITATION OF COLLOIDAL ARSENIOUS SULFIDE BY
MIXTURES OF ELECTROLYTES

(Precipitation values in milliequivalents per liter.)

LiCl	+ BaCl$_2$	NaCl	+ BaCl$_2$	KCl	+ BaCl$_2$
00.0	1.60	00.0	1.60	00.0	1.60
12.5	2.02	12.5	1.93	12.0	1.88
25.0	2.18	25.0	1.98	25.0	1.92
43.7	2.13	43.7	1.82	43.7	1.62
62.5	1.78	62.5	1.30	62.5	1.05
81.2	1.23	95.0	0.00	83.0	0.00
111.2	0.00				

HCl	+ BaCl$_2$	KCl	+ CeCl$_3$	KCl	+ NaCl
00.0	1.60	00.0	0.388	00.0	95.0
12.5	1.98	12.5	0.230	25.0	64.0
25.0	1.93	25.0	0.162	50.0	35.0
37.5	1.65	37.5	0.132	83.0	00.0
50.0	1.00	50.0	0.105		
61.5	0.00	62.5	0.067		
		83.0	0.000		

It will be seen that the precipitation values of salt pairs for the same sol, may be additive, may be greater than the additive values, or may be less than the additive values. From determinations of adsorption during the precipitation of sols, there appear to be three factors which determine the precipitation concentration of salt pairs; (1) the stabilizing action of the ion having the same charge as the sol; (2) the effect of each precipitating ion on the adsorption of the other; and (3) the relatively greater adsorbability of ions at lower concentration. Since the addition of small amounts of potassium ferrocyanide to ferrocyanide sols or of hydrochloric acid to hydrous oxide sols

[1] WEISER: *J. Phys. Chem.*, **30**, 28 (1926).

increases their stability toward electrolytes, Dhar[1] and Sen[2] are inclined to attribute all the so-called antagonistic action of salt pairs to adsorption of stabilizing ions. Thus, the addition of a small amount of potassium chloride to arsenious sulfide sol is believed to stabilize it, thereby increasing the precipitation value of barium chloride. But a small amount of potassium chloride does not stabilize arsenious sulfide sol in the same sense that hydrochloric acid stabilizes chromic oxide sol; hence, the

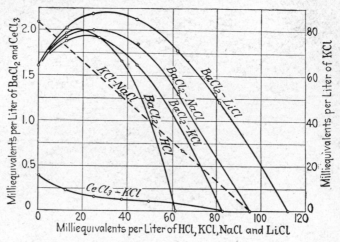

Fig. 7.—Precipitation of colloidal arsenious sulfide with mixtures of electrolytes.

precipitation concentrations for mixtures of potassium and sodium chloride are additive; and for mixtures of potassium and cerium chloride, they are below the additive value. It would thus appear that the determining factor with mixtures of barium chloride and the alkali chlorides is the antagonistic action of each precipitating ion on the adsorption of the other, while with potassium and cerium chlorides, it is the relatively greater adsorbability of the precipitating cations below the precipitation value of either taken separately. In line with this view, the adsorption of barium ion is cut down much more strongly than

[1] Ghosh and Dhar: *J. Phys. Chem.*, **29**, 659 (1925).
[2] *Z. anorg. Chem.*, **142**, 345 (1925).

cerium ion by the concentrations of alkali chlorides concerned
The precipitation values of such mixtures as NaCl and KCl,
having a common anion, are additive since the adsorption of
the precipitating cations are similar, and so the adsorption of
each is affected but slightly by the presence of the other within
the limits of the precipitation concentration.

The adsorbability of the alkalies deduced from their power to
cut down the adsorption of barium ion is in the order: K > Na >
Li.[1] From the curves in Fig. 7 it will be seen that the precipitation value of barium chloride is increased by like amounts of
alkali chlorides in the order LiCl > NaCl > KCl; while in the
presence of HCl, the precipitation value of barium salt first
rises to a point just below that in the presence of a like amount of
lithium chloride and then drops off rather sharply. The following explanation of these phenomena is suggested: For a given
alkali chloride concentration, precipitation will take place when
the combined adsorption of the two cations neutralizes the
combined adsorption of chloride and hydrosulfide ions. The
combined adsorption will be equivalent for different pairs of
cations; but the relative amounts of each that make up this
equivalent adsorption will vary, depending as it does on the
relative adsorbability of the two cations. If one may disregard
for the moment the slight variation in the amounts of chloride
added with barium chloride as compared with the relatively large
amount of this ion added with the alkali chloride, it follows that,
for a given concentration of different alkali chlorides, the varying amounts of barium that must be added will depend on the
effect of each cation on the adsorption of the other. Thus, the
adsorption of barium is cut down by lithium ion less than by
potassium ion, tending to make the precipitation concentration
of barium chloride less in the presence of lithium chloride than of
potassium chloride. Hand in hand with this is the decrease in
the adsorption of alkali by barium, which will tend to make the
precipitation concentration of barium chloride higher in the
presence of lithium. From this point of view, the latter factor
appears to predominate with the alkali chlorides. With hydrochloric acid, however, the cutting down of the adsorption of
barium by hydrogen ion is the determining factor with lower

[1] WEISER: *J. Phys. Chem.*, **29**, 955 (1925); *cf.* p. 125.

concentrations of hydrochloric acid; while with higher concentrations of acid, the second factor appears to predominate.

Precipitation of Negative Sol.—In Table XII are given the precipitation values of several electrolytes for a negative sol prepared by mixing 5 cubic centimeters of chromic chloride containing 40 grams Cr_2O_3 per liter with 45 cubic centimeters of 0.2N KOH. The precipitation value is that concentration of electrolyte which will just cause complete coagulation in 10 minutes. It will be noted that the precipitating power of cations follows the usual order: barium > lithium > sodium > potassium; and the stabilizing action of the an:ons is: sulfate > chloride > acetate.

TABLE XII.—PRECIPITATION VALUES OF SALTS

Salt	Precipitation value, milliequivalents per liter	Nature of precipitate
Barium chloride	5.15	Gelatinous
Potassium chloride	500.0	Gelatinous
Sodium chloride	210.0	Gelatinous
Lithium chloride	51.0	Gelatinous
Sodium sulfate	315.0	Gelatinous
Sodium acetate	220.0	Gelatinous

Chromic Oxide Jellies.—Mention has been made of Reinitzer's observation that a solution of chromic salt boiled with sodium acetate and rendered alkaline with caustic alkalies or ammonia sets to a jelly. Bunce and Finch[1] confirmed this observation and showed further that a jelly is formed by adding excess sodium hydroxide or potassium hydroxide to chrome alum and allowing the solution to stand. They were unable to obtain a jelly from chromic sulfate, nitrate, or chloride; but Nagel[2] succeeded in getting a jelly with sulfate by keeping down the concentration of alkali. From these observations it was logical to conclude that acetate or sulfate ions are necessary for the formation of a chromic oxide jelly.[3] That such is not the case

[1] *Cf. J. Phys. Chem.*, **17**, 769 (1913).
[2] *J. Phys. Chem.*, **19**, 331 (1914).
[3] BANCROFT: "Applied Colloid Chemistry," 244 (1921).

is evident from the series of experiments recorded in Table XIII, using chromic chloride instead of sulfate or acetate. The experiments bear out the general conclusions regarding jelly formation previously considered in detail.[1] The rapid addition of a slight excess of alkali to a chromic chloride solution produces a negative colloidal oxide that is instable and precipitates slowly, forming a jelly (Table XIII). If this precipitation is hastened by heating or by addition of a suitable amount of electrolyte, the precipitate forms so rapidly that it is gelatinous and not jelly-like (Table XII). Finally, if the hydrous oxide has been peptized by too great a concentration of alkali, the precipitate comes down very slowly and is almost granular in character, as observed by Nagel.

TABLE XIII.—CHROMIC OXIDE JELLIES FROM NEGATIVE COLLOID

Alkali	Solutions (cubic centimeters) mixed			Observations	Nature of precipitate
	Alkali 0.6 N	$CrCl_3$	Total volume		
NaOH	10.0	5.0	25	Peptization incomplete	Gelatinous
NaOH	11.5	5.0	25	Peptization incomplete	Firm green jelly
NaOH	11.75	5.0	25	Peptization almost complete	Firm green jelly
NaOH	12.0	5.0	25	Peptization complete	Firm green jelly
KOH	10.0	5.0	25	Peptization incomplete	Firm green jelly
KOH	10.75	5.0	25	Peptization almost complete	Firm green jelly
KOH	11.0	5.0	25	Peptization complete	Firm green jelly
Ba(OH)₂	20.0	5.0	25	No peptization	Gelatinous
Ba(OH)₂	24.0	1.0	25	No peptization	Gelatinous
NaOH	13.5	5.0	50	Peptization almost complete	Soft green jelly
NaOH	13.75	5.0	50	Peptization complete	Soft green jelly
KOH	12.0	5.0	50	Peptization almost complete	Soft green jelly
KOH	12.25	5.0	50	Peptization complete	Soft green jelly

The experiments under consideration corroborate the observation of Fischer and Herz that the peptizing power of potassium hydroxide is slightly greater than that of sodium hydroxide. On the other hand, they disprove the statement that hydrous chromic oxide is peptized by barium hydroxide and that the peptizing power of alkalies depends on the absolute amount present and not on the concentration. The hydroxides arranged in order of peptizing power are potassium hydroxide > sodium hydroxide > barium hydroxide. As would be expected, this is

[1] See p. 26, *et seq.*

the reverse of the order of precipitating power of the cations (Table XII).

Knowing the conditions favorable to jelly formation by precipitation of a negative colloidal hydrous chromic oxide, it is a simple matter to precipitate the positive sol as a jelly. All that is necessary is to add just enough electrolyte to cause complete coagulation in an hour or two. If too little electrolyte is used, precipitation is incomplete and the results are unsatisfactory; while if too great an excess is added, the precipitation is so rapid that a gelatinous precipitate is formed. From the results recorded in Table X, it is quite evident that jellies will form in the presence of any precipitating ion. Moreover, the hydrogen ion concentration within which jellies will form, can vary over a wide range; thus, they are obtained from strongly alkaline solution and from a colloid stabilized by hydrogen ion.

A typical jelly containing but 0.18 per cent chromic oxide will stand for days without undergoing noticeable syneresis. Shaking destroys the jelly structure, which does not re-form as in the case of more concentrated jellies.[1]

[1] *Cf.* SCHALEK and SZEGVARY: *Kolloid-Z.*, **32,** 318; **33,** 326 (1923).

CHAPTER IV

THE HYDROUS OXIDES OF ALUMINUM, GALLIUM, INDIUM, AND THALLIUM

Hydrous Aluminum Oxide

The Gelatinous Oxide.—The addition of ammonia to an aluminum salt solution throws down a very highly gelatinous precipitate of hydrous aluminum oxide. An x-radiogram of the precipitate formed in the cold with not too dilute solutions shows it to possess no crystalline character[1] even after prolonged drying at room temperature.[2] The precipitate exhibits a wide variation in properties depending on the conditions of formation and the age and history of the sample. Thus Tommasi[3] found the newly formed oxide to be quite soluble in acids and alkalies, whereas the aged product was sparingly soluble. Recently Willstätter and Kraut[4] described a number of hydrous oxides differing in reactivity and adsorptive power, by precipitating aluminum sulfate with ammonia: With concentrated ammonia, and boiling for a long time, the precipitate was a pale yellow plastic mass A; without prolonged boiling, it was a very pale yellow plastic mass B; with dilute ammonia it was a pure white, very voluminous, and very finely divided substance C. An intermediate variety b prepared by the dialysis of aluminum chloride with frequent additions of small quantities of ammonia, was claimed to be related chemically to B but resembled A in adsorptive capacity; and a modified form of C precipitated at 60° had an adsorptive capacity similar to B. Specimens of A were entirely different in properties, depending on whether they

[1] HABER: *Ber.*, **55**, 1727 (1922); *cf.* FRICKE and WEAVER: *Z. anorg. Chem.*, **136**, 320 (1924).

[2] BÖHM and NICLASSEN: *Z. anorg. Chem.*, **132**, 1 (1924); BÖHM: *Ibid.*, **149**, 203 (1925).

[3] *Compt. rend.*, **91**, 231 (1880); *cf.* PHILLIPS: *Phil. Mag.*, (3) **33**, 357 (1848).

[4] *Ber.*, **56**, 149, 1117 (1923); **57**, 58, 1082 (1924).

were still moist or subjected to a rapid preliminary drying in a high vacuum over P_2O_5. As a result of desiccation experiments, Willstätter concluded that the different gels contained a variety of different hydrates. This brings to mind earlier papers on hydrous aluminum oxide in which are described such hydrates as $Al_2O_3 \cdot H_2O$[1] corresponding to the crystalline mineral diaspore, $Al_2O_3 \cdot 2H_2O$[2] corresponding to amorphous bauxite, and $Al_2O_3 \cdot 3H_2O$[3] corresponding to crystalline gibbsite;[4] but the existence of hydrates in gelatinous alumina is rendered doubtful by the work of Carnelley and Walker[5] and of van Bemmelen.[6] The latter showed that at constant temperature the precipitated oxide takes up or gives off water until the vapor tension of the substance is the same as that of the surroundings; hence, change in temperature causes a continuous change in the water content of the substance by varying its vapor tension. Moreover, the vapor pressure of the hydrous oxide is influenced by the conditions of precipitation and the subsequent treatment. Thus an oxide adsorbs water more strongly if thrown down from a dilute solution of aluminum chloride than from a concentrated solution. The precipitate decreases in solubility in alkali and acids in proportion to the quantity of water lost by heating; after heating at various temperatures, the different oxides adsorb smaller quantities of water when placed in a saturated atmosphere, and they retain less in dry air in proportion to the water lost. By standing under water, the capacity to adsorb water and the solubility in acids and alkalies alters in proportion to the time of standing An "amorphous" hygroscopic oxide formed by ageing the gelatinous precipitate for 6 months under water and drying in air,

[1] MITSCHERLICH: *J. prakt. Chem.*, **83**, 468 (1861); BECQUEREL: *Jahresber.*, 87 (1868); RAMSAY: *J. Chem. Soc.*, **32**, 395 (1877).

[2] LÖWE: *Z. für Chemie*, **3**, 247 (1864); PÉAN de ST. GILLES: *Ann. chim. phys.*, (3) **46**, 57 (1856); CRUM: *Liebig's Ann. Chem.*, **89**, 156 (1853).

[3] ALLEN: *Chem. News*, **82**, 75 (1900); COSSA: *Z. für Chemie*, **13**, 443 (1873); TOMMASI: *Compt. rend.*, **91**, 231 (1880).

[4] Other hydrates have been described by ZUNINO: *Gazz. chim. ital.*, **30**, 194 (1900); RAMSAY: *J. Chem. Soc.*, **32**, 395 (1877); SCHLUMBERGER: *Bull. soc. chim.*, (3) **13**, 41 (1895).

[5] *J. Chem. Soc.*, **53**, 87 (1888).

[6] *Rec. trav. chim.*, **7**, 75 (1888); *cf.* SHIDEI: *Mem. Coll. Sci.*, *Kyoto*, **9a**, 42 (1924).

corresponds to a trihydrate in composition. Van Bemmelen's general conclusions were confirmed by observations on gelatinous alumina by Martin[1] and Kohlschütter[2] and on "fibrous" alumina[3] by von Zehman;[4] but Willstätter claims that vapor-pressure data do not show the absence of hydrates in preparations dried in vacuum over P_2O_5 or treated with acetone, operations which are tacitly assumed to remove all adsorbed water. On the contrary, Willstätter's predried preparations give certain temperature intervals of almost constant water content which are cited to prove the existence of hydrates. Thus the acetone-dried oxide precipitated from aluminum sulfate at low hydroxyl ion concentration analyzes approximately for a trihydrate (van Bemmelen); and the precipitates obtained with excess ammonia in the hot give what are assumed to be polyaluminum hydroxides, such as $2Al(OH)_3 \cdot H_2O$, as a result of intermolecular dehydration. Willstätter believes fresh gels to be hydrates; but his arguments are vague and unconvincing. Thus he says:

It is not known whether the hydrates found after desiccation existed originally in the gelatinous suspension with the same amount of chemically combined water. Of course, there is no need of assuming the existence of single hydrates. The formulas calculated for hydrates of alumina in the cases described are complex; they have little significance, for they can usually be looked upon as mixtures of different hydrates. Whatever may be the water content and the degree of hydration of the gel suspended in water, it follows from the drying curve of preparation C, $(Al(OH)_3 \cdot nH_2O$ which dries to $Al(OH)_3)$, that desiccated preparations with values between $(Al_2O_3)_2 \cdot H_2O$ and $Al_2O_3 \cdot H_2O$ could not be $Al(OH)_3$ in the original moist condition, but are probably mixtures of compounds of the composition $Al_n(OH)_{3n} \cdot xH_2O$, *i.e.*, polymetahydroxides.

Willstätter's observations on a variety of oxides would seem to disprove the existence of hydrates with the possible exception of van Bemmelen's trihydrate. Wide variations in the conditions of forming the oxides cause differences in their physical character and structure that determine not only the behavior toward

[1] *Mon. sci.*, (5) **5**, 225 (1915).
[2] *Z. anorg. Chem.*, **105**, 1 (1919); *Z. Elektrochem.*, **29**, 246 (1923).
[3] WISLICENUS: *Z. angew. Chem.*, **17**, 805 (1904).
[4] *Kolloid-Z.*, **27**, 233 (1920).

reagents and their adsorption capacity for dyes and enzymes, but also the amount of water they retain under given conditions. The nature and the location of the kinks or bends in the temperature-dehydration curves depend on the previous history of the sample and so are different for each sample. As might be expected, the composition of a preparation treated in a certain definite way may sometimes be represented by a Dalton formula; but this does not prove the existence of a definite compound. Van Bemmelen[1] obtained breaks in the vapor-pressure curves

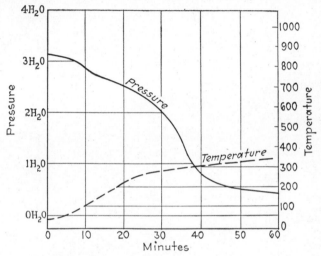

Fig. 8.—Dehydration of hydrous alumina prepared at 15°.

for gels of lower water content; but these were not due to the presence of hydrates, for the location of the breaks varied with the history of the sample, and similar breaks were observed when alcohol or benzene was substituted for water.

Guichard[2] followed the continuous dehydration of hydrous aluminas with increasing temperature by means of a specially designed hydrostatic compensation balance.[3] The form of the curves is well illustrated by Figs. 8 and 9 showing the results of experiments carried out on the gelatinous oxide precipitated (1)

[1] "Die Absorption," 257 *et seq.* (1910).
[2] *Bull. soc. chim.*, **37**, 381 (1925).
[3] Guichard: *Bull. soc. chim.*, **37**, 251 (1925).

in the cold and (2) at the boiling point. With regular increase in temperature there appears a slight slowing down of the dehydration of the oxide formed in the cold, between 150 and 200°, corresponding to a composition between $3H_2O$ and $2H_2O$. The "pseudo flat" is interpreted to indicate the existence of $Al_2O_3 \cdot 3H_2O$ with adsorbed water and possibly $Al_2O_3 \cdot 2H_2O$ with adsorbed water. Contrary to what one might have expected, the

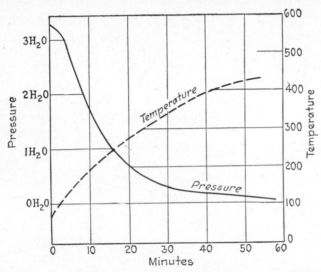

FIG. 9.—Dehydration curve of hydrous alumina prepared at 100°.

aged crystalline oxide formed in the hot gives no indication of being $Al_2O_3 \cdot 3H_2O$ or any other hydrate.

The Crystalline Hydrate.—Although the oxide formed by precipitation of aluminum chloride with ammonium hydroxide contains no definite hydrates, crystals of artificial gibbsite have been prepared in a number of ways. Bornsdorff[1] obtained such a compound by saturating a sodium hydroxide solution with gelatinous alumina and allowing the solution to stand in a closed

[1] *Pogg. Ann.*, **27**, 275 (1833); *cf.* VAN BEMMELEN: *Rec. trav. chim.*, **7**, 75 (1888); BAYER: *Chem. Ztg.*, **12**, 1209 (1889); DITTE: *Compt. rend.*, **116**, 183 (1893); ALLEN: *Chem. News*, **82**, 75 (1900); RUSS: *Z. anorg. Chem.*, **41**, 216 (1904).

vessel.[1] A similar compound is formed by passing carbon dioxide through a boiling solution of alkali aluminate; by boiling aluminum in water for many hours; by the action of hydrogen peroxide on aluminum;[2] by the action of water on aluminum amalgam;[3] by allowing potassium aluminate and aluminum chloride to mix slowly through a diaphragm;[4] by calcining hydrated aluminum nitrate;[5] and by electrolysis of an aqueous solution of alum.[6] According to Milligan[7] the composition of this compound remains constant up to 145°, when it starts losing water continuously with increasing temperature. All but 8 per cent of the water is driven off below 200°, and there is no evidence whatsoever of another hydrate. Alumina dried at as low a temperature as 275° takes up water by adsorption but does not combine to reform the hydrate. The higher the temperature of ignition the less the adsorption capacity of the oxide, doubtless on account of decreased porosity resulting from sintering. Alumina prepared from amalgamated aluminum is much denser than the ordinary precipitated hydrous oxide.[8]

The gelatinous oxide freshly precipitated in the cold dissolves in acids and alkalies forming salts and is readily peptized by certain dilute acids and salts. The precipitate thrown down from the hot solution is less reactive and less easily peptized. The newly formed oxide ages fairly rapidly in the hot and more slowly in the cold even under water. Two modifications of alumina have, therefore, been recognized, the so-called ordinary or alpha and meta or beta modifications, representing the two extremes of reactivity. But there is no temperature of inversion from the soluble alpha to the insoluble beta form; on the contrary, between these two extremes one may have all possible variation in solubility, reactivity, and adsorbability depending on the structure of the mass which in turn is determined by the conditions of precipitation and the subsequent method of treat-

[1] Wöhler: *Liebig's Ann. Chem.*, **113**, 249 (1859).

[2] Weltzien: *Liebig's Ann. Chem.*, **138**, 130 (1866).

[3] Cossa: *Z. für Chemie*, **13**, 443 (1873).

[4] Becquerel: *Compt. rend.*, **67**, 1081 (1868).

[5] Schlösing: "Traite d'analyse," Paris, **105** (1877).

[6] Dullo: *Bull. soc. chim.*, (2) **5**, 78 (1866).

[7] *J. Phys. Chem.*, **26**, 247 (1922); *cf.* Martin: *Mon. sci.*, (5) **5**, 225 (1915).

[8] Hahn and Thieler: *Ber.*, **57**, 671 (1924).

ment.[1] These conclusions have been confirmed by Kohlschütter[2] with different pseudo crystals of hydrous aluminas formed by the action of ammonia on crystals of aluminum salts.

Unlike the fresh gelatinous oxide, the crystalline trihydrate is almost insoluble in cold acids and alkalies; it is very slowly soluble in hot concentrated HCl but it dissolves readily in concentrated H_2SO_4. It is, therefore, similar in properties to the aged gelatinous oxide. By means of x-radiograms Böhm and Niclassen[3] observed the gradual transformation from an amorphous to a crystalline oxide during ageing. Naturally, this raises the question whether the ageing process consists essentially in the gradual formation of crystalline trihydrate. X-radiograms would appear to answer this in the negative, for aged oxides, obtained by precipitation in the hot or by precipitation in the cold and heating to 100° for an hour,[4] gave interference patterns corresponding to the indefinite mineral bauxite[5] and not to definite crystalline gibbsite.[6] However, from observations of the magnetic susceptibilities of a number of freshly precipitated and aged gels, as well as of crystalline trihydrate from potassium aluminate, Pascal[7] concludes that newly formed gels consist solely of anhydrous Al_2O_3 with adsorbed water. On long standing, the gels go over to van Bemmelen's unstable trihydrate, which appears to be quite distinct from the crystalline trihydrate of the same composition obtained from aluminate. We know definitely that gelatinous alumina, aged in the presence of alkali, gives trihydrate crystals identical with gibbsite; but neither x-ray nor magnetic analyses furnish conclusive evidence as to whether van Bemmelen's submicrocrystalline oxide, formed by ageing the ammonia-precipitated oxide in the cold, is really a trihydrate, and if so, whether it is identical with artificial gibbsite or an allotropic modification of the latter. For the present I am inclined to attribute the difference between the crystalline oxides aged by long standing in cold water and aged in dilute

[1] WEISER: *J. Phys. Chem.*, **24**, 505 (1920).

[2] *Z. anorg. Chem.*, **105**, 1 (1919).

[3] *Z. anorg. Chem.*, **132**, 1 (1924).

[4] MILLIGAN: *J. Phys. Chem.*, **26**, 254 (1922).

[5] FRICKE and WEAVER: *Z. anorg. Chem.*, **136**, 321 (1924).

[6] RINNE: *Z. anorg. Chem.*, **136**, 322 (1922).

[7] *Compt. rend.*, **178**, 481 (1924).

alkali to a difference in specific surface rather than in composition or chemical structure.   Five years ago, before x-ray analysis established the crystalline character of aged aluminum oxides, Fricke[1] observed a marked difference in the physical character and solubility of trihydrates obtained from aluminate under varying conditions.

The adsorption capacity of a gelatinous oxide aged for a short time is much greater than that of crystalline trihydrate from aluminate; and the heating curves of the two are quite distinct.[2] On heating the crystalline trihydrate, there appears a diminution corresponding to an endothermal change below 360°; while gelatinous alumina gives a curve with a decided hump at 850°, corresponding to an exothermal change.   Mellor and Holdcroft[3] suggest the term calorescence for the exothermic phenomenon. This calorescence or glow phenomenon, like that observed by calcining hydrous chromic oxide, is a manifestation of the energy lost by a sudden diminution of surface at some temperature.   The relatively large trihydrate crystals which precipitate from alkali aluminate do not caloresce when heated, since they possess a much smaller surface for a given mass than the aged gelatinous oxide.   The diminution in surface of the heated oxide is accompanied by a decrease in hygroscopicity, specific gravity, reactivity, and adsorbability.   X-radiograms[4] show that the ignited oxide is not a different allotropic modification.

Anhydrous Alumina.   Corundum Gems.—While there is little evidence of the existence of α and β hydrous oxides of aluminum, the anhydrous oxide has been prepared in two distinct forms:[5] α aluminum oxide, the usual trigonal, crystalline form represented by corundum; and β aluminum oxide formed in hexagonal crystals or appearing in groups of overlapping triangular plates when α aluminum oxide is melted and allowed to cool slowly.   The presence of a small amount of MgO (0.5 per cent) materially assists the formation of β aluminum oxide while small amounts of either calcium oxide or silicon diox-

---

[1] *Z. Elektrochem.*, **26,** 143 (1920).

[2] LE CHATELIER: *Compt. rend.*, **104,** 1517 (1887).

[3] *Trans. Ceram. Soc.*, **10,** 169 (1912); **13,** 83 (1914).

[4] HEDVALL: *Z. anorg. Chem.*, **120,** 327 (1922).

[5] RANKIN and MERWIN: *J. Am. Chem. Soc.*, **38,** 568 (1916).

ide favor the formation of the α variety. Since the β form does not revert to the α form even when held at temperatures above or below the melting point, it is suggested that β aluminum oxide may be monotropic with respect to the α form; but this conclusion does not follow.

The existence of these two modifications of alumina is of interest in connection with the color of corundum gems. The color of pure Al_2O_3 is white or water clear. Natural corundum occurs as blue, green, violet, yellow, and white sapphires and as ruby which varies in color from pale rose to carmine red or bluish red. The yellow, purple, and green sapphires are sometimes called oriental topaz, amethyst, and emerald, respectively. The pleochroism is marked in some gems. Thus the ruby may be deep red in the direction of the vertical axis and lighter color or colorless at right angles to this direction. Similarly, the sapphire may be deep blue in the direction of the vertical axis and greenish blue to bluish white when viewed at right angles. The various tints are due to the presence of colored oxides. By fusing aluminum and chromium oxides Fremy and Verneuil[1] synthesized ruby and also obtained crystals which, in parts, had the color of blue sapphire.[2] The difference in color was attributed to a difference in the state of oxidation of the chromic oxide. If such is the case, it would appear that the ruby may owe its color to CrO_3 and the sapphire to Cr_2O_3. In line with this, a red color can be obtained only in an oxidizing atmosphere; moreover, by heating a ruby in a reducing atmosphere it may become green or even colorless,[3] owing to the low tinctorial power of the green oxide. There are, however, two difficulties with this hypothesis. In the first place, CrO_3 is instable at the temperature of molten alumina, and so we must make the unproved assumption that the oxide is stabilized by alumina; and in the second place, we do not know whether CrO_3 when highly dispersed will give a red color to alumina. An alternative hypothesis is that the different colors of gems with chromic oxide as pigment are due to variation in the size of the particles of Cr_2O_3. While this would account for

[1] *Compt. rend.*, **111**, 667 (1890).

[2] *Cf.* DEVILLE and CARON: *Compt. rend.*, **66**, 765 (1858).

[3] BOELTER: "Edelsteinkinde," Leipsig, 88 (1893); KENNGOTT: *Neues Jahrb. Mineral. Geol.*, 313 (1867); RINNE: *Ibid.*, I, 170 (1900); II, 47 (1906).

variations in color from light blue to dark green,[1] it seems unlikely that this explanation can be extended to include the red color. The Norton Company found that artificial gems made with α Al_2O_3 and chromic oxide are red, while those made with β oxide are green. Bancroft suggests, therefore, that the different colors are due to different allotropic modifications of Cr_2O_3. Since α alumina is only partly converted into β alumina by melting and slowly cooling the oxide, Bancroft's explanation might account for red and blue patches in the same crystals, both natural and artificial.

Morozenwicz[2] claimed to get rose, yellow, greenish-yellow, red, and pale-blue corundum with iron oxide and so suggested that the coloring agent in certain gems is due to iron instead of chromium oxides. Verneuil's[3] most recent work on the synthesis of sapphires leads him to attribute the coloration of natural sapphires to iron and titanium oxides. However this may be, there is no denying that artificial sapphires may owe their color to chromium oxide.

ALUMINUM OXIDE SOLS

Since it is possible to prepare an indefinite number of hydrous aluminas differing in the size and structure of the particles and the amount of water they contain, it is possible to obtain colloidal solutions of alumina having widely varying properties depending on the method of formation. Two general methods of preparation are employed: hydrolysis of aluminum salts, and peptization of the hydrous oxide by acids and salts.

Hydrolysis of Aluminum Salts.—Gay Lussac[4] boiled a concentrated solution of aluminum acetate and obtained a precipitate of hydrous alumina which redissolved when the temperature was lowered. Crum[5] heated a more dilute and more basic solution than Gay Lussac, first in a closed vessel and subsequently in an open one, to drive off the excess acetic acid. In this way a

---

[1] WEISER: *J. Phys. Chem.*, **26**, 417 (1922).

[2] *Tschermak's mineralog. petrog. Mitt.*, (2) **18**, 456 (1899).

[3] *Compt. rend.*, **150**, 185 (1910).

[4] *Ann. chim. phys.*, (1) **74**, 193 (1810).

[5] *Liebig's Ann. Chem.*, **89**, 168 (1854).

stable but opalescent colloidal solution was formed, containing alumina and acetic acid in the ratio of 5.5:1. The conditions of formation, namely prolonged digestion at high temperature with subsequent boiling in a medium having a slight solvent action, were conducive to the formation of relatively large dense non-reactive primary particles. Accordingly, the oxide thrown down from the sol by electrolytes was an aged coagulum made up of crystalline particles that were not very soluble in acids or alkalies and had no mordanting action.

Graham[1] prepared a sol having properties similar to Crum's by heating an acetate solution for several days and then dialyzing in the cold. The time required for making Crum's sol may be materially shortened by peptizing freshly precipitated hydrous alumina with the smallest possible amount of acetic acid, diluting, and boiling to remove the excess acid.[2] Minachi and Okazaka[3] diluted a saturated solution of aluminum acetate in dilute acetic acid, added hydrogen dioxide, and dialyzed at 50 to 80°. Attempts to prepare colloidal alumina by dialysis of the chloride and nitrate[4] in the cold have not proved successful, owing to the relatively low degree of hydrolysis of even $\frac{1}{1000} M$ solutions.[5] Since the temperature coefficient of the hydrolysis is quite high,[6] Neidle[7] was able to get a 9.5 per cent conversion of a 0.05 M solution of $AlCl_3$ by dialyzing for 37 hours at 75 to 80°.

Peptization of Hydrous Alumina.—Graham[8] peptized freshly prepared and thoroughly washed hydrous alumina in a solution of aluminum chloride and then dialyzed out the excess of the peptizing agent in the cold. By this method a positively charged sol results that is very sensitive to the action of electrolytes. The precipitate formed on coagulation is highly gelatinous, is readily soluble in acids and alkalies, and is a mordant. The sol, therefore, bears the same relation to Crum's colloidal alumina

[1] *Phil. Mag.*, (4) **23,** 290 (1862); see also SCHLUMBERGER: *Bull. soc. chim.*, (3) **13,** 62 (1895).

[2] WEISER: *J. Phys. Chem.*, **24,** 525 (1920).

[3] Japanese Patent 41726 (1922).

[4] BILTZ: *Ber.*, **35,** 4432 (1902).

[5] LEY: *Z. physik. Chem.*, **30,** 219 (1899).

[6] BJERRUM: *Z. physik. Chem.*, **59,** 343 (1907).

[7] *J. Am. Chem. Soc.*, **39,** 71 (1917).

[8] *Liebig's Ann. Chem.*, **121,** 41 (1862).

that Graham's colloidal ferric oxide bears to the Péan de St. Gilles sol. Analogous to ferric oxide sols, the difference in properties of the two colloidal aluminas is closely associated with the size and physical character of the hydrous particles. Peptization of highly gelatinous alumina in the cold favors the formation of small highly hydrous primary particles that are more reactive and have a higher adsorption capacity than the more granular and denser particles formed during prolonged boiling in a medium possessing a slight solvent action.

The peptization of an alumina gel by $AlCl_3$ does not take place very readily; but Hantzsch and Desch[1] got around this difficulty by adding ammonia to an aluminum chloride solution until the precipitate first formed failed to dissolve, and then dialyzing the sol. By evaporating the transparent purified sol on the water bath, a glassy mass was obtained which was readily repeptized by water; but the new colloid was quite opalescent owing to the formation of larger crystalline[2] particles during the process of evaporation. The sol prepared by hot dialysis was also slightly opalescent, possessing properties intermediate between Graham's and Crum's sols.

Highly purified sols cannot be prepared by adding ammonia to aluminum sulfate and dialyzing, because of the precipitating action of sulfate ion. However, one may add Na_2CO_3 and $Al_2(SO_4)_3$ in the approximate ratio of 3:5 without any precipitation taking place; when the ratio is 7.5:5, half the alumina is thrown down; and when it is 12:5, all the alumina precipitates.[3]

Schneider[4] first peptized gelatinous alumina with a dilute solution of HCl. The excess acid was removed by evaporating to dryness and repeptizing with water. The sol gave no test for chloride ion with $AgNO_3$ in the cold, but AgCl precipitated out on heating; with silver oxide, both AgCl and the sol were thrown down. The failure to get a test for chloride ion in the cold was doubtless due to inhibition of the growth of AgCl particles by the protecting power of hydrous alumina. Heating caused the AgCl to show up, owing to partial agglomeration of the particles.

---

[1] *Liebig's Ann. Chem.*, **323,** 30 (1902).
[2] Böhm and Niclassen: *Z. anorg. Chem.*, **132,** 1 (1924).
[3] Mills and Barr: *J. Chem. Soc.*, **41,** 341 (1882).
[4] *Liebig's Ann. Chem.*, **257,** 359 (1890).

The addition of silver oxide introduced the strongly adsorbed hydroxyl ion which neutralized the charge on the particles precipitating the colloidal oxide together with AgCl. Müller[1] boiled freshly prepared hydrous alumina with $N/20$ HCl and found the amount of acid required for complete peptization to be one-seventy-second of that necessary to form $AlCl_3$; Pauli[2] used one-ninth of the theoretical amount; and Kohlschütter[3] showed that the quantity of acid required was determined by the history of the sample. The dissolution of hydrous alumina in concentrated HCl is always preceded by sol formation; but H_2SO_4 does not form a sol.

Hydrous alumina is peptized by ferric chloride or nitrate but not by ferric sulfate. The peptizing action of the chloride and nitrate is due to strong adsorption of ferric ions and of hydrogen ions resulting from hydrolysis of the salts. Such sols contain both hydrous alumina and hydrous ferric oxide. With ferric sulfate, the peptizing action of the cations is neutralized by strong adsorption of sulfate ion and no sol is formed. The order of peptizing power of different acids and salts on an aged gel thrown down from a boiling solution is: $HNO_3 > HCl > FeCl_3 > AlCl_3 > HC_2H_3O_2$.[4]

If we assume, as Lottermoser does, that a peptizer must contain one of the ions of the disperse phase, then the first step in the peptization of alumina by an acid or salt would be interaction with the formation of some aluminum ion. This would seem to be an unnecessary step in view of the stronger peptizing action of hydrogen ion than of aluminum ion. On account of the relatively small ionization of acetic acid, its peptizing power is less than that of HCl or HNO_3. Bentley and Rose[5] have reported many anomalies in the behavior of the sol formed by peptizing alumina with acetic acid; but for the most part, these are the result either of experimental error or of misinterpretation of data.[6]

[1] *Z. anorg. Chem.*, **57,** 311 (1908); *cf.* SCHLUMBERGER: *Bull. soc. chim.*, (3) **13,** 60 (1895).

[2] *Kolloid-Z.*, **29,** 281 (1921).

[3] *Z. Elektrochem.*, **29,** 253 (1923).

[4] WEISER: *J. Phys. Chem.*, **24,** 521 (1920).

[5] *J. Am. Chem. Soc.*, **35,** 1490 (1913); ROSE: *Kolloid-Z.*, **15,** 1 (1914).

[6] WEISER: *J. Phys. Chem.*, **24,** 522, 527 (1920).

On account of the marked tendency of aluminum salts to hydrolyze, one is not surprised to encounter a very large number of basic aluminum chlorides, sulfates, and acetates. While there may be some definite salts of this type, it is certain that by far the most of them are mixtures of indefinite composition.[1] Pauli and his collaborators[2] champion the view that the various alumina sols are highly complex basic salts of variable composition. While one cannot deny the possible existence in a sol of such compounds as Pauli describes, there seems no reason for postulating their existence until someone shows that such definite compounds are formed and defines their limits of stability.

Action of Alkalies and Ammonia.—As has been noted in the preceding chapter, hydrous chromium oxide is peptized by dilute alkalies forming a negative sol owing to preferential adsorption of hydroxyl ion, and little or no chromite results within a reasonable time. Certain investigators are of the opinion that hydrous aluminum oxide is peptized in the same way and question the existence of definite aluminates in the alkaline solution. In support of this view, Mahin[3] observed the precipitation of a greater amount of hydrous alumina on adding NH_4NO_3 to an alkaline solution of the hydrous oxide than is represented by the assumption that an aluminate is involved in the process, thus: $NaAlO_2 + NH_4NO_3 \rightarrow NH_4AlO_2 + NaNO_3$; $NH_4AlO_2 + 2H_2O \rightarrow NH_4OH + Al(OH)_3$. It was assumed, therefore, that NH_4NO_3 merely coagulates a negative alumina sol. Moreover, in electrolysis the ratio between the oxygen evolved and the alumina precipitated should be always $1:2$ if the solution were pure aluminate; but a slightly greater amount of alumina was obtained in some cases. As Blum[4] points out, Mahin's observations are not conclusive because of the inability to control the spontaneous decomposition which is going on continuously in alkali solutions of alumina. Chatterji and Dhar[5] observed no appreciable change

---

[1] ORDWAY: *Am. J. Sci.*, (2) **26**, 196 (1858); TOMMASI: *Bull. soc. chim.*, (2) **37**, 443 (1882); SCHLUMBERGER: *Ibid.*, (3) **13**, 60 (1895); LIECHTI and SUIDA: *Dinglers polytech. J.*, **251**, 177 (1883).

[2] ADOLF, PAULI, and JANDRASCHITSCH: *Kolloid-Z.*, **29**, 281 (1921); PAULI: *Ibid.*, **28**, 49 (1921).

[3] *J. Am. Chem. Soc.*, **35**, 30 (1913).

[4] *J. Am. Chem. Soc.*, **35**, 1499 (1913); **36**, 2383 (1914).

[5] *Chem. News*, **121**, 253 (1920).

in the conductivity of solutions of alkali to which alumina was added; and so concluded that a sol was formed. Their observations merely indicate the failure of their experimental method to detect any change in conductivity in the highly alkaline solu-

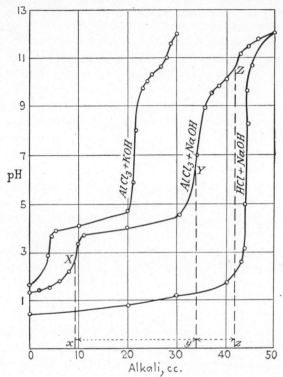

Fig. 10.—Variation in pH on titration of aluminium chloride solutions with alkali.

tion, rather than the absence of a change. The bulk of the evidence seems to indicate that alumina is acted on chemically by alkali hydroxides.[1] Thus Hildebrand and Blum followed the change in hydrogen ion concentration on adding NaOH or KOH

[1] PRESCOTT: *J. Am. Chem. Soc.*, **2**, 27 (1880); LEYTE: *Chem. News*, **51**, 109 (1885); NOYES and WHITNEY: *Z. physik. Chem.*, **15**, 695 (1894); HERZ: *Z. anorg. Chem.*, **25**, 155 (1900); HANTZSCH: *Ibid.*, **30**, 289 (1902); RUBEN-BAUER: *Ibid.*, **30**, 331 (1902); SLADE: *Ibid.*, **77**, 457 (1912); HILDEBRAND: *J. Am. Chem. Soc.*, **35**, 864 (1913); BLUM: *Ibid.*, **35**, 1499 (1913); **36**, 2383 (1914); SLADE and POLACK: *Trans. Faraday Soc.*, **10**, 150 (1914).

to a solution of aluminum salt until all the hydrous alumina is precipitated and subsequently dissolved. The results are represented in Fig. 10, together with the neutralization curve for NaOH and HCl which is included for reference. With $AlCl_3$ and NaOH, X represents the beginning of precipitation, Y the completion of precipitation, and Z the completion of solution. From X to Y, $2AlCl_3 + 6NaOH + xH_2O = 6NaCl + Al_2O_3 \cdot xH_2O$, and from Y to Z, $Al_2O_3 \cdot xH_2O + 2NaOH = 2NaAlO_2 + (x + 1)$ H_2O. Since yz is almost exactly $\frac{1}{3}xy$, the formation of $NaAlO_2$ is rendered quite certain.

The potassium salt $KAlO_2 \cdot 1.5H_2O$ has been isolated[1] in a crystalline form. The existence of alkali metaaluminates only has been established,[2] although other aluminates are believed to form under certain conditions.[3]

Even though alkalies act on hydrous alumina giving aluminate, the solutions always contain more or less colloidal alumina. Indeed, Kohlschütter found that sol formation always precedes the dissolution of alumina from aluminate, and the same is probably true of aged hydrous alumina; but it is apparently not the case with gelatinous oxides. In any event, the aluminate undergoes progressive hydrolysis with the formation first of colloidal alumina, as Pascal[4] observed; and finally, of the crystalline trihydrate which precipitates. According to Johnston,[5] this progressive hydrolysis with precipitation of alumina probably accounts for the strong alkalinity of solutions of alkali aluminates.

In analytical chemistry it is well known that the precipitation of aluminum as hydrous oxide is not quantitative in the presence of an excess of ammonia[6] on account of the solvent action of the

---

[1] ALLEN and ROGERS: *Am. Chem. J.*, **24**, 304 (1900).

[2] WOOD: *J. Chem. Soc.*, **93**, 417 (1908); CARRARA and VESPIGNANI: *Gazz. chim. ital.*, **30** II, 35 (1900); HEYROVSKY: *Chem. News*, **125**, 198 (1922).

[3] GROBET: *J. chim. phys.*, **19**, 331 (1922); HERZ: *Z. anorg. Chem.*, **25**, 155 (1900); *Z. Elektrochem.*, **17**, 403 (1911); GOUDRIAAN: *Rec. trav. chim.*, **41**, 82 (1922).

[4] *Compt. rend.*, **178**, 481 (1924).

[5] Private communication to BLUM: *J. Am. Chem. Soc.*, **35**, 1503 (1913).

[6] FRESENIUS: "Quant. Chem. Analysis," **2**, 807 (1916); WEDENHORST: "Beitrage zur Quant. Bestimmung und Trennung des Aluminiums," Göttingen (1921); BLUM: *Z. analyt. Chem.*, **27**, 19 (1888); VON WEIMARN: *Kolloid-Z.*, **4**, 38 (1909); JANDER and WEBER: *Z. anorg. Chem.*, **131**, 266 (1923).

solution. Blum observed a small but appreciable solvent action when the solution is just alkaline to phenolphthalein at a hydrogen ion concentration of 10^{-9}. Whether this is due wholly or in part to peptization of the oxide is open to some question. When potassium aluminate is precipitated with the calculated amount of ammonium chloride and an excess of ammonia added rapidly, all the alumina redissolves. Renz[1] mixed the calculated amount of ammonium sulfate with barium aluminate to which an excess of ammonia was added, and after filtering off the barium sulfate, obtained a clear solution containing 2.0 grams Al_2O_3 per liter. On evaporating to dryness, there was found a white gummy mass of hydrous oxide insoluble in ammonia. The solvent action of ammonia is most pronounced at the moment of formation, and from analogy with the alkali aluminates it is probable that aluminate is formed.[2] Blum was unable to detect the presence of this salt by determing the change in hydrogen ion concentration during the precipitation of hydrous alumina, because of the low alkalinity of the aqueous solution. If the salt exists, the maximum quantity that can be held in solution will be determined by the alkalinity of the resulting solution and its ability to repress the hydrolysis of the salt. According to Archibald and Habasian, the solubility of alumina in ammonia rises to a maximum of approximately 0.45 gram per liter at a concentration of about 0.5 N, and then decreases owing to a change in the physical character of the hydrous oxide. The solubility of Renz's preparation in excess ammonia was more than four times this maximum. Ammonium nitrate decreases the solubility in ammonia while potassium nitrate apparently increases it.

Lottermoser and Friedrich[3] prepared a very readily peptized hydrous oxide by adding $AlCl_3$ in small increments to a solution of $N/10$ NH_4OH cooled to $0°$ and stirred by air saturated with ammonia. After thorough purification by dialysis, the oxide was peptized by $AlCl_3$ slowly in the cold and rapidly at 60 to $70°$. Traces of ammonia peptized the gel forming a negative sol that was not very stable on heating. In the light of this work, Renz's experiments should be repeated to determine the

[1] *Ber.*, **36**, 2751 (1903).

[2] *Cf.* Archibald and Habasian: *Trans. Roy. Soc. Canada*, **10**, 69 (1916).

[3] *Ber.*, **57**, 808 (1924).

nature of his solutions. Jander and Weber[1] found no evidence of sol formation on shaking precipitated alumina with ammonia solutions. For a given concentration of ammonia, the solubility was the same in the presence of monovalent and univalent anions; organic solvents have no precipitating effect;[2] and the solution passes readily through an ultrafilter.

Alumina is not precipitated from an alum solution by ammonia in the presence of a tartrate owing to the formation of a complex aluminum tartrate.[3] A sol results by precipitation in the presence of glucose. In some preliminary experiments on grinding alumina in a colloid mill with glucose, Utzino[4] claimed to get a sol, the maximum stability of which does not occur with the finest state of subdivision. These observations should be repeated.

Coagulation of Sol.—The precipitating power of electrolytes for colloidal aluminum oxide sols has been studied repeatedly.[5] While the absolute precipitation values of electrolytes vary with the concentration and purity of the sol and with the experimental method, the order is always approximately the same. On account of the transparency of the gelatinous oxide, some difficulty is experienced in determining the critical precipitation concentration of electrolytes. Kawamura took advantage of the change in viscosity which the sol undergoes on coagulation, and this method was adopted by Ishazaka and Gann. The latter in collaboration with Freundlich, followed the slow coagulation of colloidal alumina by the addition of electrolytes containing univalent precipitating ions. The process which was found to be autocatalytically accelerated, takes place in accordance with the equation $\dfrac{dx}{dt} = k(1 + b_1x)\,(1 - x)$ where x is the increase in viscosity after time t expressed as a fraction of the total increase;

[1] *Z. anorg. Chem.*, **131**, 266 (1923).

[2] Yanek: *Ann. ecole mines Oural*, **1**, 45 (1919); *Chem. Abstracts*, **15**, 1239 (1921).

[3] Hakomori: *J. Chem. Soc. Japan*, **43**, 629 (1922).

[4] *Kolloid-Z.*, **32**, 149 (1923).

[5] Kawamura: *J. Coll. Sci., Imp. Univ. Tokyo*, **28**, Art. 8 (1908); Ishazaka: *Z. physik. Chem.*, **83**, 97 (1913); Gann: *Kolloidchem. Beihefte*, **8**, 125 (1916); Weiser and Middleton: *J. Phys. Chem.*, **24**, 639 (1920); Iwanitzkaja: *Kolloidchem. Beihefte*, **18**, 24 (1923).

and k and b_1 are constants. For concentrated sols the coagulation process is more nearly represented by the equation $\dfrac{dx}{dt} =$ $k_1(1 - x)^2$. The coefficient k_1 increases rapidly with the concentration of the electrolyte during slow coagulation, while for very rapid coagulation the velocity is independent of the nature of the electrolyte. In rapid coagulation, Smoluchowski[1] assumes that all the collisions of particles are inelastic because of the great attractive forces existing between particles; and in slow coagulation, only a portion of the collisions result in immediate union, because the mutual attraction is not always great enough to overcome the repulsive effect of more highly charged particles. Freundlich turns this around and assumes a constant force of attraction for a given concentration of electrolyte below that necessary for rapid coagulation; but because of repulsion between charged particles, only those collisions are inelastic in which the particles collide with sufficient force. Obviously, the greater the charge on the particles, the greater must be the velocity of collision in order to overcome the repulsive effect and so to bring about coalescence and agglomeration. The rapid increase in the velocity of slow coagulation is due to the proportionately larger number of inelastic collisions that result when the charge on the particles is reduced by adsorption of precipitating ions.

Aluminum Oxide Jellies.—A sol formed by peptizing sufficient hydrous alumina to form a viscous liquid sets to a jelly on standing.[2] If this jelly is broken up by shaking, a gelatinous precipitate settles out which is not repeptized by the acid and so cannot be reconverted into a jelly. Schalek and Szegvary[3] prepared a so by Crum's method which set to a jelly on the addition of a sulitable amount of electrolyte just below the precipitation value. This jelly was broken up on shaking, but instead of giving a gelatinous precipitate, a sol was re-formed that would again set to a jelly on standing. The reversible sol-gel transformation has been observed only with relatively concentrated sols of the hydrous oxide. A jelly may be formed by coagulating a dilute sol prepared by peptizing hydrous alumina with acetic acid;

---

[1] *Z. physik. Chem.*, **92**, 129 (1917); *Kolloid-Z.*, **21**, 98 (1917).

[2] SCHLUMBERGER: *Bull. soc. chim.*, (3) **13**, 56 (1895).

[3] *Kolloid-Z.*, **33**, 326 (1923).

but shaking converts the jelly into a gelatinous precipitate that is not repeptized.

ADSORPTION BY HYDROUS ALUMINUM OXIDE

If an electrolyte is added to a sol stabilized by preferential adsorption of cations, precipitation will take place when the anions of the electrolyte are adsorbed sufficiently to reduce the charge on the particles below a critical value. Whitney and Ober[1] first showed that the amount of various ions carried down during the precipitation of arsenious sulfide sol are not far from equivalent. This conclusion was upheld by Freundlich[2] as a result of similar observations on adsorption during the precipitation of other sols. The results with alumina given in Table XIV are frequently offered as proof of equivalent adsorption

TABLE XIV

Ions	Precipitation value, millimols per liter	Adsorption at the precipitation values	
		In millimols	In milli-equivalents
Salicylate.........	8.0	0.30	0.30
Picrate...........	4.0	0.18	0.18
Oxalate..........	0.36	0.18	0.36
Ferricyanide......	0.10	0.09	0.27
Ferrocyanide......	0.08	0.073	0.29

during the precipitation of sols with precipitating ions of varying valence although the variation from equivalence is quite appreciable. The investigations of Freundlich on aluminum oxide sol have been extended by Middleton[3] with the results given in Table XV. The adsorption for different ions is not even approximately equivalent, and the variation cannot be attributed to experimental errors, as Freundlich assumes. While the latter is doubtless right in concluding that neutralization of the charge is accomplished by adsorption of equivalent amounts, the

[1] *J. Am. Chem. Soc.*, **23**, 1842 (1901).

[2] "Kapillarchemie," 579 *et seq.* (1922).

[3] WEISER and MIDDLETON: *J. Phys. Chem.*, **24**, 630 (1920).

TABLE XV

Anion	Adsorption, milliequivalents per liter	Precipitation value of salt, milliequivalents per liter
Ferrocyanide..............	1.280	0.375
Ferricyanide...............	1.214	0.400
Sulfate....................	0.997	0.538
Oxalate...................	1.142	0.700
Chromate..................	0.870	1.300
Dithionate................	0.657	1.625
Dichromate...............	0.269	1.775

actual amount carried down is determined (*a*) by adsorption of the electrically charged particles during neutralization and (*b*) by adsorption of salt by electrically neutral particles during the agglomeration process. The amounts of (*a*) will be approximately equivalent, but the amounts of (*b*) will vary with the nature and concentration of the electrolyte. Owing to salt adsorption by neutralized particles, Freundlich's conclusion that equivalent amounts are adsorbed at the precipitation concentration cannot be generally true, since this would mean either that the neutralized particles do not act as an adsorbent or adsorb all ions to the same extent. Moreover, the variability of the precipitation concentration will necessarily result in variation in the degree of saturation of the adsorbent by the adsorbed phase. One should expect the adsorption value to approach equivalence more nearly, the less the adsorption capacity of the precipitated particles. This probably accounts for the values being more nearly equivalent with an arsenious sufide sol than with a hydrous oxide sol having many times the adsorption capacity.

If the variation from equivalence arises from adsorption after neutralization, the adsorption values might appear *a priori* to give directly the order of adsorption of the ions. This is not necessarily true, however, because there are variable factors other than the adsorbability of the precipitating ions that determine the amount of adsorption after neutralization; for example, the nature and degree of ionization and the degree of hydrolysis of the salt; the hydrogen ion concentration; the effect of different salts on the physical character of the precipitate; etc. From the observations recorded in Table XV, the order of adsorbability expressed in equivalents would appear to be as follows: ferrocyanide > ferricyanide > oxalate > sulfate > chromate > dithionate > dichromate. Considering the precipitation value of the several potassium salts, we find the order of precipitating power beginning at the greatest to be: ferrocyanide > ferricyanide > sulfate > oxalate > chromate > dithionate > dichromate. The order of adsorption determined directly is the same as the order deduced from precipitation data with the exception of oxalate and sulfate, which are reversed. The cause of this exception is not known; but in this connection, attention may be called to some unpublished work of Everett E. Porter which disclosed that the order of precipitating power of oxalate and sulfate for chromic oxide sol is determined by the hydrogen ion concentration of the precipitating solution.

If the adsorption value is expressed in equivalents, as seems logical, since neutralization is determined by the number of adsorbed charges, the results given in Table XV are in accord with the usual interpretation of Schulze's law that the ion of highest valence is most readily adsorbed. At the same time, the qualitative nature of the rule is indicated by the different adsorption value for ions of the same valence. Schilow[1] found a wide variation in the adsorption of cations of the same valence by ignited alumina; but the ions of highest valence were most strongly adsorbed.

It is unfortunate that a comparison of the relationship between the precipitation values of electrolytes and the adsorption of precipitating ions cannot be made directly with salts containing univalent precipitating ions since the precipitation values and adsorption values for multivalent ions are likely to be so close together that it is hazardous to draw conclusions, particularly when the differences may be of the same order of magnitude as the errors inherent in the experimental method. The direct determination of adsorption of univalent ions that precipitate only in high concentration, is impracticable since the change in concentration resulting from adsorption is too low to measure accurately. It is possible, however, to determine the relative

[1] *Z. physik. Chem.*, **100**, 425 (1922).

adsorbability of univalent precipitating ions during the precipitation of sols by an indirect method consisting essentially in determining the extent to which the presence of different univalent ions cuts down the adsorption of an easily estimated multivalent ion.[1] This is illustrated by the results recorded in Table XVI. The extent to which the adsorption of barium ion

TABLE XVI

Cubic centimeters electrolyte added to 100 cubic centimeters sol, total volume 200 cubic centimeters.	Barium adsorbed		Precipitation value, milliequivalents per liter
	Grams	Milliequivalents per gram	
30 $N/50$ BaCl₂..........................	0.0109	0.058	BaCl₂	2.74
30 $N/50$ BaCl₂ + 30 $N/2$ LiCl...........	0.0037	0.019	LiCl	88.7
30 $N/50$ BaCl₂ + 30 $N/2$ NaCl.........	0.0025	0.014	NaCl	73.5
30 $N/50$ BaCl₂ + 30 $N/2$ KCl...........	0.0018	0.009	KCl	63.7
30 $N/50$ BaCl₂ + 30 $N/2$ HCl...........	0.0013	0.007	HCl	52.5

by arsenious sulfide is cut down by the presence of the same amount of different alkali chlorides is in the order Li < Na < K < H. Since, under otherwise constant conditions, one should expect the adsorption of a given cation to be cut down by the presence of a second, in proportion to the adsorbability of the latter, it follows that the order of adsorbability of univalent ions is H > K > Na > Li. This is exactly the same as the order deduced from the precipitation values of the salts, assuming that the salt containing the most readily adsorbed cation precipitates in lowest concentration.

Weak adsorption of the precipitating ions of electrolytes requiring a high concentration to effect neutralization, is indicated by the ease of reversibility of precipitation. Thus hydrous alumina precipitated from a sol with a relatively high concentration of KCl, NaCl, or NaC₂H₃O₂ is readily carried back into colloidal solution by washing, whereas the precipitation is more nearly irreversible if K₂SO₄ is the precipitating electrolyte. Similarly, a precipitated alumina thrown down from an alum solution with alkali can be washed until most of the sulfate is removed before peptization begins,[2] whereas the precipitate from chloride solution is very easily dispersed by washing. The

[1] WEISER: *J. Phys. Chem.*, **29**, 963 (1925).
[2] BRADFIELD: *J. Am. Chem. Soc.*, **44**, 969 (1922).

difference in degree of reversibility of precipitation is determined by the relatively weak adsorption of univalent chloride as compared with bivalent sulfate. Rakuzin[1] reports that hydrous alumina adsorbs gum arabic reversibly; but the adsorption from sodium and potassium silicate is partly reversible.

The adsorption of chromate by hydrous alumina is sufficiently strong to impart a yellow color to the precipitate formed in the presence of alkali chromate or precipitated and subsequently shaken with alkali chromate solutions. Charriou[2] found little alkali metal in the precipitate and so attributed the color to the formation of aluminum chromate on the surface of the alumina. There is no justification for this conclusion and it is probably erroneous. If well-washed alumina is shaken with alkali chromate, the solution becomes alkaline owing to stronger adsorption of acid than of base. The yellow color is due to chromic acid rather than aluminum chromate. Ishazaka[3] found that potassium dichromate was converted to chromate in the presence of powdered alumina. The explanation of this phenomenon is as follows: The equilibrium in solution between dichromate and chromate ion may be represented by the equation $Cr_2O_7'' + H_2O \rightleftarrows 2H^{\cdot} + 2CrO_4''$. Alumina shows such a strong preferential adsorption for hydrogen ion that the presence of the oxide in a finely divided condition shifts the equilibrium to the right with the formation of chromate ion at the expense of dichromate. Colloidal alumina stabilized by preferential adsorption of hydrogen ion has a comparatively slight effect on the equilibrium.[4]

Adsorbed chromate is displaced but slightly by washing with 5 per cent solutions of the more weakly adsorbed chloride, bromide, iodide, nitrate, or acetate; while chromate is displaced by ions the adsorption of which is of the same order of magnitude, such as carbonate, sulfate, sulfide, oxalate, tartrate, phosphate, or arsenate. Similarly, sulfate is not displaced by weakly adsorbed univalent ions but is displaced by bivalent ions. Charriou[5] generalized that an adsorbed ion is displaced by one of the same

[1] *J. Russ. Phys.-Chem. Soc.*, **53**, 357 (1921).
[2] *Compt. rend.*, **176**, 679, 1890 (1923).
[3] *Z. physik. Chem.*, **83**, 97 (1913).
[4] WEISER and MIDDLETON: *J. Phys. Chem.*, **24**, 648 (1920).
[5] *Compt. rend.*, **176**, 1890 (1923).

kind having the same or a higher valence; but is not displaced by one of lower valence. With two ions of the same valence the less concentrated is displaced the most. These generalizations may be approximately true in certain cases, but they are necessarily not quantitative, since they are based on the erroneous impression that ions of like valences are all adsorbed to the same extent and that trivalent ions are always more strongly adsorbed than bivalent and bivalent ions always more strongly adsorbed than univalent. Generalizations based on Schulze's law are of value only in so far as the limitations of Schulze's law are fully recognized.[1]

From the practical point of view, in the quantitative estimation of alumina one may avoid the contamination by such ions as chromate by carrying out the precipitation with NH_4HCO_3 instead of NaOH, or one may remove the adsorbed ion by washing the precipitate with NH_4HCO_3.

Miller[2] investigated the simultaneous adsorption of sulfate and oxalate ions during the precipitation of alumina. The adsorbabilities of the two ions are not far apart, and it is claimed that the sum of the adsorption expressed in mols per mol of hydrous alumina may be considered constant, although the observed values really show variations of more than 20 per cent both above and below the mean value. The distribution ratios $\dfrac{\text{ion in solution}}{\text{ion in precipitate}}$ at equilibrium were also calculated, and the values for the same ion were considered to be of the same order of magnitude, although here the variations from a constant value were more than 100 per cent from the mean. As a result of these observations, the taking up of anions by the hydrous oxide was considered to be a solid-solution phenomenon. This conclusion seems hardly justified by the evidence. Of course, one cannot expect too much from data obtained on such a complex system where such factors as the hydrogen ion concentration and the physical character of the precipitate are not subject to control. But one cannot be certain of the effect of eliminating all variable factors other than the relative amounts of oxalate and sulfate. In case the adsorbabilities of the two ions are

[1] WEISER: *J. Phys. Chem.*, **29**, 963 (1925).
[2] *U. S. Pub. Health Repts.*, **39**, 1502 (1924).

very similar, one should expect the total adsorption to be approximately equivalent, irrespective of the relative amounts of each; but if the adsorbabilities of the ions are widely different, there is likely to be an antagonistic action between the two which will cause the total adsorption to vary with the relative amounts of each in the solution. But even should the adsorption be equivalent and the displacement follow the law of distribution between solutions, it does not follow that the taking up of ions is a true solid-solution phenomenon rather than a surface phenomenon. If in certain cases there should be a reciprocal displacement of adsorbed ions, there is probably no real objection to calling the system a homogeneous single-phase solid solution as Miller does, provided one recognizes that this designation is probably not strictly accurate.

If a small amount of ferric salt is added to the test tube containing the precipitate thrown down from an alumina sol by the required amount of ferrocyanide, no Prussian blue is formed until after an appreciable interval of time.[1] This is not due to the slow rate of reaction between ferrocyanide and ferric ions as a result of the colloidal nature of ferric salt solutions;[2] but is due to the very strong adsorption of ferrocyanide ion which removes it from the field of action. If another strongly adsorbed precipitating ion is added to the sol either before or after precipitation, the ferrocyanide is displaced and the time necessary for the appearance of Prussian blue is diminished appreciably. In the same way, the transformation of Congo blue to Congo red by dilute alkali is slowed down in the presence of hydrous alumina on account of the strong adsorption of Congo blue by the hydrous oxide.[3]

The selective adsorption of alumina seems to offer a great many possibilities to the biochemist,[4] although the observations to date are somewhat fragmentary. Rakuzin[5] reports that casein is adsorbed by alumina without splitting the molecule,

---

[1] Reitstötter: *Kolloid-Z.*, **21**, 197 (1917); Freundlich and Reitstötter: *Ibid.*, **23**, 23 (1918).

[2] Vorländer: *Kolloid-Z.*, **22**, 103 (1918).

[3] Bayliss: *Proc. Roy. Soc. London*, **84**, 81 (1912).

[4] Euler and Erikson: *Z. physiol. Chem.*, **128**, 1, 9 (1923).

[5] *Ber.*, **56**, 1385 (1923); *Z. Immunitäts.*, **34**, 155 (1922).

whereas most proteins are broken up. Thus egg albumin is separated into two components differing in optical rotatory power; chondrin is separated from chondroitin sulfuric acid which remains in solution, while the colloidal chrondrin residue is adsorbed reversibly. Koch's tuberculin and Deny's tuberculin can be distinguished by their difference in adsorbability. Alumina is also recommended for the purification of pepsin and of diphtheria antitoxin; therapeutically, it is suggested for use in intestinal infections.

It cannot be emphasized too strongly that comparative data on adsorption by hydrous alumina or any other substance cannot be obtained unless particular attention is paid to the physical character of the adsorbent.[1] To make the most rapid progress it would seem to be essential for biochemists to get together on some well-defined arbitrary methods of procedure for making a series of preparations that could serve as standards. The systems with which the biochemists deal are so complicated at best that there seems no justification for carrying out adsorption experiments with adsorbents that are not standardized in some way.

The important rôle which hydrous aluminum oxide plays in the soil and in such important technical processes as water purification and dyeing will be considered in later chapters.

HYDROUS GALLIUM OXIDE

Hydrous gallium oxide requires a very slight hydroxyl ion concentration for its precipitation and is thrown down in a highly gelatinous form not only by both strong and weak alkalies but by salts of weak acids,[2] such as carbonate, bicarbonate, sulfide, sulfite,[3] etc. Tartaric acid prevents the precipitation, presumably because complex tartrates are formed.[4] Unlike hydrous alumina, the gel is fairly soluble in an excess of strong ammonia, doubtless owing to the formation of a complex gallium-ammonium ion; like alumina, it is very soluble in alkalies apparently forming gallates.[5] From the alkali solution, the oxide

[1] EULER and NILSSON: *Z. physiol. Chem.*, **131**, 107 (1923); **134**, 22 (1924).
[2] LECOQ DE BOISBAUDRAN: *Chem. News*, **35**, 148, 157, 167 (1877).
[3] DENNIS and BRIDGEMAN: *J. Am. Chem. Soc.*, **40**, 1531 (1918).
[4] LECOQ DE BOISBAUDRAN: *Compt. rend.*, **93**, 293, 329, 815 (1881).
[5] FRICKE and BLENCKE: *Z. anorg. Chem.*, **143**, 183 (1925).

precipitates very slowly out of contact with air, but it is readily thrown down by carbon dioxide as a flocculent mass entirely different from the granular crystals of $Al_2O_3 \cdot 3H_2O$ which precipitate from aluminate solution.[1]

Owing to the highly gelatinous nature of the precipitate, one should expect sol formation to result from thorough washing of the gel. Moreover, it is not unlikely that a small amount of gallic chloride or hydrochloric acid would peptize the gel, forming a positive sol; or a slight excess of alkali, a negative sol; but there is no record of such experiments having been performed. There is some evidence that in the presence of excess alkali a part, at least, of the hydrous oxide is in the sol form. Thus, if CO_2 conducted into an alkali solution newly formed in the cold, one obtains a very voluminous gel, quite different in appearance and properties from the flocculent precipitate thrown down from an old alkali solution. Moreover, the solubility of the hydrous oxide in KOH solution is appreciably less than in NaOH solution,[1] as would be expected from the higher precipitating power of K· ion than of Na· ion for negative sols.

Hydrous gallium oxide, like hydrous alumina, ages fairly rapidly even at ordinary temperatures, as evidenced by a progressive loss of adsorbed water and a decrease in the solubility in alkalies.[1] As already intimated, the ageing progresses more rapidly in the presence of alkali.

No definite hydrate of Ga_2O_3 has been established, and the available evidence indicates the non-existence of such compounds. The hydrous oxide precipitated from ammonia contains less water than corresponds to the hydrate $Ga_2O_3 \cdot 3H_2O$ when dried in a vacuum desiccator over H_2SO_4 or heated on the water bath. The water content of an oxide obtained from an old alkali solution and dried over H_2SO_4 is greater than required for a trihydrate; but the more gelatinous precipitate from a newly formed alkali solution falls considerably below that for a trihydrate, even when dried in the air at ordinary temperatures.[1] Apparently, the hydrous precipitate is Ga_2O_3 with adsorbed water in amount depending on the conditions of formation and the method of drying.

[1] FRICKE: *Z. Elektrochem.*, **30**, 393 (1924).

HYDROUS INDIUM OXIDE

Hydrous indium oxide in a highly gelatinous form is precipitated by adding alkali, ammonia, hydroxylamine,[1] or dimethylamine[2] to a solution of an indium salt. The oxide loses water continuously on heating, and there is no indication of the existence of a hydrate.[3] The last traces of the adsorbed water are not removed until a temperature of 650° is reached; but the oxide undergoes no appreciable decomposition below 850°.[4] Like hydrous gallia and alumina, the precipitate ages slowly at ordinary temperature but rapidly at the boiling point, particularly in the presence of alkali. The newly formed oxide dissolves in the cold in excess alkali but soon precipitates out in a much less reactive form.[5] This precipitation is almost quantitative in the hot.[6] Unfortunately we do not know whether in the cold the oxide is dissolved by excess alkali forming an indate or whether it is peptized forming a negative sol, although the latter seems more likely. Nor do we know whether the precipitate which comes down on standing is an aged hydrous oxide as in the case of chromic oxide or a definite hydrate as in the case of alumina. These problems should be investigated.

As ordinarily prepared, hydrous indium oxide is but slightly soluble in ammonia. Renz[7] claimed at one time to have obtained an ammonia-soluble form of the gel; but later he was not sure about it. It is, of course, altogether possible that the hydrous oxide may be thrown down under special conditions in a more soluble or more readily peptizable form than that ordinarily obtained; and if so, there should be little difficulty in determining whether a sol is formed, as has been suspected.[8]

Whatever may be the nature of the alkali solution of hydrous indium oxide, the gel is readily converted into a sol by thorough washing with distilled water. Even the denser gel thrown

---

[1] DENNIS and GEER: *Ber.*, **37**, 961 (1904).

[2] RENZ: *Ber.*, **34**, 2763 (1901); **36**, 1847, 2751, 4394 (1904); **37**, 2111 (1904).

[3] CARNELLEY and WALKER: *J. Chem. Soc.*, **53**, 88 (1888).

[4] THIEL and KOELSCH: *Z. anorg. Chem.*, **66**, 288 (1910).

[5] MEYER: *Liebig's Ann. Chem.*, **150**, 137 (1869).

[6] RICHARDS and BOYER: *J. Am. Chem. Soc.*, **41**, 133 (1919).

[7] *Ber.*, **36**, 1848, 2754 (1903).

[8] THIEL: *Z. anorg. Chem.*, **40**, 322 (1904); *cf.*, however, THIEL and KOELSCH: *Ibid.*, **66**, 300 (1910).

down at 100° is peptized in this way. The colloidal solutions obtained by Thiel precipitated out in a few weeks' time; but there is no doubt that very stable sols could be formed by supercentrifugal washing. To prevent sol formation during quantitative washing, it is only necessary to follow the time-honored practice of adding a little ammonium salt to the wash water.

A stable colloid is easily obtained by passing air through a cold solution of indium monoiodide.[1] The reaction $2InI + xH_2O + O_2 = In_2O_3 \cdot xH_2O + 2HI$ goes slowly, practically all of the oxide remaining colloidally dissolved. If desired, there seems no reason why this sol should not be purified by dialysis.

By carrying out the oxidation of indium monoiodide in the hot, 99 per cent of the indium is converted into hydrous oxide most of which precipitates out. Obviously, the oxide ages quite rapidly, or it would not precipitate from dilute acid solution in which the newly formed gel is very soluble. Indeed, the oxide thrown down in this way is almost insoluble in the cold in dilute acids and dissolves but slowly in concentrated ones, a behavior analogous to the ageing of the better-known hydrous oxides of aluminum and chromium.

Anhydrous indium oxide likewise furnishes a good example of the influence of the physical character of an oxide on its chemical properties. Not only is an oxide heated to 850° acted on much more readily than one ignited at 1200°;[2] but a newly formed oxide decomposes into In_3O_4 and O_2 between 1200 and 1500° much more rapidly than a dense preparation aged by long ignition[3] at a low red heat.

Hydrous Thallic Oxide

The most hydrous form of thallic oxide is obtained by adding ammonia or alkali in slight excess to a thallic salt solution in the cold. The very insoluble[4] voluminous precipitate is reddish brown in color like hydrous ferric oxide; it adsorbs alkali strongly, and in consequence, ammonia is always used as the precipitant in the estimation of thallium as trioxide.[5] If the solution after

---

[1] THIEL and KOELSCH: *Z. anorg. Chem.*, **66**, 300, 304 (1910).

[2] RENZ: *Ber.*, **36**, 1848 (1903); THIEL and KOELSCH: *Z. anorg. Chem.*, **66**, 296 (1910).

[3] THIEL: *Z. anorg. Chem.*, **40**, 322 (1904).

[4] ABEGG and SPENCER: *Z. anorg. Chem.*, **44**, 379 (1905).

[5] MEYER: *Z. anorg. Chem.*, **24**, 364 (1900).

precipitation is heated to boiling, the brown mass of hydrous oxide loses practically all its water becoming a dark granular powder; in this respect it behaves like blue hydrous cupric oxide. The oxide precipitated in the cold and dried in the air has a composition approaching $Tl_2O_3 \cdot H_2O$.[1] It has, therefore, been tacitly assumed that the red-brown slimy precipitate is a monohydrate. While this may be true, it is probably purely accidental that the composition at room temperature can be formulated $Tl_2O_3 \cdot H_2O$, particularly since it loses water continuously above room temperature, becoming almost anhydrous at 100°.[2]

By treating an alkaline solution of a thallous salt with hydrogen peroxide at room temperature,[3] one obtains a dark-brown flocculent precipitate of hydrous oxide which changes slowly to small lustrous crystals of almost anhydrous Tl_2O_3. If the reaction is carried out at 80 to 100°, the oxide is a black sandy powder. The density of the black oxide is 5.6 per cent higher than the brown; and the latter dissolves much more readily in acids and is more readily reduced to the thallous state by boiling water. It is probable that these difference in properties are due entirely to variations in the physical character of the mass, as determined by the conditions of formation, and not to allotropy as assumed by Rabe.[4] Indeed, by heating the brown oxide to 500° the primary particles sinter together and assume permanently the properties of black oxide.

A crystalline hydrate of thallic oxide, $Tl_2O_3 \cdot 3H_2O$ or $Tl(OH)_3$,[5] stable to a temperature of 340°, is said to be formed by prolonged fusion of Tl_2O_3 with KOH and subsequently treating the yellow mass with water. These observations should be repeated, as the formula was derived from thallium analyses the accuracy of which is not known.

Thallous oxide forms a definite crystalline hydrate, $Tl_2O \cdot H_2O$ or TlOH, soluble in water and possessing basic properties of the same order of magnitude as the caustic alkalies.

[1] CARNELLEY and WALKER: *J. Chem. Soc.*, **53**, 88 (1888).

[2] BIRNBAUM: *Liebig's Ann. Chem.*, **138**, 133 (1866); WERTHER: *J. prakt. Chem.*, (1) **91**, 385 (1864); *cf.*, however, LAMY: *Compt. rend.*, **54**, 1255 (1862); **58**, 442 (1863).

[3] RABE: *Z. anorg. Chem.*, **48**, 427 (1906); **50**, 158 (1906).

[4] *Z. anorg. Chem.*, **55**, 130 (1907).

[5] CARNEGIE: *Chem. News*, **60**, 113 (1889).

CHAPTER V

THE HYDROUS OXIDES OF COPPER, COBALT, NICKEL, SILVER, AND GOLD

Although the compounds of cobalt and nickel are usually studied in connection with those of iron, it seems advisable to consider their hydrous oxides along with copper. Thus, the most common oxide of iron is ferric oxide, whereas the most common oxides of nickel and cobalt are the "ous" oxides which are more nearly related to cupric oxide than to ferrous oxide. Moreover, the relationship between the blue and rose oxides of cobalt is similar in certain respects to that between the blue and black oxides of copper.

Hydrous Cupric Oxide

The gelatinous mass obtained by the addition of dilute alkali to a cuprous salt is usually considered to have the composition $Cu(OH)_2$ or $CuO \cdot H_2O$. This is because the precipitate, washed rapidly until free from the mother liquor and dried over H_2SO_4, has the composition corresponding to a monohydrate. Van Bemmelen[1] found the freshly precipitated blue substance to be highly hydrous, containing more than 20 mols of water to 1 of cupric oxide even after pressing between porous earthenware for 2 hours. When the precipitate is exposed at ordinary temperatures to an artificially dried atmosphere, it loses water continuously until the vapor pressure is equal to that of the atmosphere. From $\pm 2H_2O$ to $\pm 1H_2O$, the water is held more firmly than above $\pm 2H_2O$, and at a pressure of zero, the oxide approaches the properties and composition of a crystalline hydrate, $CuO \cdot H_2O$. The ease with which water is eliminated decreases with the age of the sample; but even the freshly prepared oxide does not lose all its water at 100°. Neither a dihydrate nor a trihydrate is formed,[2] and van Bemmelen considers

[1] Z. anorg. Chem., **5**, 466 (1894).
[2] Cf. Spring: Z. anorg. Chem., **2**, 195 (1892).

the evidence insufficient to establish the existence of a definite amorphous oxide of the composition $CuO \cdot H_2O$; hence, the gelatinous body must be looked upon as hydrous cupric oxide rather than hydrous hydrated cupric oxide.

Besides the familiar blue gelatinous oxide, a crystalline compound can be obtained in a number of ways. Becquerel[1] prepared the latter by the action of dilute potassium hydroxide on a basic cupric nitrate, and Böttger,[2] by the action of concentrated sodium hydroxide on crystalline basic cupric sulfate. Péligot[3] hydrolyzed crystalline blue-violet copper ammonium nitrate; while Villiers[4] claimed that a crystalline hydrate was formed from the amorphous hydrous oxide by suspending the latter in water which was subsequently frozen and allowed to stand several hours. Villiers' observation supports van Bemmelen's view that the amorphous hydrous oxide goes over gradually to a crystalline monohydrate on standing. While the transformation of the oxide from the amorphous to the crystalline state on standing is an established fact, there is a difference in opinion as to whether the crystals are monohydrate. By electrolyzing a solution of alkali nitrate,[5] one obtains blue hydrous copper oxide, the physical character and hence the properties of which depend on the concentration of solution and the current density.[6] Müller and Spitzer[7] electrolyzed an alkaline copper ammonium salt solution with a platinum anode and obtained a black deposit containing 95 per cent CuO. In the latter case, dehydration took place at the same time as the precipitation. The blue oxide did not darken appreciably when suspended for an hour in alkali; but if a current was passed through the solution, the particles moved to the anode, where partial dehydration and darkening

[1] *Compt. rend.*, **34**, 573 (1852); *cf.* van Bemmelen: *Z. anorg. Chem.*, **5**, 468 (1894).

[2] *Jahresber.*, 198 (1858); Habermann: *Z. anorg. Chem.*, **50**, 318 (1906).

[3] *Compt. rend.*, **53**, 209 (1861); *cf.* Bonsdorff: *Z. anorg. Chem.*, **41**, 132 (1904).

[4] *Compt. rend.*, **120**, 322 (1895).

[5] Lorenz: *Z. anorg. Chem.*, **12**, 438 (1896); Elbs: *Z. angew. Chem.*, **17**, 291 (1903).

[6] Kohlschütter and Tüscher: *Z. anorg. Chem.*, **111**, 193 (1920); Kohlschütter and Sedelinovich: *Z. Elektrochem.*, **29**, 30 (1923).

[7] *Kolloid-Z.*, **1**, 44 (1906); *Z. anorg. Chem.*, **50**, 322 (1906).

took place by electrical endosmose. Similar observations were made with the blue crystalline oxide but the dehydration was considerably slower. Müller and Spitzer believe that definite hydrate water would not be removed by electrical endosmose and suggest that the chemical hydrate, so called, goes over to an unstable adsorption compound or that an unstable peroxide results at first which later decomposes to the ordinary oxide containing less water. A more plausible guess is that the crystalline compound is not a definite monohydrate at all but a hydrous oxide possessing a dense structure that retains adsorbed water more tenaciously than a gelatinous mass.[1] Since the vapor pressure of hydrous copper oxide becomes practically zero at a composition closely approximating $CuO \cdot H_2O$, it cannot be determined by vapor-pressure measurements whether a definite hydrate exists. This could probably be decided by comparing x-radiograms of the black oxide and the blue crystalline compound. Hedvall[2] made such a comparison of black oxides prepared in a variety of ways and found them to be identical. He also obtained an x-radiogram of the blue compound, but no comparison of the latter with the black oxide was recorded. Bancroft[3] points out that, if a definite compound, $CuO \cdot H_2O$, exists with a practically zero vapor pressure, it should form from cupric oxide in the presence of water; but the reverse process is the one that actually takes place. Kohlschütter and Tüscher[4] get around this by assuming that the dehydration is not simply a molecular splitting off of water, thus: $Cu(OH)_2 = CuO + H_2O$; but depends on intramolecular neutralization of the $H^{\cdot}$ and OH' ions resulting from amphoteric dissociation of $Cu(OH)_2$ as follows:

$$Cu(OH)_2 \rightleftarrows Cu^{\cdot\cdot} + 2OH'$$
$$Cu(OH)_2 \rightleftarrows CuO_2'' + 2H^{\cdot}$$
$$OH' + H^{\cdot} = H_2O$$
$$CuO_2'' + Cu^{\cdot\cdot} = 2CuO$$

This interpretation of the mechanism of the dehydration process is superfluous, if the blue compound having zero vapor pressure

---

[1] KOHLSCHÜTTER and SEDELINOVICH: *Z. Elektrochem.*, **29**, 30 (1923).
[2] *Z. anorg. Chem.*, **120**, 327 (1922).
[3] "Applied Colloid Chemistry," 246 (1921).
[4] *Z. anorg. Chem.*, **111**, 193 (1920).

is not $Cu(OH)_2$, and may be open to serious question even should a monohydrate exist.

Stability of Blue Cupric Oxide.—The instability of gelatinous cupric oxide is one of its most characteristic properties. If allowed to stand in contact with its mother liquor, it loses water and changes in color from blue to green, brown, and finally black,[1] the process going on slowly at room temperature and with increasing velocity as the temperature is raised.[2] To obtain a clear blue product, precipitation should be carried out at 0° and the mother liquor removed by washing with iced water as rapidly as possible.[3] Analogous to the hydrous oxides of iron and chromium, the blue oxide aged at low temperatures holds on to its water more strongly than the newly formed product.

Unlike the gelatinous oxide, the blue crystalline compound is stable in boiling water and maintains its blue color when heated for hours at 100°. However, it darkens gradually on long standing even at room temperature. Thus, 10-year-old samples made by the methods of Böttger and Péligot were reported by Fowles[4] to have a bluish-slate tint, while a 12-year-old sample was quite black. In the light of these observations Fowles concludes that the crystalline oxide is a highly stable form of the blue oxide in a state of suspended transformation.

While alkalies and certain salts tend to decrease the stability of the blue gelatinous oxide, Tommasi[5] found a retardation of the blackening in the presence of a number of salts, notably $MnSO_4$. Bancroft[6] attributed the stability to adsorption of the hydrous oxide of manganese which acts as a protective colloid. Although this conclusion was reaffirmed by Blucher and Farnau[7] as a result of observations with salts of a number of heavy metals other than manganese, it seems questionable, since (1) relatively high concentrations of colloidal hydrous oxides are

[1] SCHAFFNER: *Liebig's Ann. Chem.*, **51**, 168 (1844); HARMS: *Arch. Pharm.*, (2) **89**, 35 (1857); *Bull. soc. chim.*, (2) **37**, 197 (1882).

[2] SPRING and LUCION: *Z. anorg. Chem.*, **2**, 195 (1892); VAN BEMMELEN: *Ibid.*, **5**, 468 (1894); EULER and EULER: *Z. anorg. Chem.*, **124**, 70 (1922).

[3] VILLIERS: *Compt. rend.*, **120**, 322 (1895).

[4] *Chem. News*, **128**, 2 (1924).

[5] *Bull. soc. chim.*, (2) **37**, 197 (1882); *Compt. rend.*, **99**, 38 (1884).

[6] *J. Phys. Chem.*, **18**, 118 (1914).

[7] *J. Phys. Chem.*, **18**, 629 (1914).

not effective, and (2) copper sulfate is as effective as manganous sulfate or chromic sulfate. The first experiment is not especially impressive, since there is no necessary reason why the adsorption of a colloidal oxide by the separately precipitated copper oxide gel should give the same result as adsorption of the oxide from a salt solution; but the second observation is fairly conclusive, since it is inconceivable that blue hydrous cupric oxide should stabilize itself.[1] Inasmuch as the only salts effective in low concentration are those which give an acid reaction by hydrolysis there still remains the possibility that the stabilizing agent is a basic salt[2] or an adsorption complex.

Since there is a marked change in the physical character of hydrous cupric oxide during heating in the presence of salts which hydrolyze to give an acid reaction, I postulated[1] a slight solvent action which was supposed to destroy the gelatinous structure, giving a denser modification that loses water and darkens less readily than a loose voluminous mass. Fowles[3] accepts the essential part of this view, that the stability is a result of change in the physical character of the hydrous oxide; but he very properly rules out any solvent action as an important factor in the process. Instead, he believes the heavy metal salts remove adsorbed alkali[4] as basic salts; thus, the stabilization consists in removing alkali, a catalyzer, and allowing the unstable gelatinous substance to pass to the more stable crystalline form. Fowles' hypothesis is not particularly helpful or constructive, since it does not attempt to define the nature of the alleged catalytic action of alkali on the dehydration process.

Like bases, certain alkali salts increase rather than retard the spontaneous dehydration of hydrous cupric oxide. Since the effect is not appreciable except with relatively high concentrations of the salts, it probably results from their dehydrating action.[5] An alternative hypothesis is suggested by the behavior of hydrous cupric oxide toward alkali salts. Tommasi[6] found

[1] WEISER: *J. Phys. Chem.*, **27,** 501 (1923).
[2] KRÜGER: *J. prakt. Chem.*, **108,** 278 (1924).
[3] *Chem. News*, **128,** 5 (1924).
[4] JORDIS: *Z. Elektrochem.*, **18,** 553 (1912).
[5] POMA and PATRONI: *Z. physik. Chem.*, **87,** 196 (1914).
[6] *Bull. soc. chim.*, (2) **37,** 197 (1882).

that solutions of sodium chloride and sodium sulfate show an alkaline reaction after shaking with hydrous cupric oxide. This is due to hydrolysis of the salts owing to stronger adsorption of acid than of base. The slight decrease in stability in the presence of alkali salts may be due to the slight alkalinity of the solution in which the particles are suspended.

Recently, hydrogen peroxide has been found by Quartaroli[1] to accelerate the darkening of hydrous cupric oxide suspended in a definite amount of alkali at 50°. This action is still perceptible with 1 part of peroxide in 200 million of water. In view of the presence of minute traces of hydrogen peroxide in ordinary distilled water, this compound is believed to bring about the spontaneous decomposition of the hydrous oxide or, at least, to accelerate the process. Such sensitive action of extremely minute amounts of substance has been found only in the action of copper in provoking the oxidation of sulfites and in the quantity of substance required to break up metastable states. Various electrolytes, especially magnesium salts, retard the blackening when present in amounts hundreds of times less than that of the hydrous oxide; but the action of such electrolytes exhibits striking irregularities. Quartaroli concludes that the blackening of the oxide suspended in alkali solution is not a simple dehydration process but is a phenomenon connected with oxidations and reductions with the formation of saline hydrates containing copper atoms with various grades of oxidation. This conclusion is so hopelessly vague and indefinite that the observations should be confirmed and extended.

By dehydrating the blue oxides under suitable conditions, compositions approximating the formulas for hydrates have been obtained.[2] Recently, Losana[3] obtained temperature-composition, vapor-pressure, and electromotive-force curves indicating the formation of hydrates in which the ratios $CuO : H_2O$ are 3, 4, and 8:1 when the dehydration takes place in the presence of liquid and 3, 4, 6, 7, and 8:1 when the compound has been dried before dehydrating. The presence of alkali and other

[1] *Gazz. chim. ital.*, **55**, 264 (1925).

[2] See MELLOR: "Treatise on Inorganic and Theoretical Chemistry," **3**, 142 (1923).

[3] *Gazz. chim. ital.*, **53**, 75 (1923).

salts influences the dehydration temperature, and in some instances, loss of water occurs below what was regarded as the true inversion point. Such behavior is not characteristic of well-defined stable hydrates.

Color.—As already noted, hydrous copper oxide may be blue, green, olive, brown, or black in color. The change in color is not necessarily associated with loss of water, as De Forcrand[1] observed a change in Peligot's oxide at 85° from blue to green without loss of weight. De Forcrand dissolved the blue, green, olive, and brown hydrous oxides and the black anhydrous oxide in sufficient nitric acid to form the nitrate; and Sabatier[2] and Joannis[3] carried out similar experiments on the oxides dehydrated at 440° and at red heat. From these data De Forcrand concludes that the different colored oxides are isomers involving definite heat changes in the transformation from one form to another. It would seem, however, that thermochemical evidence of this sort is altogether insufficient to establish the existence of definite isomers. Many hydrous oxides, when heated quickly, undergo a decrease in surface energy which is sufficient to raise the temperature of the whole mass to incandescence. Thermochemical data obtained before and after glowing might be interpreted to mean that an isomeric transformation had taken place; but such a conclusion would be erroneous. It is much more probable that the differences in color result from differences in the physical character and size of particles. Kohlschütter and Tüscher believe the blue compound to be amorphous or pseudocrystalline $Cu(OH)_2$, consisting of rather large particles, and the black compound to be CuO made up of distinctly smaller particles. The conclusion that the blue particles are larger than the black seems to have been reached without taking all the facts into consideration. Everyone knows that copper oxide can be obtained in quite large particles which are black and the hydrous oxide in very much more highly dispersed, gelatinous particles which are blue. A clump of the blue hydrous oxide consists of very finely divided primary particles that have adsorbed water strongly, forming a gelatinous mass. On heating, the relatively

[1] *Compt. rend.*, **157**, 441 (1913).
[2] *Compt. rend.*, **125**, 301 (1897).
[3] *Compt. rend.*, **102**, 1161 (1886).

large gelatinous clump is broken up and the particles constituting it coalesce to larger particles that appear black. From this point of view, anhydrous cupric oxide would be blue and not black if coalescence during dehydration were prevented. In support of this, Schenck,[1] in Bancroft's laboratory, observed that a mixture of the hydrous oxides of copper and aluminum containing 5 per cent cupric oxide remained blue after ignition. In one instance[2] the excess of alumina was dissolved out with alkali, giving a distinctly blue powder containing CuO and Al_2O_3 in the ratio of approximately $4:1$.

The hypothesis of Kohlschütter that the blue and black oxides are $Cu(OH)_2$ and CuO, respectively, stands or falls on the unproved assumption that there is a definite amorphous hydrate and that this dehydrates not by the molecular splitting off of water but by "internal neutralization as a result of amphoteric dissociation."

The wide variation in color of anhydrous CuO is utilized in coloring glass and pottery glazes. That cupric oxide imparts a blue or green color to glass under certain conditions was known to the ancients and the later alchemists. An old blue Venetian glass contained 1.32 per cent CuO.[3] Artificial emeralds have been prepared with this pigment. The color imparted to a glaze by CuO depends on the constituents of the glaze and the conditions of firing. In a reducing atmosphere, a red glaze is obtained consisting probably of colloidal copper or cuprous oxide; blue and green glazes develop in an oxidizing atmosphere.[4]

Cupric Oxide Sols.—To prepare sols of hydrous cupric oxide, it is usually necessary to employ some protective agent. Graham[5] prepared a fairly stable sol by adding alkali to a solution of cupric chloride containing cane sugar. It was deep blue at first but changed to green on dialyzing; the precipitate obtained on boiling the sol or on adding salts or acids was bluish green in color. A more stable sol can be prepared using Paal's[6] sodium

---

[1] *J. Phys. Chem.*, **23**, 283 (1919).

[2] PARSELL: *J. Phys. Chem.*, **26**, 501 (1922).

[3] SCHWARZ: *Dinglers polytech. J.*, **205**, 425 (1872).

[4] RAUTER: *Z. angew. Chem.*, **14**, 753 (1901).

[5] *Phil. Trans.*, **151**, 183 (1861); *Compt. rend.*, **59**, 174 (1864).

[6] *Ber.*, **39**, 1550 (1906); *Kolloid-Z.*, **30**, 1 (1922).

salts of lysalbinic or protalbinic acids as protective colloid. Other stabilizing agents that have proved effective are agar,[1] casein,[2] milk and grape sugar,[3] and soap. Thorium and uranyl nitrate[4] peptize the gelatinous oxide owing to strong adsorption of the salt cations. Biltz[5] attempted to prepare the colloidal oxide by dialysis of a solution of cupric nitrate; but the salt passed unchanged through the dialyzer owing to its low hydrolysis constant. Ley[6] hydrolyzed the copper salt of succinimide, obtaining a very satisfactory sol that changed in color, slowly at room temperature but rapidly at 70°, from blue green to yellow brown and finally dark brown. Succinimide is a protector, since its removal by dialysis causes agglomeration of the sol.

Cupric oxide sols have been prepared without the use of a protective colloid by oxidizing a copper sol[7] and by what Kohlschütter called "discharge electrolysis."[8]   In the latter process, a passivifying layer of oxide was deposited on the anode and subsequently dispersed in the liquid by a rapidly oscillating discharge. The sol was perfectly clear in transmitted light; it was bluish green in color at the outset but changed to brown on standing. By means of the ultramicroscope, Kohlschütter[9] observed the formation of blue hydrous cupric oxide sol when a current of relatively high density was passed between copper electrodes dipped in dilute $CuSO_4$ solution or in water.

By passing a spark between copper wires under water, there is formed a positive sol of cupric oxide instead of copper.[10]   Stirring accelerates the velocity of coagulation of this sol by electrolytes, particularly when ions of high coagulating power are employed and when the concentration of electrolyte is in the region of the

---

[1] LUDWIG: *Brandes Archiv*, **82**, 157 (1855).

[2] RITTENHAUSEN: *J. prakt. Chem.*, [2] **5**, 215 (1873); **7**, 361 (1874).

[3] SALKOWSKY: *Pflüger's Arch.*, **6**, 221 (1872); SEN and DHAR: *Kolloid-Z.*, **33**, 193 (1923).

[4] SZILARD: *J. chim. phys.*, **5**, 636 (1907).

[5] *Ber.*, **35**, 4431 (1902).

[6] *Ber.*, **38**, 2199 (1906); LEY and WERNER: *Ibid.*, **39**, 2178 (1906).

[7] LOTTERMOSER: "Anorganische Kolloide," Stuttgart (1901).

[8] KOHLSCHÜTTER: *Z. Elektrochem.*, **25**, 309 (1919).

[9] *Z. Elektrochem.*, **30**, 164 (1924).

[10] BURTON: *Phil. Mag.*, [6] **11**, 436 (1906).

precipitation value.   Prolonged stirring alone, without the addition of precipitating electrolyte, lowers the charge on the particles sufficiently to allow agglomeration and finally complete precipitation.[1]

· Hooker prepared a very satisfactory blue sol[2] by thorough washing of the gelatinous oxide formed by adding alkali to copper sulfate solution until the supernatant liquid was just colorless. The washing may be carried out by sedimentation, but a more stable sol results by repeated washing with the supercentrifuge.[3] The colloidal oxide has high fungicidal action against apple scab and apple black in concentrations of 1 part of hydrous oxides to 5000 of water; at this concentration it causes very slight burning. This sol possesses excellent sticking properties due to its positive charge and can be used in conjunction with lead arsenate and nicotine sulfate, if desired.   Since the sol can be prepared at relatively low cost, it is suggested as a substitute for Bordeaux mixture and lime sulfur.

Hydrous cupric oxide dissolves but slightly in dilute alkali, but is appreciably soluble in concentrated alkali forming deep-blue solutions.[4]   As might be expected, the unstable blue gelatinous oxide is more soluble than the black compound, and the latter separates gradually from a solution of the former, provided the alkali (NaOH) concentration does not exceed 17 N.[5]   Both copper, in the presence of air, and anhydrous CuO dissolve in alkalies, forming blue solutions which are stable on boiling and do not precipitate out on standing.[6]   The bulk of the evidence supports the view that the blue coloration is due to CuO_2'''[7] ion and not to colloidal cupric oxide.   Fischer[8] added alkali to copper salts short of precipitation and obtained blue solutions which were supposed to be colloidal, because hydrous copper oxide settled

[1] FREUNDLICH and BASU: *Z. physik. Chem.*, **115**, 203 (1925).

[2] *J. Ind. Eng. Chem.*, **15**, 1177 (1923).

[3] BRADFIELD: *J. Am. Chem. Soc.*, **44**, 965 (1922).

[4] LÖW: *Z. anal. Chem.*, **9**, 463 (1870); DONATH: *Ibid.*, **40**, 137 (1901).

[5] MÜLLER: *Z. physik. Chem.*, **105**, 73 (1923).

[6] CREIGHTON: *J. Am. Chem. Soc.*, **45**, 1237 (1923).

[7] MELBYE: *Meddel. Vetenskapsakad. Nobelinst.*, **4**, 8 (1922); *Chem. Abstracts*, **17**, 1572 (1923).

[8] *Z. anorg. Chem.*, **40**, 39 (1904); CHATTERJI and DHAR: *Chem. News*, **121**, 253 (1924).

out on standing or could be filtered out. The discoloration of the solution by filtering was believed by Creighton to result from interaction between the cellulose of the filter and the blue component, since the filtrate was blue after several portions were passed through the same filter. This observation is not quite conclusive, since the filter may have become more porous owing to peptization of the filter paper by the alkali. However, Müller prepared a cobalt-blue crystalline cuprite from the alkali solution; so there is no doubt of the existence of such a salt. It is altogether probable that sol formation precedes cuprite formation when alkali acts on the gelatinous oxide.

The solubility of hydrous cupric oxide in alkali may be increased enormously by the presence of other substances. Thus, the addition of alkali to copper sulfate in the presence of tartrate forms the deep-blue solution known as Fehling's solution, so widely used in detecting small amounts of reducing sugar. The copper in this solution is not present as cupric oxide sol but as a cupric tartrate complex.[1] The same is apparently true for the alkali solution formed in the presence of higher valent alcohols, such as glycerin and mannite, and of certain amines.[2] Gelatinous copper oxide is adsorbed strongly by hydrous chromic oxide, and the colloidal solution of the latter in alkali carries a considerable amount of the former into colloidal solution.[3]

Cupric Oxide Jellies.—A cupric oxide jelly forms on hydrolysis of a solution of cupric ammonium acetate of the formula $Cu(C_2H_3O_2)_2 \cdot 2NH_3$.[4] It is unnecessary to start with this salt, and much more stable jellies are obtained by precipitation of a suitable amount of colloidal oxide at a suitable rate. The desired conditions may be realized[5] by adding ammonia to cupric acetate in the presence of a small amount of sulfate[6] and allowing the instable colloidal solution to precipitate spontaneously.

[1] Küster: *Z. Elektrochem.*, **4**, 112 (1897); Masson and Steele: *J. Chem. Soc.*, **75**, 725 (1899); Kahlenberg: *Z. physik. Chem.*, **17**, 577 (1895).

[2] Traube: *Ber.*, **55**, 1899 (1922); **56**, 1653 (1923); Donnan: Abegg's "Handbuch anorg. Chem.," **2**, 547 (1908).

[3] *Cf.* Knecht, Rawson, and Löwenthal: "A Manual of Dyeing," **1**, 241 (1916); Prud'homme: *Bull. soc. chim.*, (2) **17**, 253 (1872).

[4] Foerster: *Ber.*, **25**, 3416 (1892); Finch: *J. Phys. Chem.*, **18**, 26 (1914).

[5] Weiser: *J. Phys. Chem.*, **27**, 685 (1923).

[6] Finch: *J. Phys. Chem.*, **18**, 26 (1914).

The solution obtained is perfectly clear at the outset, but precipitation starts after intervals varying from a few seconds to several minutes depending on the relative amounts of the three components. In view of the great importance of rate of precipitation on jelly formation, the most favorable conditions are pretty sharply defined. A firm jelly that remained unbroken for weeks is obtained by mixing 5 cubic centimeters of 3 N NH_4OH to 25 cubic centimeters of 0.75 N $Cu(C_2H_3O_2)_2$ containing 2 cubic centimeters of N K_2SO_4. The presence of sulfate is necessary in order to get a sol of sufficient concentration. Gelatinous precipitates instead of jellies are obtained by adding ammonia directly to copper sulfate, chloride, or nitrate, on account of the high velocity of precipitation.

HYDROUS CUPROUS OXIDE

The yellow or orange precipitate thrown down from a cuprous salt solution by sodium hydroxide[1] or carbonate[2] is not $CuOH$ but hydrous cuprous oxide in an amorphous state.[3] The yellow compound is best prepared by reduction of $Cu^{..}$ in the presence of OH' or by electrolysis of alkali salts in the cold with a copper anode.[4] For the chemical reduction, a variety of reducing agents may be used, such as dextrose,[5] maltose,[6] and phenylhydrazine;[7] hydroxylamine hydrochloride[8] is particularly satisfactory. The yellow oxide is formed in the cold by the reduction of Fehling's solution with dextrose or in the hot when the amount of tartrate is too small to convert all the $Cu^{..}$ into a complex. The clear-yellow amorphous product goes over rapidly to orange or reddish yellow, probably with the loss of water. By drying in the absence of air, a stable product is obtained. This is changed

[1] MITSCHERLICH: *J. prakt. Chem.*, **19**, 450 (1840); PROUST: *J. phys.*, **51**, 182 (1800); KLASON: *Svensk Kem. Tid.*, **36**, 202 (1924).

[2] FREMY: *Ann. chim. phys.*, [3] **23**, 391 (1848).

[3] GRÖGER: *Z. anorg. Chem.*, **31**, 326 (1902); MOSER: *Ibid.*, **105**, 112 (1919).

[4] LORENZ: *Z. anorg. Chem.*, **12**, 438 (1898).

[5] SANDMEYER: *Ber.*, **20**, 1494 (1887); MILLER and HAGEN: *Pflüger's Arch.*, **23**, 221 (1880).

[6] GLENDENNING: *J. Chem. Soc.*, **67**, 999 (1895).

[7] CHATTAWAY: *Chem. News*, **97**, 19 (1908).

[8] MOSER: *Z. anorg. Chem.*, **105**, 112 (1919); *cf.* EBLER: *Ber.*, **35**, 3055 (1902).

to a brick-red amorphous powder by heating for 60 hours at 500°; and by igniting in a stream of nitrogen, it goes over to the familiar crystalline red form which is commonly obtained by reducing Fehling's solution at 100°. Similarly, by electrolyzing alkali salts, the oxide is yellow at room temperature, bright red at 100°, and intermediate colors in between.[1] Red cuprous oxide is prepared on a commercial scale by electrolysis of a hot solution of sodium chloride with copper anodes.

Red crystalline Cu_2O appears to bear the same relation to the yellow hydrous oxide that black CuO bears to the blue gelatinous oxide. The change in the color of hydrous cuprous oxide from yellow, through orange, brick red, and bright red results from a gradual increase in particle size and loss of absorbed water. With this change from the finely divided hydrous precipitate having a high specific surface to the granular red product having a low specific surface, the reactivity with oxygen and the solubility in acids and alkalies fall off. The varicolored products are not definite isomeric modifications of Cu_2O.

The colorless solution of hydrous cuprous oxide in ammonia turns blue in the air owing to the formation of $Cu(NH_3)_4^{··}$, thereby furnishing a delicate test for oxygen.

Red cuprous oxide is largely used in coloring glass red, a property known to the ancients and in the middle ages. The manufacture of this ancient red glass was revived by Bontemps in France and Englehardt in Germany about 1827. The oxide is also used for the production of a red glaze on pottery[2] and as a poisonous pigment in antifouling compositions for painting the bottoms of vessels.

Cuprous Oxide Sols.—A sol of hydrous cuprous oxide is nearly always obtained in the reduction of alkali solutions of copper salts.[3] Similarly, during the reduction of cupric sulfate solution with $SnCl_2$[4] or hydrazine, yellow hydrous[5] cuprous oxide first appears, which goes over to the red oxide and finally to black

---

[1] MILLER: *J. Phys. Chem.*, **13**, 256 (1909); MOSER: *Z. anorg. Chem.*, **105**, 112 (1919).

[2] LOUTH and DUTAILLY: *Mon. Ceram. et Verr.*, **19**, 237.

[3] *Cf.* RUOSS: *Z. anal. Chem.*, **58**, 193 (1919).

[4] LOTTERMOSER: *J. prakt. Chem.*, (2) **59**, 492 (1899).

[5] GUTBIER and HOFMEIER: *Z. anorg. Chem.*, **32**, 355 (1902); **44**, 227 (1905); *cf.* PAAL and LEUZE: *Ber.*, **39**, 1550 (1906).

copper sol. Reduction of a neutral solution of copper sulfate in the presence of gum arabic or gelatin[1] gives a cuprous oxide sol which is stable in the absence of air. Gröger[2] obtained a stable sol on attempting to purify the orange hydrous oxide by prolonged washing in the absence of air.

Hydrous Cobaltous Oxide

If alkali is added in excess to a solution of rose-colored cobaltous salt, there is formed, at first, a blue hydrous mass which goes over into rose hydrous cobalt oxide or hydroxide, the transformation taking place more rapidly the higher the temperature.[3] The gradual transformation can be observed by boiling cobaltous carbonate with a solution of potassium hydroxide. The voluminous blue oxide formed at first turns to violet and then to rose red.[4] On the other hand, if insufficient akali to react with all the cobalt ion is used, the precipitate retains its blue color indefinitely. At one time, the blue compound was believed to be a basic salt which was decomposed by excess alkali, forming rose-colored hydrate. Hantzsch[5] disproved this view by showing that the blue oxide, precipitated from sulfate or acetate solution with insufficient alkali, absorbs the respective salts or basic salts strongly; but most of the latter can be removed by repeated boiling of the precipitate with water free from air, without altering the blue color in any way. Hence, the blue color is that of the oxide and not of a basic salt.

The blue and rose precipitates differ quite appreciably in their chemical properties. Thus, the blue compound loses practically all its water at 150° and is completely dehydrated at 170°; whereas the rose compound still retains some water after heating for several hours at 300°. Moreover, the blue oxide reacts slowly with acetyl chloride, while the red reacts so rapidly that the chloride boils. After drying the preparations in a desiccator, each analyzes experimentally for a monohydrate or hydroxide.

---

[1] Lobry De Bruyn: *Rec. trav. chim.*, **19**, 236 (1900).

[2] *Z. anorg. Chem.*, **31**, 326 (1902).

[3] Winkelblech: *Liebig's Ann. Chem.*, **13**, 148 (1835); Betz: *Pogg. Ann.*, **61**, 472 (1844).

[4] Fremy: *Jahresber.*, 637 (1851).

[5] *Z. anorg. Chem.*, **73**, 304 (1911).

Hantzsch concludes, therefore, that the two compounds are hydrate isomers differing in the way in which the water is held, the blue being $CoO \cdot H_2O$ and the red $Co \genfrac{}{}{0pt}{}{- OH}{- OH}$.

As has been pointed out, the gelatinous oxide does not go over to rose in the absence of alkali or in the presence of a little cobalt salt. Benedict[1] observed that the change in color from blue to rose in the presence of excess alkali is retarded by the addition of a small amount of nickel salt. The retardation is sufficiently marked to serve as a delicate test for nickel. To account for this behavior, Benedict postulates the formation of a deep-blue nickel cobaltite which masks the rose-colored hydrate. This assumption cannot be correct, since increasing the amount of nickel salt does not increase the intensity of the blue color. Apparently, hydrous nickel oxide is adsorbed by the blue oxide, thereby stabilizing it to a certain extent. The phenomenon recalls the stabilization of blue hydrous cupric oxide by salts, but it differs from the latter in that salts of metals other than nickel have little or no effect. Thus the presence of the sulfates of iron(ous), zinc, manganese, magnesium, chromium, copper, and aluminum; the chlorides of tin and calcium; and the nitrates of lead, cadmium, thorium, and strontium produces no marked retardation.[2] The specific effect of nickel oxide may be due to its having the same crystal lattice as cobalt oxide.

Both the blue and rose compounds thrown down by mixing solutions of cobalt salt and alkali are gelatinous and appear amorphous. It is possible that both are hydrous oxides when first formed but, like cadmium oxide, go over into microcrystalline hydrates on standing. This is certainly true of the rose compound, as shown by x-ray examination.[3] Large crystals of rose hydroxide come down from a solution made by adding 250 grams of potassium hydroxide to 10 grams of cobalt chloride hexahydrate in 60 cubic centimeters of water, and heating in the absence of air until solution is complete. The crystals are elongated rhombic prisms that analyze for $Co(OH)_2$.[4] They are

[1] *J. Am. Chem. Soc.*, **26**, 695 (1904).
[2] CHATTERJI and DHAR: *Chem. News*, **121**, 253 (1920).
[3] HEDVALL: *Z. anorg. Chem.*, **120**, 327, 338 (1924).
[4] DE SCHULTEN: *Compt. rend.*, **109**, 266 (1889).

pleochroic, appearing rose colored along n_g, rose yellow along n_m, and pale brownish yellow along n_p. Unlike the gelatinous oxide, the large crystals are not altered by contact with air.

Since a crystalline rose-colored oxide is known with certainty, and there is only an analysis of an apparently amorphous mass to indicate the nature of the blue preparation, it might be concluded that the blue compound is a hydrous oxide and the rose, a hydroxide. This hypothesis, like that of Hantzsch's, cannot be correct, since it is based on the manner in which water is held by the oxide, and apparently we may have either a blue or a rose oxide in the absence of water. Thus cobalt glass owes its color to the blue anhydrous oxide; and the brown anhydrous powder obtained by drying the precipitated hydrate melts without decomposition and gives rose-colored crystals on cooling.[1] This suggests the possibility of the color of cobalt oxide and hydroxide being determined by the size of particles. In glass the particles are obviously highly dispersed and appear blue, while the oxide in mass is red. Similarly, the precipitated oxide is most finely divided when first formed and so is blue; but in the presence of a slight excess of alkali, the highly hydrous mass ages, losing water and becoming denser, the color at the same time changing from blue through lavender to rose. The rate of this transformation is, of course, hastened by raising the temperature, and is retarded or stopped by the presence of basic cobalt salts or hydrous nickel oxide.

If one objects to attributing the difference in color to the size of particles, an alternative hypothesis is that there are two allotropic forms of cobalt oxide, an instable blue one and a stable rose. As a matter of fact, the transformation of the blue gelatinous oxide to rose in the presence of alkali has led people to regard the former as the alkali instable modification and the latter as the alkali stable modification.[2] The existence or non-existence of allotropic forms could probably be settled by comparing x-radiograms of the blue and rose oxides or hydrates.[3]

[1] MOISSAN: *Ann. chim. phys.*, (7), **4**, 136 (1895); HEDVALL: *Z. anorg. Chem.*, **86**, 210 (1914); HANTZSCH: *Z. anorg. Chem.*, **73**, 304 (1912).

[2] HANTZSCH: *Z. anorg. Chem.*, **73**, 304 (1912); FARNAU and WITTEVEEN: *J. Ind. Eng. Chem.*, **13**, 1060 (1921).

[3] *Cf.* HEDVALL: *Z. anorg. Chem.*, **120**, 338 (1922).

Both blue and rose cobalt oxide dissolve in concentrated alkali, giving a solution with a deep-blue color. A similar color results on electrolyzing a solution of alkali, 4 N or stronger, with a cobalt anode. The blue solution was thought by Tubandt[1] to be colloidal cobalt oxide; but the results of exact potential measurements of cobalt against the blue solutions containing different amounts of cobalt in 8 N potassium hydroxide show conclusively that the blue color is due to potassium cobaltite, K_2CoO_2, and not to colloidal cobalt oxide.[2] Thus the behavior of cobalt oxide in excess alkali is similar to that of cupric oxide. In the light of these observations, it is unlikely that the alkaline solution in the presence of glycerin is colloidal.[3] Positive sols have been formed both by peptization of the blue oxide with dilute hydrochloric acid[4] and by thorough washing of the fresh gelatinous precipitate;[5] but they are quite instable, settling out in the course of a few hours.

Liesegang rings of $Co(OH)_2$ are formed by pouring ammonia on a gelatin gel containing cobalt chloride. Under certain conditions a spiral is obtained instead of a series of rhythmic bands.[6]

Cobaltous oxide is used by enamelers and porcelain manufacturers for the production of the finest blue glaze and color in porcelain, glass, and other vitrifiable substances; 1 part of oxide in 100,000 imparts a faint blue while 1 part in 1000 gives a deep blue. When heated with certain oxides, colored compounds are formed, and with others, colored solid solutions which are widely used as pigments. With aluminum oxide, a blue compound $CoO \cdot Al_2O_3$ known as cobalt blue or Thenard's blue is formed at 1100°, and above this temperature a green one, said to have the composition $4CoO \cdot 3Al_2O_3$.[7] The exact tint of cobalt blue depends on the conditions of formation and on the relative amounts of the two oxides fused. A similar valuable

---

[1] Z. anorg. Chem., **45**, 368 (1905); cf. DONATH: Monatschefte für Chemie, **14**, 93 (1893).

[2] GRUBE and FEUCHT: Z. Elektrochem., **28**, 568 (1922).

[3] Cf., however, SEN and DHAR: Kolloid-Z., **33**, 193 (1923).

[4] MÜLLER: Z. anorg. Chem., **57**, 311 (1908).

[5] TOWER and COOKE: J. Phys. Chem., **26**, 733 (1922).

[6] WOLFGANG OSTWALD: Kolloid-Z. (Zsigmondy Festschrift), **36**, 390 (1925).

[7] HEDVALL: Archiv Kemi, Mineral. Geol., **5**, 18, 1 (1914); Z. anorg. Chem., **96**, 71 (1916).

pigment known as cobalt green or Renneman's green is obtained by fusing cobalt oxide with zinc oxide. The green color is due to cobalt zincate which forms solid solutions with excess zinc oxide.[1] Stannic oxide likewise forms a green stannate,[2] and chromic oxide, a green chromite[3] on fusion with cobalt oxide. The chromite dissolves in excess of either oxide, giving various shades of blue. Many combinations with other oxides have been reported, but in the majority of cases these are either mixtures or solid solutions.[4] Magnesium oxide forms mixed crystals varying in color from light to dark red, depending on the relative proportions of the two oxides.[5] Mixed crystals are also formed with the isomorphous oxides of nickel and manganese.[6] It is probable that cobalt oxide is dissolved or dispersed by silica although violet cobalt orthosilicate and ruby-red metasilicate have been reported.[7] Obviously, the deep-blue color of cobalt glass is not due to the formation of these alleged compounds.

Cobalt oxide proves to be a very good "dryer" for paints.[8] Since the action of dryers is to catalyze the oxidation of the oil, this behavior is in line with the observations that the spontaneous oxidation of cobaltous hydrate induces the oxidation of the stable nickelous hydrate.[9]

HYDROUS COBALTIC OXIDE

Cobaltic oxide, Co_2O_3, in a highly hydrous state is precipitated on treating a solution of a cobaltous salt with alkaline hypochlorite[10] or persulfate;[11] or by electrolysis of an alkaline solution

[1] HEDVALL: *Z. anorg. Chem.*, **93**, 313 (1915); **96**, 71 (1916); *cf.*, however, *Ibid.*, **86**, 201 (1914).

[2] HEDVALL: *Archiv Kemi, Mineral. Geol.*, **5**, 18, 1 (1914).

[3] ELLIOT: "On the Magnetic Combinations," Göttingen, 33 (1862).

[4] FARNAU and WITTEVEEN: *J. Ind. Eng. Chem.*, **13**, 1061 (1921).

[5] HEDVALL: *Z. anorg. Chem.*, **86**, 296 (1914).

[6] HEDVALL: *Ibid.*, **92**, 381 (1915).

[7] RÜGER: *Keram. Rundschau*, **31**, 79, 87, 99, 110 (1923); *C. A.*, **18**, 156 (1924).

[8] GARDNER and PARKS: *Paint Mfrs.' Assoc. U. S.*, *Circ.* 186 (1923).

[9] MITTRA and DHAR: *Z. anorg. Chem.*, **122**, 146 (1922).

[10] CARNOT: *Compt. rend.*, **108**, 610 (1889); SCHRÖDER: *J. Chem. Soc.*, **58**, 1213 (1890).

[11] MAWROW: *Z. anorg. Chem.*, **24**, 263 (1900); HÜTTNER: *Ibid.*, **27**, 81 (1901).

of cobalt sulfate.[1] It forms a brownish-black mass that loses water readily, the composition depending on the method of drying. The dark-brown anhydrous powder is transformed into black cobaltous cobaltic oxide, Co_3O_4, corresponding to magnetic oxide of iron, by heating below 910°.[2]

Hydrous Co_3O_4 results when cobaltous hydroxide oxidizes in the air. A fairly pure preparation is obtained by warming cobaltous hydroxide with an excess of ammonium persulfate, washing and heating the product with dilute nitric acid.[3] The substance obtained by fusing an oxide of cobalt with caustic potash which was thought to be a potassium cobaltite, Co_9O_{16}-$K_2 \cdot 3H_2O$,[4] is probable cobalto-cobaltic oxide with adsorbed potash.[5]

HYDROUS NICKELOUS OXIDE

The addition of potash or soda to a solution of nickel salt throws down a voluminous apple-green precipitate of hydrous nickel oxide which goes over to crystalline[6] $Ni(OH)_2$.[7] The purest preparation is obtained by using nickel nitrate or nickel ammonium nitrate rather than sulfate or chloride, since nitrate ion is said to be least strongly adsorbed by the hydrous precipitate.[8] The gelatinous oxide is readily soluble in ammonia forming a deep-blue solution from which a green crystalline powder is precipitated by boiling.

Anhydrous NiO is an olive-green powder which becomes deep yellow on heating but returns to the original green on cooling to room temperature.[9] Like cobalt oxide, it forms a variety of

---

[1] COEHN and GLÄSER: *Z. anorg. Chem.*, **33**, 9 (1903).

[2] BURGSTALLER: *Chem. Zentr.*, II, 1525 (1912).

[3] MAWROW: *Z. anorg. Chem.*, **24**, 263 (1900).

[4] SCHWARZENBERG: *Liebig's Ann. Chem.*, **97**, 212 (1856); PEBAL: *Ibid.*, **100**, 257 (1856); MAYER: *Ibid.*, **101**, 266 (1857).

[5] McCONNELL and HANES: *J. Chem. Soc.*, **71**, 585 (1897).

[6] HEDVALL: *Z. anorg. Chem.*, **120**, 338 (1922).

[7] TOWER: *J. Phys. Chem.*, **28**, 176 (1924).

[8] BONSDORFF: *Z. anorg. Chem.*, **41**, 136 (1904); TEICHMANN: *Liebig's Ann. Chem.*, **156**, 17 (1870).

[9] MOISSAN: *Ann. chim. phys.*, [5] **21**, 238 (1880); ZIMMERMAN: *Liebig's Ann. Chem.*, **232**, 344 (1880).

pigment colors for glazes[1] when fused with other metallic oxides. Thus alumina gives a blue aluminate, and zinc oxide, a blue zincate; but a variety of tints is possible, as the compounds form solid solutions with the excess of either oxide. Mixed crystals result on fusing nickel oxide with the isomorphous oxides of magnesium, nickel, and cobalt.[2]

To prepare the active form of $Ni(OH)_2$ for the Edison storage battery, the oxide is precipitated from sulfate solution with an excess of sodium hydroxide. The gel is dried slowly with the enclosed salts and alkali which are subsequently washed out. Excess of alkali increases the porosity of the product.[3]

As early as 1906, Ipatiev[4] employed nickel oxides as catalytic agents for hydrogenation, working at temperatures around 250° and at 100 atmospheres pressure. Later Bedford and Erdmann[5] found nickel oxides to be efficient catalyst for the hydrogenation of oils The oxides were considered to be superior to metallic nickel: first, because the velocity of hydrogenation is more rapid with the former; and second, because the oxides are much less sensitive to the action of poisons such as sulfur, chlorine, and carbon monoxide. The latter gas is especially poisonous to nickel, but in technical hydrogenation with oxides, it can be allowed to accumulate in the system without having any effect except to dilute the system. Nickelous and nickelic oxides are effective at 250°; at temperatures as low as 180°, the most efficient catalyst appears to be suboxide, possibly Ni_2O, which forms colloidal solutions in oil. Indeed, the increased activity of the higher oxides, after using for a short time, is attributed to the formation of a colloidal solution of nickel suboxide.

Since nickel oxide is reduced by hydrogen at 190°, it is claimed by some that the actual hydrogen carrier in Erdmann's experiments was metallic nickel.[6] This does not seem to be the case, since the catalyst freed from the hardened oil is a strongly mag-

[1] *Cf.* WHITNER: *J. Am. Ceram. Soc.*, **4**, 357 (1921).

[2] HEDVALL: *Z. anorg. Chem.*, **103**, 249 (1918).

[3] EDISON: U. S. Patents 1083355–1083356 (1914); 1167484 (1916).

[4] *J. Russ. Phys.-Chem. Soc.*, **38**, 75 (1906); **39**, 693 (1907); **40**, 1 (1908).

[5] *J. prakt. Chem.*, (2) **87**, 245 (1913); *J. Russ. Phys.-Chem. Soc.*, **45**, 616 (1913); British Patent 29612 (1910); 18122 (1913).

[6] MEIGIN and BARTELS: *J. prakt. Chem.*, (2) **89**, 290 (1914).

netic black powder which does not form a carbonyl and does not conduct the current as does nickel. Moreover, finely divided nickel is a hydrogenation catalyst either in the presence or absence of moisture, whereas the suboxide is inactive except in the presence of moisture.[1] According to Erdmann, the suboxide forms an additive product with the oil which assists in preventing reduction to metallic nickel.

Sabatier and Espel[2] prepared what they took to be Ni_4O by reducing NiO with hydrogen at 220°; but this differs from the catalyst, as it forms a carbonyl. Erdmann prepared an oxide very similar in properties to that obtained from the hardened oil by electrical reduction of potassium nickel cyanide.[3] The product was colloidally dispersed by oil and proved to be a good catalyst for hydrogenation. While the evidence points to the existence of a catalytically active suboxide of nickel, its composition has not been established with certainty.[4]

A sol of nickel hydroxide results on mixing solutions containing equivalent amounts of nickel tartrate and potassium hydroxide. If the solutions are as concentrated as normal, precipitation takes place slowly giving a transparent green jelly; but if the solutions are dilute, say $N/10$, a sol forms which can be purified by dialysis.

The gel precipitated from nickel chloride solution by alkali is peptized by washing. Using $N/10$ solutions, six or seven washings by decantation suffice. Tower[5] attributes the stabilization to potassium chloride, since sol formation is retarded or prevented by washing either too little or too much. One mol of KCl to 200 mols of $Ni(OH)_2$ was found to be the limiting ratio for a stable sol.[6]

---

[1] SENDERENS and ABOULENC: *Bull. soc. chim.*, (4) **17,** 14 (1915).

[2] *Compt. rend.*, **158,** 668 (1914).

[3] *Cf.* MOORE: *Chem. News*, **71,** 82 (1895).

[4] MÜLLER: *Pogg. Ann.*, **136,** 59 (1869); GLASER: *Z. anorg. Chem.*, **36,** 18 (1903); TSCHUGAEV and ICHLOPINE: *Compt. rend.*, **159,** 62 (1914); BERGER: *Compt. rend.*, **158,** 1798 (1914); **174,** 1341 (1922); *cf.*, however, WÖHLER and BALZ: *Z. Elektrochem.*, **27,** 406 (1921); LEVI and TACCHINI: *Gazz. chim. ital.*, **55,** 28 (1925).

[5] TOWER and COOKE: *J. Phys. Chem.*, **26,** 728 (1922); TOWER: *Ibid.*, **28,** 176 (1924).

[6] PAAL and BRÜNJES: *Ber.*, **47,** 2200 (1914).

Hydrous Nickelic Oxide and Nickel Peroxide

By passing chlorine or bromine through a suspension of nickel hydroxide or by warming a nickel salt with an alkali hypochlorite or hypobromite, a black precipitate is thrown down which was assigned the formula, $Ni_2O_3 \cdot 3H_2O$.[1] This is in error in two respects: Not only is the water content indefinite,[2] but the degree of oxidation of the nickel varies with the nature of the oxidizing agent, the rapidity of oxidation, and the temperature.[3] Under no conditions is pure hydrous Ni_2O_3 precipitated; and with bromine at $0°$, the ratio of nickel to oxygen approaches $1:2$ Howell[4] showed that both hydrous Ni_2O_3 and NiO_2 are formed simultaneously during the action of alkali and hypochlorite on $Ni(OH)_2$. Since Ni_2O_3 is not oxidized, there is a limit to the oxygen content of the precipitate. Moreover, unlike cobalt dioxide, NiO_2 is instable, decomposing to NiO without the intermediate formation of Ni_2O_3. The rate of decomposition of the dioxide is accelerated by heat; but excess alkali stabilizes it by adsorption. Ni_2O_3 has the structure represented by $NiO \cdot NiO_2$.[5]

A greenish-gray compound having the composition $NiO_2 \cdot xH_2O$ is obtained by mixing 30 per cent hydrogen peroxide with a dilute alcoholic solution of nickel chloride cooled to $50°$, followed by the addition of alcoholic potassium hydroxide.[6] Unlike the black dioxide, the green compound behaves like hydrogen peroxide. The latter is, therefore, regarded as a true peroxide $Ni\langle\!\!\begin{smallmatrix}O\\|\\O\end{smallmatrix}$; and the former as $Ni\langle\!\!\begin{smallmatrix}O\\\\O\end{smallmatrix}$.[7] A peroxide of nickel is formed by the electrolytic oxidation of the metal and plays a part in the Edison battery.[8]

[1] Wachter: *J. prakt. Chem.*, **30**, 327 (1843); Veil: *Compt. rend.*, **180**, 211 (1925).

[2] Carnelley and Walker: *J. Chem. Soc.*, **53**, 91 (1888).

[3] Bellucci and Clavari: *Atti accad. Lincei*, **14**, II, 234 (1905).

[4] *J. Chem. Soc.*, **123**, 669, 1772 (1923).

[5] Clark, Asbury, and Wick: *J. Am. Chem. Soc.*, **47**, 2661 (1925).

[6] Pellini and Meneghini: *Z. anorg. Chem.*, **60**, 178 (1908).

[7] Tubandt and Riedel: *Ber.*, **44**, 2565 (1911); *Z. anorg. Chem.*, **72**, 219 (1911); *cf.*, however, Tanatar: *Ber.*, **42**, 1516 (1909).

[8] Foerster: *Z. Elektrochem.*, **13**, 414 (1907); **14**, 17 (1908); Riesenfeld: *Ibid.*, **12**, 621 (1906); *cf.*, however, Zedner: *Ibid.*, **11**, 809 (1905); **12**, 463 (1906); **13**, 752 (1907).

The black hydrous dioxide of nickel is peptized by small amounts of organic acids, such as acetic, citric, and tartaric, forming a very stable colloid. Peptization results simply on washing the hydrous oxide with cold water, but the sol obtained in this way is not stable.[1]

HYDROUS SILVER OXIDE

By mixing a dilute solution of silver nitrate and KOH in 90 per cent alcohol at $-45°$, hydrous silver oxide comes down as a flocculent mass almost pure white in color.[2]   As the temperature rises, it changes in color from pale brown to brown, owing to loss of adsorbed water and agglomeration of the particles.   The hydrous oxide precipitated at room temperature is brown, but becomes black on drying at temperatures as low as 50 to 60°. Pure Ag_2O decomposes slightly even at 100°[3] and it does not give up all its adsorbed water until a temperature of 280° is reached; accordingly, pure Ag_2O cannot be obtained.[4]

A silver oxide sol is formed both by heating silver wire to redness and plunging it suddenly into water,[5] and by mixing a dilute $N/40$ solution of $AgNO_3$ with a slight excess of KOH of similar concentration.[6]   A stable sol is obtained only when the hydrous oxide is formed in the presence of a protective colloid such as tannin[7] or Paal's sodium protalbinate and lysalbinate.[8]

THE HYDROUS OXIDES OF GOLD

Auric Oxide.—The hydrous oxide formed by treating auric chloride with alkali or by decomposing potassium aurate with acid is always contaminated with adsorbed alkali or salt which

[1] TUBANDT and RIEDEL: *Z. anorg. Chem.*, **72**, 219 (1911).

[2] BRUCE: *Chem. News*, **50**, 208 (1884).

[3] ROSE: *Pogg. Ann.*, **85**, 314 (1852).

[4] MADSEN: *Z. anorg. Chem.*, **79**, 200 (1913); HARDIN: *J. Am. Chem. Soc.*, **18**, 994 (1898); LEA: *Am. J. Sci.*, (3) **44**, 240 (1892).

[5] KIMURA: *Mem. Coll. Sci., Kyoto Imp. Univ.*, **5**, 211 (1913).

[6] LOTTERMOSER: *J. prakt. Chem.*, (2) **72**, 39 (1905).

[7] SENSBURG: German Patent 208189 (1907).

[8] PAAL and VOSS: *Ber.*, **37**, 3862 (1904); LOTTERMOSER: *J. prakt. Chem.*, (2) **71**, 296 (1905).

cannot be removed by washing.[1] It may be obtained pure by heating a solution of gold chloride with magnesia and decomposing the residue with nitric acid.[2] The hydrous oxide is yellow or olive green, depending on the method of formation, and becomes brown to black on drying. A sample precipitated from potassium aurate with acid contained more than $8H_2O$ to $1Au_2O_3$;[3] and one thrown down from the chloride solution with barium hydroxide approached the composition $Au_2O_3 \cdot 3H_2O$[4] when dried in vacuum over calcium chloride, and $Au_2O_3 \cdot H_2O$[5] when dried over phosphorus pentoxide. These data offer no proof of the existence of a definite hydrate, and it is altogether likely that none is formed. Like hydrous silver oxide, the gold compound decomposes below the temperature at which all of the adsorbed water can be driven off. At 160° a composition corresponding to the formula, Au_2O_2, gold dioxide,[6] has been obtained, but the identity of such a compound has not been established.

Aurous Oxide.—If a solution of an aurous salt[7] is treated with potassium hydroxide, a dark-violet precipitate results, which is said to be aurous hydroxide; but there is no evidence to support this view, and it is probably Au_2O with adsorbed water. A similar product is obtained by hydrolysis of an aurous salt[8] or by reduction of an auric salt with mercurous nitrate.[9] The hydrous oxide appears to give up all its adsorbed water at 200°, and oxygen is not evolved until a somewhat higher temperature. The freshly precipitated and washed gel is peptized by shaking with water[10] forming a fairly stable indigo-blue sol with a brown fluorescence.[11] The sol shows a maximum adsorption between

[1] SCHOTTLÄNDER: *Liebig's Ann. Chem.*, **217**, 312 (1883).

[2] PELLETIER: *Ann. chim. phys.*, (2) **15**, 113 (1820); LENHER: *J. Am. Chem. Soc.*, **25**, 1137 (1903); MORRIS: *Ibid.*, **40**, 917 (1918).

[3] FIGUIER: *Ann. chim. phys.*, (3) **11**, 336 (1844).

[4] WITTSTEIN: *Pharm. Vierteljahr*, **15**, 21 (1866).

[5] KRÜSS: *Ber.*, **19**, 2541 (1886).

[6] KRÜSS: *Loc. cit.;* DUDLEY: *Am. Chem. J.*, **28**, 61 (1902).

[7] BERZELIUS: *Jahresber.*, 199 (1846); KRÜSS: *Liebig's Ann. Chem.*, **237**, 274 (1887); PRAT: *Compt. rend.*, **70**, 840 (1870).

[8] SCHOTTLÄNDER: *Liebig's Ann. Chem.*, **217**, 312 (1883).

[9] FIGUIER: *Ann. chim. phys.*, (2) **41**, 167 (1829); (3) **11**, 336 (1844).

[10] KRÜSS: *Ber.*, **19**, 2541 (1886); *Liebig's Ann. Chem.*, **237**, 274 (1887).

[11] VANINO: *Ber.*, **38**, 462 (1905).

$\gamma = 586.5$ and 597.5;[1] while the maximum adsorption for colloidal gold is $\gamma = 535$. By boiling the sol or by allowing it to stand several days, the dark-violet hydrous oxide is precipitated. The stability of the sol would probably be increased by more thorough washing, preferably with a centrifuge, before shaking with water.

[1] VOGEL: "Die prakt. Spektralanalyse iridischer Stoffe," Berlin, **1**, 489 (1889).

CHAPTER VI

THE HYDROUS OXIDES OF BERYLLIUM, MAGNESIUM, ZINC, CADMIUM, AND MERCURY

HYDROUS BERYLLIUM OXIDE

Hydrous beryllium oxide is obtained in a gelatinous condition by adding ammonia to a solution of beryllium salt. In this form it possesses a high adsorption capacity and cannot be washed free from the mother liquor. The washing must be carried out in the absence of carbon dioxide, since Parsons and Roberts[1] found that the freshly formed oxide will take up as much as one-third of an equivalent of the gas. The hydrous oxide is readily soluble in dilute acids, alkalies, ammonium carbonate, and alkali bicarbonates as well as in solutions of beryllium salts. The great solubility of the hydrous oxide in sodium bicarbonate serves to distinguish beryllium and to separate it quantitatively from iron and aluminum.[2] Like most gelatinous oxides, the adsorbability and solubility of hydrous beryllia decrease slowly on standing at room temperature and rapidly at higher temperatures, particularly if heated in a current of steam or in the presence of a solution of ammonia or of alkali hydroxide or carbonate.[3] The ageing is accompanied not only by a marked diminution in specific surface but by a change from amorphous to a definite crystalline form, as shown by x-radiograms.[4] Böhm and Niclassen[5] obtained a complete series of photographs showing the transformation from the amorphous to the stable crystalline modification. In this

[1] *Science*, **24**, 39 (1906).

[2] PARSONS: "The Chemistry of Beryllium," 9, 27 (1908).

[3] HABER and VAN OORDT: *Z. anorg. Chem.*, **38**, 377 (1904); VAN OORDT: German Patent 165488 (1903).

[4] FREUNDLICH: "Kapillarchemie," 2d ed., 456 (1922).

[5] *Z. anorg. Chem.*, **132**, 1 (1924).

instance the ageing is a concomitant of crystallization as well as of the formation of a hydrated oxide or hydroxide from a hydrous oxide. A similar thing happens with hydrous aluminum oxide and with hydrous cupric oxide under certain conditions; but these cases constitute the exceptions rather than the rule. Indeed, the hydrous oxides of chromium and zirconium exhibit the ageing phenomenon to a marked degree without even undergoing crystallization.

The water content of the amorphous gelatinous oxide is indefinite, depending on the temperature and vapor pressure of the surrounding air.[1] The various hydrated beryllium hydroxides described by Atterberg[2] and others merely represent different stages in the removal of adsorbed water from a hydrous oxide. When heated a little above 150°, the amorphous compound goes over into a different chemical individual, crystalline $Be(OH)_2$ or $BeO \cdot H_2O$, which does not dissociate until a temperature of approximately 215° is reached. The crystalline hydroxide thrown down by heating a solution of gelatinous oxide in alkali has the composition $BeO \cdot H_2O$ when dried over sulfuric acid at 15° and maintains it up to above 200°. The monohydrate is slightly hygroscopic, adsorbing as much as $0.5H_2O$ from saturated air but giving it up again in dry air; after losing $0.5H_2O$ by heating above 200°, the constitution of the compound is definitely changed, for it will then adsorb as much as a mol of water in moist air, giving it up entirely in dry air; similarly, by heating to 280°, the water content is reduced to $0.13H_2O$ and again it will adsorb a mol or more of water, which it gives up in dry air until the composition is $BeO \cdot 0.18H_2O$. X-radiograms of the monohydrate and of the compound heated to 280° should be obtained to determine whether the increased power of the latter to adsorb water is due to the transformation to an amorphous compound or one with a different crystal lattice. When either the gelatinous oxide or the crystalline hydroxide is heated to red heat, the anhydrous oxide no longer adsorbs water, probably owing to the cutting down of the extent of surface by sintering.

---

[1] VAN BEMMELEN: *J. prakt. Chem.*, (2) **26**, 227 (1882); *Z. anorg. Chem.*, **18**, 126 (1898).

[2] *Köngl Svenska Vet. Akad. Hand.*, **12**, 1 (1873).

The solubility of the gelatinous oxide in dilute alkalies and alkali bicarbonates has been determined by a number of investigators,[1] but the values are not constant, since they depend on the method of preparation and the age of the sample, as recognized clearly by Haber and van Oordt.[2] Bleyer and Kaufmann[3] recognize three modifications of the oxide; A, the readily soluble gelatinous form to which they assign the formula, $2BeO \cdot H_2O$ or $H_2Be_2O_3$; B, the less soluble crystalline monohydrate thrown down from alkali solutions; and C, a still less soluble monoydrate obtained by drying C. Obviously, one may obtain intermediate modifications with intermediate properties between A and B and between B and C, if one desires. In other words, the gelatinous precipitate may show a continuous variation in properties from the instable, voluminous, and highly soluble oxide to the stable, relatively insoluble, and slightly adsorptive crystalline monohydrate. Similarly the crystalline compound possesses properties which may vary continuously through certain limits depending on the size of the crystals and the physical structure of the mass. The rapidity with which the highly adsorptive gelatinous oxide goes over into a slightly adsorptive condition, particularly at 100°, may account for Prud'homme's[4] observation that beryllia does not act as a mordant.

Beryllium hydroxide possesses a very slight acidic character[5] and forms beryllates with alkalies. The salts, $Be(OK)_2$ and $Be(ONa)_2$, have been obtained in a crystalline form from alcoholic solution.[6] About 40 per cent of an aqueous solution of the sodium salt is hydrolyzed in a $0.1 N$ solution.[7] According to Hantzsch the solution of hydrous beryllia in alkali is partly beryllate. From a concentrated solution, $Be(OH)_2$ precipitates spontaneously on standing for a long time or rapidly on heating.

[1] GMELIN: *Pogg. Ann.*, **50**, 175 (1840); SCHAFFGOTSCH: *Ibid.*, **50**, 183 (1840); HANTZSCH: *Z. anorg. Chem.*, **30**, 289 (1902); RUBENBAUER: *Ibid.*, **30**, 331 (1902); WOOD: *J. Chem. Soc.*, **97**, 878 (1910).

[2] *Z. anorg. Chem.*, **38**, 377 (1904).

[3] *Z. anorg. Chem.*, **82**, 71 (1913).

[4] *Bull. soc. chim.*, [3] **13**, 509 (1895).

[5] HANTZSCH: *Z. anorg. Chem.*, **30**, 289 (1902); LEY: *Z. physik. Chem.*, **30**, 218 (1899).

[6] KRÜSS and MORAHT: *Liebig's Ann. Chem.*, **260**, 173 (1890).

[7] WOOD: *J. Chem. Soc.*, **97**, 878 (1910).

It seems likely that the first step in the solution process is peptization by preferential adsorption of hydroxyl ion. This is followed by the formation of beryllate, the breaking down of which gives granular crystals of the difficullty soluble crystalline hydroxide. As Ostwald[1] points out, the stable hydroxide is not present in the original solution which soon becomes supersaturated with respect to it; but precipitation can commence only after the first traces have come down, a step that occurs slowly at ordinary temperatures, but rapidly when the solution is heated. Unlike alumina, hydrous beryllia is neither peptized nor dissolved by ammonia[2] or by methyl- or ethylamine.[3]

To prepare beryllium hydroxide free from adsorbed material, Parsons, Robinson, and Fuller[4] dissolve the impure gelatinous hydrous oxide in ammonium carbonate, and precipitate the basic carbonate with steam. The latter compound is decomposed by boiling with frequently renewed portions of water while a stream of air is passed through the liquid. The product is almost free from adsorbed ammonia[5] or carbonate.

Concentrated solutions of normal beryllium salts can dissolve 2 to 6 equivalents of hydrous beryllia; thus, the oxalate or sulfate dissolves nearly 3 equivalents, the chloride 4, and the acetate nearly 6. In every case the hydrous oxide precipitates on dilution, although the precipitation is not complete. This solution is not due to the formation of a molecular complex nor is there any evidence of sol formation.[6] Parsons[7] believes the dissolved beryllium salt merely acts as a solvent for hydrous beryllium oxide in the same manner as a water solution of acetic acid dissolves camphor which is itself insoluble in water; or as a solution of potassium iodide dissolves iodine without forming the hypothetical KI_3.

If hydrous beryllium oxide is precipitated in the presence of boric acid, the distribution of the latter between the hydrous

---

[1] "The Principles of Inorganic Chemistry," London, 546 (1902).

[2] WEEREN: *Pogg. Ann.*, **92**, 91 (1854).

[3] RENZ: *Ber.*, **36**, 2751 (1903).

[4] *Cf.* BRITTON: *J. Chem. Soc.*, **121**, 2612 (1922).

[5] *J. Phys. Chem.*, **11**, 651 (1907); *cf.* PARSONS and BARNES: *J. Am. Chem. Soc.*, **28**, 1589 (1906).

[6] PARSONS, ROBINSON and FULLER: *J. Phys. Chem.*, **11**, 651 (1907).

[7] *J. Phys. Chem.*, **11**, 659 (1907).

oxide and water is independent of the concentration of boric acid, both at 20 and 100°. Similarly, the composition of the precipitate formed by mixing sodium borate and beryllium sulfate varies with the concentration and the relative proportion of the reacting substances. It is evident, therefore, that the so-called beryllium borates,[1] like a large number of alleged beryllium compounds,[2] are, in reality, solid solutions of boric acid and hydrous beryllium oxide.[3] Arsenious oxide likewise seems to form solid solutions with beryllium oxide at 100°; but at room temperature, the acid is adsorbed by the gel giving a well-defined adsorption isotherm.[4] A freshly formed hydrous oxide adsorbs[5] acid dyes, such as eosin and Congo red, the latter being taken up more strongly than by hydrous alumina. It also adsorbs invertin and amylase more strongly than alumina. Basic dyes, such as methylene blue, are adsorbed very slightly, and the same is true for acetic acid, grape sugar, and tributyrin. The adsorption capacity of gels decreases rapidly with age on account of the rapid change from a gelatinous to a granular structure.

While colloidal solutions of hydrous beryllium oxide have not been described in detail, Böhm and Niclassen[6] prepared a clear concentrated sol by peptizing freshly made gelatinous oxide with a small amount of 0.05 N hydrochloric acid. Since the gelatinous oxide runs through the filter paper when an attempt is made to wash out adsorbed salts, there is little doubt that a pure sol could be prepared by thorough washing of the hydrous gel using the centrifuge or supercentrifuge.

So far as known, hydrous beryllium oxide has no industrial applications, but anhydrous beryllia finds an important application in the manufacture of incandescent gas mantles. A very small amount of BeO gives greater strength to the mantle and so is of particular value for mantles which are given special shapes, such as those for use with a pressure system. In this connection it may be mentioned that beryllium nitrate is sometimes added

---

[1] BLEYER and PAZUSKI: *Kolloid-Z.*, **14**, 295 (1914).

[2] PARSONS: "The Chemistry of Beryllium," 69 (1908).

[3] KRÜSS and MORAHT: *Ber.*, **23**, 727 (1890).

[4] BLEYER and MÜLLER: *Arch. Pharm.*, **251**, 304 (1913); *Z. anorg. Chem.*, **75**, 285 (1913).

[5] KLEEBERG: *Kolloid-Z.*, **37**, 17 (1925).

[6] *Z. anorg. Chem.*, **132**, 5 (1924).

to the collodion for mantle coating to increase the protection given the mantle.[1] The crystals of beryllia obtained from an electric arc furnace are almost as hard as corundum, and so it is sometimes mixed with other substances as an abrasive.[1] The oxide would also seem to possess certain advantages over magnesia as a refractory for crucibles. It has a high melting point, 2450°, and after calcination it resists acid corrosion much more effectively than magnesia.[2] The oxide has also shown some promise as a body in paints and in the manufacture of certain dental products and synthetic gems.

HYDROUS MAGNESIUM HYDROXIDE

Magnesium hydroxide in a flocculent hydrous condition is formed by the action of water on magnesia obtained from the naturally occurring carbonate, magnesia alba.[3] The precipitated mass is not a hydrous oxide as is so frequently the case, but is a hydrous hydrate[4] made up of very finely divided particles which adsorb alkali so strongly[5] that its presence prevents the adsorption of sulfate and chloride.[6] The oxide is more soluble when first formed, going over to a less soluble crystalline form quickly when the magnesium ion concentration is high, and more slowly when it is low.[7] X-radiograms show the microcrystalline particles to possess a structure identical with natural brucite.[8] Large crystals of the hydrate are formed by heating magnesium chloride with an excess of potash in a limited volume of water.[9] The flocculent hydroxide dried over sulfuric acid at 100 to 200° adsorbs more than 1.5 H_2O, which it gives up in a dry atmos-

---

[1] Cf. JAMES: Metal Ind., **11**, 66 (1917).

[2] BERZELIUS: Schweigger's J., **15**, 236 (1815); LEBEAU: Compt. rend., **123**, 818 (1896); Ann. chim. phys., (7) **16**, 457 (1899).

[3] DEVILLE: Compt. rend., **61**, 975 (1865); DITTE: Ibid., **73**, 191 (1871).

[4] VAN BEMMELEN: J. prakt. Chem., **26**, 238 (1882).

[5] GROUVELLE: Ann. chim. phys., (2) **17**, 354 (1821); MARCHAND and SCHÜRER: J. prakt. Chem., (1) **50**, 385 (1850).

[6] PATTEN: J. Am. Chem. Soc., **25**, 186 (1903).

[7] GJALDBAEK: Z. anorg. Chem., **144**, 145, 269 (1925).

[8] BÖHM and NICLASSEN: Z. anorg. Chem., **132**, 6 (1924).

[9] DE SCHULTEN: Compt. rend., **101**, 72 (1885).

phere.[1] The amount of adsorbed water taken up decreases with the temperature of ignition and the anhydrous oxide obtained at high temperatures hydrates very slowly. Campbell[2] burned magnesite between 600 and 800°, obtaining an impure oxide which hydrates completely in 3 days. Between 1000 and 1100°, the magnesia was said to undergo a change resulting in a marked decrease in the rate of hydration until at 1450°, about the temperature used in burning Portland cement, the oxide, immersed in water for 18 months, combines with 60 per cent of that necessary to form $MgO \cdot H_2O$. Le Chatelier[3] gave 1600° as the transformation temperature, and Parravano and Mazzetti[4] placed it at 800°, at the same time calling attention to the effect of impurities on the transformation temperatures; thus, ferric oxide hastens it. Mellor[5] pointed out the absence of a definite transformation temperature and showed the change to proceed more quickly the higher the temperature of calcination. Mellor attributed the change to a conversion from amorphous to crystalline periclase; but this cannot be the case, as Hedvall[6] found the oxide formed at various temperatures to have a cubic-lattic crystal structure which underwent no change on heating. The specific gravity of calcined magnesia varies, however, between 3.0 and 3.6, depending not only on the method of preparation but on the temperature of calcination. The low-temperature low-specific-gravity oxide not only reacts much more rapidly with water than the oxide formed at high temperatures, but the former possesses a greater adsorption capacity for gases and moisture, and dissolves more rapidly in acids.[7] Although the melting point of magnesia is in the neighborhood of 2500°, it undoubtedly sinters at a much lower temperature, and this change in physical character probably accounts for the difference in reactivity of the oxide ignited at different temperatures.

[1] VAN BEMMELEN: "Die Absorption," 369 (1910).
[2] *J. Ind. Eng. Chem.*, **1**, 665 (1909).
[3] *Compt. rend.*, **102**, 1243 (1883).
[4] *Atti accad. Lincei*, (5) **30** I, 63 (1921).
[5] *Trans. Ceram. Soc.*, **16**, 85 (1917).
[6] *Z. anorg. Chem.*, **120**, 327 (1922).
[7] DITTE; *Compt. rend.*, **73**, 111, 191, 220 (1871); ANDERSON: *J. Chem. Soc.*, **87**, 257 (1905).

Magnesia Cement.—It is an interesting fact that magnesia prepared by heating the chloride or nitrate to redness possesses hydraulic properties similar to Portland cement in that it sets to a rigid mass when mixed with a limited quantity of water.[1] If the nitrate is calcined at as low a temperature as 350°, the resulting magnesia will not set; if calcined at 440 to 500°, the magnesia hardens under water and at the end of 2 months is like polished marble; but if heated to 1200° or more, the oxide loses its power to set.   The oxide obtained by gentle ignition of natural magnesite also possesses hydraulic properties but that obtained from synthetic carbonates will not set, although it appears to react readily with water.   This difference cannot be due to the presence of impurities in the natural product, since an hydraulic oxide is formed by converting the synthetic carbonate to nitrate and igniting the latter.   As will be discussed in Chap. XVIII, the setting of such substances as Portland cement and plaster of Paris involves the formation of a gel structure,[2] and the same is probably true in the setting of magnesia.   The temperature of ignition and the structure of the calcined substance determine the physical character of the oxide, and these, in turn, determine the rate of hydration and the nature of the resulting product.   As in the preparation of jellies by precipitation, a suitable rate of agglomeration of highly hydrous particles is essential for obtaining a firm jelly structure.

Magnesia possessing setting properties is sometimes used in conjunction with lime for mortar making in districts where only magnesium limestone is available.   Similarly, gently calcined magnesia is mixed with crushed dead-burnt magnesia in manufacturing firebricks so widely used in the basic Bessemer steel process.   The hydraulic magnesia gives plasticity to the paste formed by mixing the materials with water to permit of molding.

Sorel's magnesia cement consists of a mixture[3] of magnesia with a concentrated solution of magnesium chloride, sp. gr. 1.16 to 1.26.   This sets in a short time to a compact mass made up of

[1] DEVILLE: *Compt. rend.*, **61**, 975 (1865); SCHWARZ: *Dinglers polytech. J.*, **186**, 25 (1867); KNAPP: *Ibid.*, **202**, 513 (1872).

[2] *Cf.* MICHAELIS: *Kolloid-Z.*, **5**, 9 (1909); **7**, 320 (1910); KEISERMANN: *Kolloidchem. Beihefte*, **1**, 423 (1910).

[3] SOREL: *Compt. rend.*, **65**, 102 (1867).

minute interlacing crystals[1] of what has been assumed to be basic chloride. People are unable to agree on the formula of the hypothetical salt, and it is probably only an indefinite solid solution of magnesium oxide and chloride. The chloride may be dissolved out completely with boiling water, leaving hard magnesium oxide. The cement can be prepared by adding water to a suitable mixture of dry components.[2] It possesses marked mechanical strength and is used for cementing glass and metal and for making artificial stones; *e.g.,* *xylolith* is made from sawdust, cement, and water.

The tendency of calcined magnesia to take up water and expand is of importance in the cement industry, since the presence of as much as 2 to 3 per cent of uncombined magnesia would give a concrete that would disintegrate from excessive expansion.[3]

In addition to the applications mentioned, hydrous magnesium hydroxide has been substituted for charcoal as a clarifier in the refining of sugar.[4] Its mild basic action has been utilized in pharmaceutical preparations as an antacid. Milk of magnesia is a fairly stable suspension of the hydrous oxide that is widely employed as a mouth wash; in the preparation of modified milk for infants; and in combating hyperacidity of the stomach.

Rhythmic Bands.—The precipitation of magnesium hydroxide in gelatin in the form of rhythmic bands has been investigated quantitatively by Popp.[5] When ammonia diffuses into gelatin containing magnesium chloride, it is found that with increasing concentration of magnesium salt, the rings increase in number and thickness, and the space between them decreases; with diminishing ammonia concentration, the rings decrease in number and thickness, and the space between them increases; adding ammonium chloride causes the number and thickness of the rings to decrease and the space between them to increase; with diminishing gelatin concentration, both the rings and the space between them increase, the number remaining the same. The rhythmic precip-

---

[1] LUHMANN: *Chem. Ztg.*, **25**, 345 (1901); KRIEGER: *Ibid.*, **34**, 246 (1910).

[2] *Cf.* KRANER: German Patent 143933 (1902); LYTE and TATTERS: British Patent 11545 (1890).

[3] CAMPBELL and WHITE: *J. Am. Chem. Soc.*, **28**, 1273 (1906); CAMPBELL: *J. Ind. Eng. Chem.*, **1**, 665 (1909).

[4] HAKE: *J. Soc. Chem. Ind.*, **2**, 149 (1883).

[5] *Kolloid-Z.*, **36**, 208 (1925).

itation takes place also in clay, agar, silica gel, fine sand, and glass beads in water.   To account for these and other Liesegang phenomena, Wolfgang Ostwald[1] postulates the existence of three principal diffusion waves in all reacting systems giving typical periodic precipitates: The added electrolyte diffuses into the gel; the electrolyte in the gel diffuses outward; and the electrolyte produced by the reaction may diffuse in both directions.   In many instances the soluble reaction product possesses a higher rate of diffusion than one or both of the reactants.   Ostwald assumes further that many and probably all reactions giving Liesegang rings are balanced reactions.   Precipitation, therefore, depends on certain critical concentrations of reactants which vary over wide ranges through the interference of diffusion waves. In support of the theory, it was shown that many Liesegang rings are destroyed by subsequent introduction, by diffusion, of the electrolyte produced in the reaction.   Thus, bands of magnesium hydroxide are destroyed by allowing ammonium chloride to diffuse into the gel supporting them.   The converse of rhythmic precipitation, namely rhythmic solution, may sometimes be produced by adding a reaction product.   Thus a uniform precipitate of lead sulfate in gelatin gel containing ammonia is converted into rings by the interdiffusion of concentrated ammonium chloride.   Continuous precipitation results if one reactant is replaced by a compound not giving a balanced reaction, as evidenced by the failure to get bands when alkali is substituted for ammonia in the precipitation of magnesium hydroxide in gelatin.   The distribution of chloride ions in a gelatin jelly containing magnesium chloride was found after the diffusion of ammonia, to show periodic variation between values much higher and much lower than those in the original gel.

Wolfgang Ostwald's theory of rhythmic banding is merely an extension of Holmes'[2] diffusion theory based on Frick's law of diffusion.   The influence of such phenomena as supersaturation,[3] peptization and coagulation of the precipitate,[4] adsorption

---

[1] *Kolloid-Z.* (*Zsigmondy Festschrift*), **36**, 380 (1925).

[2] *J. Am. Chem. Soc.*, **40**, 1187 (1918).

[3] OSTWALD: "Lehrbuch allgem. Chemie," 2d ed., **2**, 778.

[4] FREUNDLICH: "Kapillarchemie," 2d ed., 1009 (1922); SEN and DHAR: *Kolloid-Z.*, **34**, 270 (1924).

of reacting solutes by the precipitate,[1] etc. is looked upon as a secondary factor in the banding process.

Stable sols of hydrous magnesium hydroxide in water have not been prepared without the aid of a protective colloid; but a typical sol of great stability is formed by shaking magnesia with methyl alcohol.[2]

HYDROUS ZINC OXIDE

The voluminous precipitate obtained by adding the calculated amount of ammonia or alkali to a solution of zinc salt is hydrous zinc oxide, the amount of adsorbed water depending on the exact method of formation, the temperature, and the age of the sample.[3] If the precipitation is carried out at 100°, it contains less than 1 per cent of adsorbed water. Although the oxide newly formed in the cold is a transparent gel,[4] it quickly becomes flocculent and later powdery, the change being accompanied by a gradual transformation into the crystalline state.[5] The hydrous oxide ages more rapidly if precipitated from chloride rather than from nitrate; and in the presence of alkali rather than water. As in the case of hydrous beryllium oxide, the microcrystalline mass formed on standing in the cold always contains more water than corresponds to $ZnO \cdot H_2O$, and in this state, it is probably hydrous zinc hydroxide. Kaufmann[6] observed a gradual loss of water on heating a precipitated hydrous zinc oxide to 125°, where it had the composition $Zn(OH)_2$ which it maintained to 180°, and then broke down gradually, giving anhydrous ZnO at a low red heat. There are no hydrates of $Zn(OH)_2$, as assumed by De Forcrand[7] and Boedecker.[8]

[1] BRADFORD: *Biochem. J.*, **10**, 169 (1905).

[2] NEUBERG and REWALD: *Kolloid-Z.*, **2**, 354 (1908).

[3] GOUDRIAAN: *Rec. trav. chim.*, **39**, 505 (1920).

[4] LINDER and PICTON: *J. Chem. Soc.*, **61**, 130 (1892).

[5] FRICKE and AHRNDTS: *Z. anorg. Chem.*, **134**, 344 (1924); FRICKE: *Ibid.*, **136**, 48 (1924); BÖHM and NICLASSEN: *Ibid.*, **132**, 1 (1924).

[6] Dissertation, München, 69 (1913); *cf.* PASCAL: *Compt. rend.*, **177**, 765 (1923).

[7] *Compt. rend.*, **135**, 36 (1902).

[8] *Liebig's Ann. Chem.*, **94**, 358 (1855).

The hydrous precipitates adsorb chloride, nitrate, and especially sulfate[1] so strongly that they cannot be purified completely by washing.[2]   Large crystals of $Zn(OH)_2$, exhibiting a very slight adsorption capacity, precipitate spontaneously from the alkali solution prepared in a variety of ways.   Thus, Goudriaan obtained long prismatic needles from a solution of normal zinc sulfate to which normal potassium hydroxide was added until the precipitate first formed just failed to redissolve; and Fricke and Ahrndts obtained the usual dense rhombic crystals by diluting a solution of the hydroxide in strong alkali.

The newly formed gel dissolves readily in alkali, 1 atom of $Zn^{..}$ being taken up by approximately 6 of OH'.[3]   On account of the ageing of the oxide, the solubility in alkali and ammonia is less the older and less hydrous the preparation.[4]   The variation in the solubility has naturally led to the assumption that the oxide exists in different polymerized forms or allotropic modifications.   Klein[5] recognizes an easily soluble form $2ZnO \cdot H_2O$ and two insoluble forms having the composition, $Zn(OH)_2$, analogous to Bleyer and Kaufmann's A, B, and C beryllium oxides.   But as in the latter case, the solubility is not definite but varies continuously from the loose highly gelatinous to the most massive granular form.

Although the alkali solution of hydrous $Zn(OH)_2$ has been the subject of repeated investigations during the past 25 years, there is still a difference of opinion as to the exact nature of such solutions.   On account of the very weak acidic character of $Zn(OH)_2$, Hantzsch[6] believed that alkalies peptize the latter, forming an insoluble sol from which most of the hydroxide precipitates on standing, leaving the remainder in solution as

[1] KURILOFF: *Chem. Zentr.*, 1222 (1901).

[2] GOUDRIAAN: *Rec. trav. chim.*, **39**, 505 (1920); FRICKE and AHRNDTS: *Z. anorg. Chem.*, **134**, 344 (1924); LORENZ: *Ibid.*, **12**, 439 (1896); HALL: *Am. Chem. J.*, **19**, 901 (1897).

[3] RUBENBAUER: *Z. anorg. Chem.*, **30**, 331 (1902); HERZ: *Ibid.*, **28**, 274 (1901).

[4] HANTZSCH: *Z. anorg. Chem.*, **30**, 289 (1902); KUNSCHERT: *Ibid.*, **41**, 337 (1904).

[5] *Z. anorg. Chem.*, **74**, 157 (1912); *cf.* DE FORCRAND: *Compt. rend.*, **134**, 1426 (1902); **135**, 36 (1902); MASSOL: *Bull. soc. chim.*, [3] **15**, 1104 (1896).

[6] *Z. anorg. Chem.*, **30**, 300 (1902).

zincate. As Hantzsch worked with dilute alkali solutions, he was probably right in concluding that most of the hydroxide was peptized; but diffusion experiments[1] and electrometric measurements[2] on solutions in concentrated alkali showed the presence of alkali zincate. The more concentrated the alkali, the more hydroxide it will take up and the more zincate will form.[3] Goudriaan[4] determined the 30° isotherm for the system, Na_2O-ZnO-H_2O. The saturation concentration increases rapidly to the triple point, ZnO-$Na_2ZnO_2 \cdot 4H_2O$, where the composition of the solution in weight per cent is 27.8 per cent Na_2O and 16.5 per cent ZnO. The zincate forms well-developed crystals decomposed by water and is stable from the triple point to the quadruple point, $NaZnO_2 \cdot 4H_2O$-$Na_2O \cdot 3H_2O$-H_2O, at 39.2 per cent Na_2O and 9.7 per cent ZnO. Sodium zincate forms an incongruent solution, the addition of water to the solid salt or the dilution of the solution causing ZnO to precipitate. This accounts for a number of so-called sodium zincates[5] which are either metastable or non-existent. While Na_2ZnO_2 appears to be the stable salt in strong alkali solution, electromotive determinations of fixed $H^{\cdot}$ion, on adding sodium hydroxide to solutions of zinc salts, indicate the formation of acid zincate in relatively dilute alkali.[6] Such solutions always contain colloidal zinc hydroxide stabilized by preferential adsorption of hydroxyl ion. Fricke and Ahrndts claim that potassium hydroxide forms chiefly $KHZnO_2$ even in concentrations above 8 N.

By dipping red-hot zinc into water, a sol is formed consisting of both colloidal zinc and zinc hydroxide.[7] A dilute sol results by allowing zinc to stand in water for a long time in contact with

[1] COTTRELL: *Z. physik. Chem.*, **42**, 418 (1902); KAUFMANN: Dissertation, München, 45 (1913); KREMANN: *Z. anorg. Chem.*, **35**, 48 (1903).

[2] DUTOIT and GROBET: *J. Chim. phys.*, **19**, 324 (1921); FRICKE and AHRNDTS: *Z. anorg. Chem.*, **134**, 344 (1924).

[3] KLEIN: *Z. anorg. Chem.*, **74**, 157 (1912); RUBENBAUER: *Ibid.*, **30**, 331 (1902); WOOD: *J. Chem. Soc.*, **97**, 878 (1910).

[4] *Rec. trav. chim.*, **39**, 505 (1920).

[5] *E.g.*, see COMEY and JACKSON: *Am. Chem. J.*, **11**, 145 (1889).

[6] HILDEBRAND and BOWERS: *J. Am. Chem. Soc.*, **38**, 785 (1916); *cf.* also KUNSCHERT: *Z. anorg. Chem.*, **41**, 337 (1904); FOERSTER: *Z. Elektrochem.*, **6**, 301 (1899).

[7] KIMURA: *Mem. Coll. Sci., Kyoto Imp. Univ.*, **5**, 211 (1913).

air.[1] With the exception of alkali-peptized colloids, concentrated sols have been obtained only in the presence of protective colloids, such as potassium soaps[2] and sodium protalbinate.[3]

Zinc oxide in the finely divided or colloidal state finds its most important application in the anhydrous rather than the hydrous condition. Thus, zinc white alone, or mixed with finely ground silica or calcium carbonate and ground with linseed oil, forms a white paint that does not discolor in the presence of H_2S. A suitable mixture of zinc white and of finely divided zinc hydroxide precipitated in the cold is said to form a useful enamel pigment.[4] Zinc oxide has a mild antiseptic action, and a sol consisting of the oxide, gutta percha, and Venice turpentine is applied to cloth in the manufacture of surgeons' adhesive tape. Like magnesia, a wet mixture of zinc oxide and chloride sets to a solid gel. A strong dental cement consists of a mixture of zinc oxide and aluminum phosphate. The oxide also finds some applications in face powders, in glazes, and as a filler in oilcloth and celluloid; but by far the greatest demand is as a filler and pigment in rubber goods, especially automobile tires.

Hydrous Cadmium Oxide

Hydrous cadmium oxide precipitates in a very voluminous and highly hydrous form when a concentrated solution of cadmium salt is treated with alkali.[5] The precipitate loses water on heating, becoming a flocculent microcrystalline mass of hydrous $Cd(OH)_2$. The purest form is obtained from nitrate solution, since it adsorbs nitrate less strongly than chloride or sulfate. Like the corresponding zinc compound, cadmium hydroxide is soluble in excess ammonia; but unlike the former, it is only slightly soluble in dilute alkalies. Hot, highly concentrated solutions of potassium hydroxide carry considerable amounts into solution from which hexagonal plates of $Cd(OH)_2$

[1] TRAUBE-MENGARINI and SCALA: *Kolloid-Z.*, **10**, 115 (1912); NORDENSON: *Kolloidchem. Beihefte*, **7**, 106 (1915).

[2] KURILOFF: *Z. Elektrochem.*, **12**, 213 (1906); ROTH: German Patent 228139 (1908).

[3] PAAL and HARTMANN: *Ber.*, **51**, 894 (1918); AMBERGER: German Patent 229306 (1909).

[4] JOANNIS: *J. Soc. Chem. Ind.*, **25**, 486 (1906).

[5] FOLLENIUS: *Z. anal. Chem.*, **13**, 272 (1874).

crystallize.[1] Alkali sulfides react with the voluminous oxide formed in the cold, giving yellow cadmium sulfide, and with the aged oxide formed in the hot, giving red cadmium sulfide. Since the yellow and red sulfides were thought to be polymers, Büchner[2] assumed the existence of two forms of $Cd(OH)_2$; but it now appears that the difference in color of the sulfides is not due to polymorphism or to crystal structure, but to a difference in the size and nature of the surface of the particles.[3] Rapid action of the voluminous compound with alkali sulfides gives small yellow particles, while slower action with the denser aged hydroxide gives larger particles that appear red.

Hydrous Oxides of Mercury

Mercuric Oxide.—Hydrous mercuric oxide is thrown down as a yellow flocculent mass on adding alkali to a cold mercuric solution. It does not form the monohydrate or hydroxide $HgO \cdot H_2O$, as claimed by Carnelley and Walker,[4] nor does it retain its adsorbed water very strongly, but is readily dried to the anhydrous oxide.[5] If the yellow oxide is boiled with aqueous solutions of salts or the dried oxide is heated, the color changes to orange red. This red compound is formed directly by the thermal decomposition of mercuric nitrate. As usually obtained, the yellow oxide decomposes at a lower temperature, is more soluble in water, and reacts more readily with acids, alkalies, and salts than the red compound. These distinct differences in physical and chemical properties were attributed by Gay Lussac[6] and later by W. Ostwald[7] and others to a difference in the degree of fineness of the particles, the greater activity of the yellow oxide resulting from the greater surface of the smaller

---

[1] De Schulten: *Compt. rend.*, **101**, 72 (1885).

[2] *Ber.*, **20**, 681 (1887); *cf.* Klobulkoff: *J. prakt. Chem.*, (2) **39**, 412 (1887).

[3] Allen and Crenshaw: *Am. J. Sci.*, (4) **34**, 341 (1912).

[4] *J. Chem. Soc.*, **53**, 59 (1888); *cf.* Schaffner: *Liebig's Ann. Chem.*, **51**, 182 (1844).

[5] Schoch: *Am. Chem. J.*, **29**, 321 (1902); *cf.* Millon: *Ann. chim. phys.*, (3) **18**, 33 (1846).

[6] *Compt. rend.*, **16**, 309 (1843).

[7] *Z. physik. Chem.*, **18**, 159 (1895); **34**, 495 (1900); Schick: *Ibid.*, **42**, 155 (1903); Varet: *Compt. rend.*, **120**, 622 (1895).

particles.   This view was called in question by Glazebrook and Skinner[1] and by Cohen[2] who showed that the E.M.F. of the chain: Hg|HgO red, KOH, HgO yellow|Hg, was 0.685 millivolt, indicating the existence of two isomeric modifications of the oxide; but Ostwald and Allmand[3] traced these results to the variation in solubility of particles of different size.[4]   Schoch[5] attributed the difference in properties to a difference in crystal structure, the yellow oxide consisting of quadratic plates and the red of prisms.   Allmand confirmed Schoch's observation but showed conclusively that either type of crystal may be yellow or red, depending altogether on the state of subdivision of the particles.

A stable yellow sol is obtained by precipitating hydrous mercuric oxide in the presence of Paal's[6] sodium salt, of protalbinic and lysalbinic acids which act as protective colloids.   After dialysis, this is agglomerated by acids and certain salts, giving a gelatinous precipitate.   By adding mercuric chloride to a normal solution of potassium hydroxide containing 40 cubic centimeters of acetone, a sol is obtained which sets to a firm jelly on standing, the time required depending on the concentration of sol.[7]   The setting may be hastened by adding a small amount of acid or by heating; but too much heating causes agglomeration to a gelatinous precipitate.   For some unknown reason, the presence of even a small amount of mercurous salt seems to retard or prevent jelly formation.

Mercurous Oxide.—Hydrous mercurous oxide, obtained by adding alkali to a mercurous salt solution, cannot be obtained free from mercuric oxide.   Bird[8] claims to get mercurous hydroxide by mixing mercurous nitrate with alcoholic potassium hydroxide at −42°; but this has not been proved.

[1] *Proc. Roy. Soc.*, **51,** 60 (1892).

[2] *Z. physik. Chem.*, **34,** 69 (1900).

[3] *Z. Elektrochem.*, **16,** 254 (1910).

[4] HULETT: *Z. physik. Chem.*, **37,** 385 (1901).

[5] *Am. Chem. J.*, **29,** 321 (1902).

[6] *Ber.*, **35,** 2219 (1902); *cf.* KALLE and Co.: *Z. angew. Chem.*, **20,** 1374 (1907); MAY: German Patent 248526 (1911).

[7] BUNCE: *J. Phys. Chem.*, **18,** 269 (1914); REYNOLDS: *Proc. Roy. Soc.*, **19,** 431 (1871).

[8] *Am. Chem. J.*, **8,** 426 (1886); *cf.* REICHARD: *Ber.*, **30,** 1914 (1887).

CHAPTER VII

THE HYDROUS OXIDES OF SILICON AND GERMANIUM

HYDROUS SILICON DIOXIDE

SILICA GEL

Composition.—The classic investigations of van Bemmelen on the composition of the hydrous oxides were climaxed by his exhaustive study of the hydration and dehydration of hydrous silica[1] thrown down from alkali silica solutions with dilute hydrochloric acid. A silica jelly containing 300 mols of water to 1 of silica is very soft, and when broken into pieces, it flows together like a viscous liquid. A gel with a water content of 30 to 40 mols is brittle; and with 6 mols, it can be pulverized, giving an apparently dry powder. On further dehydration, the vapor-pressure curve drops continuously, giving no indication of a definite hydrate. The highly hydrous oxide is almost perfectly clear, but when the water content drops to a point usually between 1.5 and 3.0 mols, depending on the method of preparation and the history of the sample, the gel becomes opaque and chalky but clears up once more when the water content is reduced to 0.5 to 1.0 mol. The clouding is due to the appearance of air bubbles in the pores of the gel and lasts until the pores are completely filled with air. Owing to capillary action, the water which evaporates from the outer surface of the capillaries is replaced from the inside of the gel leaving a vapor space in the center of the jelly and thus producing an opacity which lasts until the pores are free from capillary water. The remaining 0.5 to 1.0 mol is adsorbed very strongly on the surface of the particles and can be removed only by heating to a relatively high temperature.

In Fig. 11 is given van Bemmelen's schematic representation of the pressure-concentration relations at 15° for a freshly formed hydrous silica. The *A* curves represent the first dehydration

[1] VAN BEMMELEN: "Die Absorption," 196, 214, 232 (1910).

over sulfuric acid; and the *Z* curves are for an oxide which has
been dehydrated once, more or less completely. The direction
of the arrows shows whether water is being taken up or given
off. Starting with a fresh gel, the vapor pressure falls below
that of pure water and decreases along the curve *Aβ*, the volume
decreasing simultaneously. There is no actual break at *O* where
the gel begins to cloud. The volume does not change much
after reaching *O*, and the loss of water along the curve *Aαβ*
causes the capillaries to fill up with air, the gel becoming cloudy.
At O_1, the capillaries are filled with air except for a small amount
of very strongly adsorbed water and the gel is clear again.

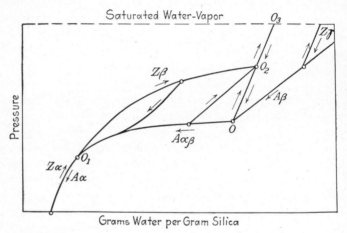

Fig. 11.—Vapor pressure diagram for hydrous silica.

Along *Aα*, the last trace of adsorbed water is driven off. If the
dehydration is stopped at some point along the curve *Aβ* and the
gel is subsequently subjected to a higher partial pressure of
water vapor, the hydration is not reversible, but a curve *Zγ* is
obtained. This is because the gel shrinks along *Aβ* and as it does
not swell to any marked extent, the water is not taken up under
the same conditions. The *Z* curves represent reversible phenomena at least until they cut the curve *Aβ*. If dehydration is
stopped at any point along OO_2, hydration curves like *Zγ* and
Zγ are obtained which usually meet in the point O_2. From O_2
to O_3 and from O_2 to *O*, the pressure-concentration curves are

reversible. It is possible to pass along the path OO_1O_2O as often as one pleases but only in the one direction indicated. The existence of this hysteresis loop was confirmed by Anderson with the systems gel-water, gel-alcohol, and gel-benzene. Both van Bemmelen and Anderson[1] explained the hysteresis from the known fact that a liquid in a capillary tube has a greater vapor pressure when being filled than when being emptied, as in the former there is a diminution of the curvature of the liquid meniscus, due to incomplete wetting. Zsigmondy[2] attributed the marked hysteresis to adsorbed air which prevents the capillaries from being wetted readily. As a matter of fact, Patrick and McGavack[3] found no hysteresis in the adsorption of sulfur dioxide by silica gel when special precautions were taken to remove all air from the system. Moreover, no hysteresis was observed in the adsorption of sulfur dioxide, alcohol, carbon tetrachloride, and benzene by a dynamic method which consists in passing a mixture of air and the vapor in question over the adsorbent until equilibrium is attained.[4] On the other hand, Patrick and Opdycke[4] were unable to eliminate the hysteresis with water by removal of all air. They ascribed the phenomenon to an increase in the viscosity of adsorbed water due to the decrease in internal pressure brought about by capillary and surface-tension forces.

Since the point O may represent approximately 2 mols of water to 1 of silica, and the point O_1, approximately 1 mol of water to 1 of silica, there is a temptation to conclude that the dehydration process consists in the decomposition of a hydrate. Van Bemmelen showed this point of view to be untenable, since the points O and O_1 do not correspond in the vast majority of cases with 2 mols and 1 mol of water, respectively, but vary with the history of the sample between 1.5 and 3 with the former and 0.5 and 1 with the latter. Moreover, one gets the same form of curves and optical phenomena by substituting for water such liquids as alcohol, benzene, and carbon tetrachloride. Van Bemmelen's work has been confirmed and extended and his conclusions reaffirmed by a number of investigators, among whom may be

[1] *Z. physik. Chem.*, **88**, 191 (1914).

[2] "Kolloidchemie," 161 (1912).

[3] *J. Am. Chem. Soc.*, **42**, 946 (1920).

[4] PATRICK and OPDYKE: *J. Phys. Chem.*, **29**, 601 (1925).

mentioned Löwenstein,[1] Zsigmondy,[2] Thiele,[3] Anderson,[4] Bachmann,[5] Vanzette,[6] Lenher,[7] and Behr and Urban.[8] Tschermak,[9] on the other hand, champions the view that the action of hydrochloric acid on mineral silicates yields definite silicic acids corresponding to the salts from which they are obtained. Tschermak's conclusions from dehydration experiments were shown to be altogether unwarranted, by Jordis,[10] van Bemmelen,[11] Mugge,[12] Serra,[13] and Thiele,[14] since the breaks in the composition curves are determined by the temperature at which the drying takes place, the nature of the drying agent, and the age and history of the sample. In spite of the evidence piled up against the existence of definite silicic acids, people are still attempting to establish their identity. Thus Schwarz and Menner[15] claim to remove adsorbed water by Willstätter's method of washing the gelatinous oxide with alcohol and acetone. By a suitable choice of the conditions of preparation and dehydration, the existence of H_2SiO_3, $H_2Si_2O_5$, $H_2Si_3O_7$, and $H_4Si_3O_8$ is regarded as definitely established; and the individuality of $12SiO_2 \cdot 10H_2O$ and $12SiO_2 \cdot 9H_2O$ is believed probable. As a matter of fact, these observations merely confirm what everybody knows, that one can get a composition for a gelatinous body corresponding to almost any desired formula provided one

[1] Z. anorg. Chem., **63**, 69 (1910).

[2] ZSIGMONDY, BACHMANN, and STEVENSON: Z. anorg. Chem., **75**, 189 (1912).

[3] Dissertation, Leipsig (1913).

[4] Z. physik. Chem., **88**, 191 (1914).

[5] Z. anorg. Chem., **100**, 77 (1917).

[6] Atti ist. Veneto, **75**, 621 (1915–1916); Gazz. chim. ital., **47**, I, 167 (1917).

[7] J. Am. Chem. Soc., **43**, 391 (1912).

[8] Z. angew. Chem., **36**, 57 (1923).

[9] Z. physik. Chem., **53**, 351 (1905); Zentr. Mineral., Geol., 225 (1908); Z. anorg. Chem., **63**, 230 (1910); **87**, 300 (1914); NORTON and ROTH: J. Am. Chem. Soc., **19**, 832 (1897); cf. HILLEBRAND: Sitzb. Akad. Wiss. Wien, **115**, 697 (1906).

[10] Z. angew. Chem., **19**, 1697 (1906).

[11] Z. anorg. Chem., **59**, 225 (1908).

[12] Zentr. Mineral., Geol., 129, 326 (1908).

[13] Atti accad. Lincei, **19**, I, 202 (1910).

[14] Dissertation, Leipsig (1913).

[15] Ber., **57** B, 1233 (1924); **58** B, 73 (1925).

chooses the conditions properly. Pascal[1] analyzed three types of hydrous silicon dioxide magnetically and found all of them to behave like a mixture of anhydrous oxide and water.[2]

Structure.—Silica gel consists of minute hydrous particles joined together into an enmeshing network which holds water in the fine pores or capillaries.[3] Precipitated silica is completely amorphous, giving no x-ray interference pattern. Quartz is, of course, crystalline, but quartz glass is amorphous. When precipitated gelatinous silica is heated to 1300°, interference rings appear, indicating a partial conversion to crystobalite.[4]

The properties of hydrous silica show the usual variations with the temperature of precipitation. The gel precipitated by hydrolysis of silicon fluoride at 0° is much more readily soluble in hydrofluoric acid and sodium hydroxide and has a much stronger adsorptive capacity for methylene blue than the oxide formed at 100°. Schwarz and Leide[5] consider the two oxides to be distinct modifications of silica, but there is no justification for this assumption. The difference is due to the size and physical character of the particles, and any member of intermediate products between the 0 and 100° oxide could be made by a suitable choice of the conditions of formation. Indeed, Schwarz and Leide[6] have studied the gradual spontaneous loss of water and agglomeration of oxide particles and find it to be a continuous process. They regard the ageing as a definite chemical condensation from $(SiO_2)_x$ to $(SiO_2)_{2x}$. Until there is some definite proof of polymerization, I prefer the more probable assumption that the ageing is a physical process involving a growth of the primary colloidal particles with the attending decrease in specific surface and loss of adsorbed water.

Although silica is classified as a non-elastic body, the freshly formed jelly possesses an elasticity[7] of the same order of magnitude

[1] *Compt. rend.*, **175,** 814 (1922).

[2] LE CHATELIER: *Compt. rend.*, **147,** 660 (1908).

[3] *Cf.* p. 12.

[4] KYROUPOULOS: *Z. anorg. Chem.*, **99,** 197 (1900); GROSS: *Umschau*, **34,** 510 (1920).

[5] *Ber.*, **53** B, 1680 (1920).

[6] *Ber.*, **53** B, 1509 (1920); SCHWARZ and STÖWENER: *Kolloidchem. Beihefte*, **19,** 171 (1924).

[7] PRASAD: *Kolloid-Z.*, **33,** 279 (1923).

as that of a gelatin jelly.[1]   Like the latter, the elasticity modulus
varies greatly with the water content of the sample.   Silica jellies
possess the interesting property of vibrating like a rigid body
under certain conditions.[2]   Holmes, Kaufmann, and Nicholas[3]
obtained jellies in a glass tube that gave a tone two octaves
above middle C when the vessel was struck.   If the jellies were
prevented from touching the walls of the glass tube by coating the
latter with vaseline, the vibration frequency was much lower
than for similar jellies adhering to the walls.   The vibration
frequency is increased by decreasing the concentration of silica
and by the presence of excess mineral acid, factors which increase
the tension and thus the effective rigidity.   The same factors
increase the tendency of the jelly to synerize, thus showing that
both vibration and syneresis have a direct relation to tension.
Holmes believed the vibration to be transverse, the vibration
frequency varying approximately inversely as the diameter of
the cylinder of jelly.   Prasad[4] failed to confirm these conclusions
for gels removed from the vessel in which they were made.   The
tone emitted by a given jelly showed wide variation depending
on how it was held.   Moreover, by applying Newton's formula
for the velocity of propagation of a longitudinal wave, the vibrations were shown to be longitudinal rather than transverse.

On account of the ease with which electrolytes diffuse into
silica jellies, a number of interesting reactions have been carried
out in this medium.   The usual method of procedure consists
in adding one electrolyte to the silica sol before it sets, after
which a solution of a second electrolyte is poured on the jelly
and allowed to diffuse into the mass where interaction takes
place.   If a crystalline precipitate is formed by the reaction, the
crystals will be much larger and better formed than if the solutions are mixed directly.   In this way, Hatschek and Simon[5]
prepared large gold crystals by reducing gold salts with several

[1] LEICK: *Drude's Ann.*, **14**, 139 (1904); SHEPPARD and SWEET: *J. Am. Chem. Soc.*, **43**, 539 (1921).

[2] KOHLRAUSCH: *Z. physik. Chem.*, **12**, 773 (1893).

[3] *J. Am. Chem. Soc.*, **41**, 1329 (1919).

[4] *Kolloid-Z.*, **33**, 279 (1923).

[5] *J. Soc. Chem. Ind.*, **31**, 439 (1912); *Mining Eng. World*, **37**, 280 (1912); *cf.* HATSCHEK: *Kolloid-Z.*, **10**, 77 (1912).

reducing agents; and Holmes[1] prepared magnificent crystals of a number of metals and salts. The function of the jelly is to prevent rapid mixing of the interacting solutions, thereby avoiding rapid precipitation and the consequent formation of amorphous particles or small crystals. Under certain conditions, reactions in jellies give rhythmic bands or Liesegang[2] rings of precipitates instead of large crystals.[3] What actually happens appears to be determined in large measure by the nature of the jelly. Thus silver chromate forms bands in gelatin but not in agar, lead chromate forms bands in agar but not in gelatin; while neither silver nor lead chromate forms bands in silica jelly, although copper chromate does. The varicolored bands of gold in silica described by Holmes[4] are obtained only in changing light and are not true Liesegang rings; in the dark, large crystals only are formed.[5]

Reactions in jellies are important as offering a plausible explanation of certain formations in nature. Thus gold salts may have been reduced to gold in gelatinous silica which subsequently become quartz. Similarly, agate has probably been produced from gelatinous silica into which iron and other salts have diffused and deposited rhythmic bands.[6]

Adsorption of Gases.—The adsorption of gases by silica gel has been studied in great detail by Patrick and his collaborators. The absorbent used in these investigations was prepared by mixing suitable concentrations of a solution of silicate of soda and hydrochloric acid under violent agitation. After setting to a firm jelly, the material was thoroughly washed and dried *in vacuo* at a temperature varying from 110 to 300°, the most active samples being obtained by heating at 250 and 300° for a half hour or more.[7]

[1] *J. Phys. Chem.*, **21**, 709 (1917).
[2] "Chemische Reaktionen in Gallerten" (1898).
[3] *Cf.* p. 167.
[4] *J. Am. Chem. Soc.*, **40**, 1187 (1918).
[5] DAVIS: *J. Am. Chem. Soc.*, **44**, 2700 (1922); **45**, 2261 (1923).
[6] LIESEGANG: *Zentr. Mineral., Geol.*, 593 (1910); 497 (1911); *cf. Kolloid-Z.*, **10**, 273 (1912).
[7] PATRICK and GREIDER: *J. Phys. Chem.*, **29**, 1031 (1925).

Adsorption isotherms for sulfur dioxide were obtained at varying temperatures between -80 and $+100°$.[1]   The empirical equation of Freundlich,

$$\frac{x}{m} = kP^{1/n} \tag{1}$$

where x is the amount adsorbed by the mass of adsorbent m at pressure P, and k and n are constants, was found to hold over almost the entire range studied, exceptions being at points where the saturation pressure was appreciable.[2]   The straight lines obtained by plotting logarithm $\frac{x}{m}$ against logarithm P at various temperatures were separated widely.

Patrick considers the adsorption by a porous substance, such as silica gel, to be a condensation in the capillaries that is independent of the chemical nature of the adsorbent.   Capillary adsorbents will differ, therefore, in the extent of their total internal volume and also in the dimensions of the pores that make up the internal volume.   If such be the case, the form of the adsorption isotherm merely expresses the distribution of the internal volume as a function of the dimensions of the pores. From this point of view, it would appear logical to seek a relation between the volume occupied by the adsorbed gas and the equilibrium pressure rather than between the weight of adsorbed gas and the pressure.   As a matter of fact, when the logarithms of the volume V of liquid sulfur dioxide obtained by dividing the weight of adsorbed gas by the density of liquid sulfur dioxide at the corresponding pressure are used as ordinates, the curves are brought closer together.   The next step is to plot logarithm V against logarithm of the "corresponding pressure" $\frac{P}{P_o}$, where P_o is the vapor pressure of the condensed gas at the temperature in question.   In this way it was found that greater volumes were taken up at lower temperatures at the same partial pressures, probably because the condensed phase is more compressible at the higher temperatures, the surface tension being smaller.[3]

[1] PATRICK and McGAVACK: *J. Am. Chem. Soc.*, **42,** 946 (1920).
[2] *Cf.* RAY: *J. Phys. Chem.*, **29,** 74 (1925).
[3] PATRICK and McGAVACK: *J. Am. Chem. Soc.*, **42,** 976 (1920).

As an empirical relationship, dividing the volume of condensed sulfur dioxide by the value of the surface tension σ raised to a fractional power gives a correction in the right direction. The Freundlich equation thus takes the form

$$\frac{v}{\sigma^{1/n}} = k \left(\frac{P}{P_o}\right)^{1/n} \tag{2}$$

or assuming the same value of $\frac{1}{n}$ to hold for $\frac{P}{P_o}$ and σ,

$$V = k\left(\frac{P\sigma}{P_o}\right)^{1/n} \tag{3}$$

This equation appears to be a general one for capillary adsorbents[1] and has been applied by Patrick and his pupils to the adsorption of sulfur dioxide, butane,[2] benzene, carbon tetrachloride, alcohol,[3] and ammonia,[4] after correcting for the amount dissolved in the gel water.[5]

Since adsorption of gases takes place above the critical temperature where no condensation to liquid occurs under ordinary conditions, Patrick, Preston, and Owen[6] studied the adsorption of carbon dioxide and nitrous oxide in the region of the critical temperature. When the equation $V = k\left(\frac{P\sigma}{P_o}\right)^{1/n}$ was applied to the experimental results, it was found that k at 0° was not equal to k at higher temperatures near the critical point. This variation in k was attributed to an increase in surface tension of the liquid in the capillaries at temperatures near the critical temperature, owing to capillary forces. After correcting the surface tension, the equation was found to apply, indicating that in all cases the constants k and $\frac{1}{n}$ depend only on the struc-

[1] Recently Munro and Johnson [*J. Phys. Chem.*, **30**, 172 (1926)] found the equation to hold for the adsorption of water vapor by alumina except when the partial pressure approaches the vapor pressure of the liquid at the temperature of the adsorbent.

[2] PATRICK and LORN: *J. Phys. Chem.*, **29**, 336 (1925).

[3] PATRICK and OPDYKE: *J. Phys. Chem.*, **29**, 601 (1925).

[4] DAVIDHEISER and PATRICK: *J. Am. Chem. Soc.*, **44**, 1 (1922).

[5] *Cf.* NEUHAUSEN and PATRICK: *J. Phys. Chem.*, **25**, 693 (1921).

[6] *J. Phys. Chem.*, **29**, 419 (1925).

ture of the silica gel. Since the theory applies even above the critical temperatures for CO_2 and N_2O, Patrick suggests that the critical temperature is raised in the pores of the gel.

Although the most active gel is obtained by heating *in vacuo* to 250 to 300°, the oxide calcined at 1000° still adsorbs more water than charcoal up to 70 per cent humidity. The cutting down of adsorption by calcining at 1000° is due in part to coalescence of primary particles and in part to crystallization.[1] By igniting at a high temperature, the adsorption capacity for water is reduced to zero.[2] The heat of wetting of silica gel by water is 19.22 calories per gram of gel at 25°.[3] It has been usual to attribute the heat of wetting of adsorbents by liquids to compression of the adsorbed liquids.[4] Patrick, on the other hand, attributes the heat of wetting of silica gel to the filling up of the pores with water, whereby the water surface is reduced from its original very large value to practically zero. In support of this view he showed the net heat of adsorption (mean heat of adsorption minus heat of liquefaction) at 0° to be positive and to be equal to the heat of wetting, within the limits of experimental error.[5]

Attention has been called to the absence of hysteresis in the adsorption of vapors other than water when care is taken to exclude air from the system.

Adsorption of Liquids from Solution.—The adsorption from solution by silica gel was investigated in Patrick's[6] laboratory for the following systems: formic acid, butyric acid, acetic acid, benzoic acid, and iodine from a series of solvents; nitrobenzene from kerosene; and acetic acid from carbon bisulfide throughout the entire range of concentration. A few of the results are shown graphically in Figs. 12 and 13. Contrary to Freundlich's[7] view that very little adsorption would be expected to take place from organic solvents which have a relatively low surface tension, it is

[1] BEHR and URBAN: *Z. angew. Chem.*, **36,** 57 (1923); *cf.* GUICHARD: *Bull. soc. chim.*, **31,** 647 (1922).

[2] VAN BEMMELEN: *Arch. Néerland. sci.*, **6,** II 607 (1901).

[3] PATRICK and GRIMM: *J. Am. Chem. Soc.*, **43,** 2144 (1921).

[4] LAMB and COOLIDGE: *J. Am. Chem. Soc.*, **42,** 1146 (1920).

[5] PATRICK and GREIDER: *J. Phys. Chem.*, **29,** 1031 (1925).

[6] PATRICK and JONES: *J. Phys. Chem.*, **29,** 1 (1925).

[7] "Kapillarchemie," 259 (1922).

evident that adsorption does take place to a very marked degree and that the amount adsorbed bears no relation to the surface tension of the solvent. Thus, the greatest adsorption of acetic acid occurs from benzene solution, and becomes less and less from the following solvents in order: carbon bisulfide, gasoline, carbon tetrachloride, toluene, and nitrobenzene; while the surface

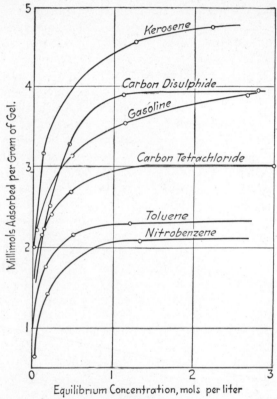

Fig. 12.—Adsorption of acetic acid from various solvents by silica gel.

tensions of these substances, respectively, are: 32, 15, 25, 29, 43. The same order of solvents holds in the adsorption of the other acids investigated.

In general, Patrick finds the adsorption of a solute to increase as its solubility in the solvent decreases. For example, the adsorption of benzoic acid from the several solvents is in inverse order of its solubility in these solvents. Similarly, formic acid is much more strongly adsorbed from toluene than is the more soluble butyric acid; iodine is adsorbed to a small extent in accord with the same laws. Moreover, nitrobenzene is adsorbed to a very great extent from kerosene with which it is only partially

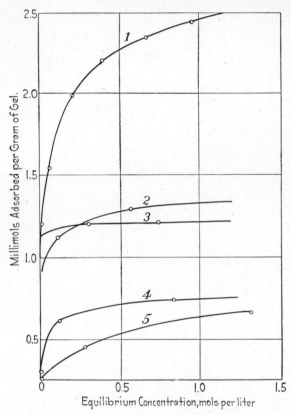

Fig. 13.—Adsorption by silica gel of (1) nitrobenzene from kerosene and of benzoic acid from (2) carbon tetrachloride (3) kerosene (4) benzene (5) chloroform.

miscible, while benzene, which is much closer to kerosene in the solubility series, is adsorbed to a considerably smaller extent.

In a system of V-shaped capillaries such as silica gel is assumed to be, the magnitude of the radius of curvature of a liquid surface adsorbed in the capillaries depends on the amount of liquid adsorbed. As the capillary forces are stronger the smaller the capillary, a minute amount of liquid adsorbed means that the liquid surfaces are very concave. Patrick concludes that adsorption by silica gel is due to a phase separation in the capillaries caused by preferential wetting of the pores by the solute, followed by the production of highly concave surfaces of solute which effects a lowering of solubility of solute in the solvent. For example, when a solution of acetic acid in sulfur dioxide is brought in contact with silica gel, the acetic acid preferentially wets the gel, the pores of which fill up with a phase rich in acetic acid owing to the marked concave curvature that this phase presents to the body of the solution. In other words, although acetic acid is miscible with carbon bisulfide in all proportions when the surfaces are plain, this is not the case if the curvatures of the separating surfaces are sufficiently concave.

This interpretation of adsorption from solution is analogous to the mechanism proposed by Patrick to explain adsorption from the gas phase. In the latter, the adsorption or condensation in capillaries at pressures lower than the saturation pressure at the given temperature is accounted for by assuming that the pores of the gel are presented to the main body of the gas. The empirical formula (3) which satisfactorily explains the adsorption of gases by silica gel has been changed in order to apply it to adsorption from solution.[1] The modified equation is

$$V = k \left(\frac{S\sigma}{S_o} \right)^{1/n} \tag{4}$$

where V is the volume of liquid solute adsorbed per gram of gel, σ is the interfacial tension, S the equilibrium concentration of the solute in the surrounding solvent and S_o the "solubility." Since S_o is analogous to P_o in Eq. (3), it might be taken to represent the ordinary maximum solubility of the solute in the solvent at the given temperature. But if this were true, S_o would be infinity for completely miscible liquids, whereas it has been found always to have a finite value. By applying Eq. (4) to adsorption from solution, in several cases S_o has been calculated to be always less than the ordinary solubility. S_o is, therefore,

[1] PATRICK and EBERMAN: *J. Phys. Chem.*, **29**, 220 (1925).

defined as the dissolving power of the solvent as uninfluenced by molecules of the solute subsequently entering.

It should be pointed out that the capillary theory of adsorption is strictly applicable only in case there is not a specific adsorption factor in addition to the purely capillary phenomenon. Thus in the case of activated carbon the chemical polarity of the adsorbent cannot be disregarded and the results cannot be interpreted solely in terms of the physical nature of the capillaries.[1] Moreover, the adsorption of solids from solution does not come within the scope of the capillary theory. Finally, Chaney remarks:

Attention might be called also to the fact that when Dr. Patrick rationalized his vapor-adsorption curves by calculating the liquid volumes of his adsorbed vapors, the success of this operation was probably due to the fact that the limiting factor in the adsorption of a given vapor was the total available capillary volume. In this case the total adsorptive capacity for the various gases would necessarily correspond with the specific volumes of the latter in liquid state, regardless of whether the condensation was caused by specific polar forces or by capillary depression of the vapor tension. If this correctly states the case, the rationalization of data affected by these calculations throws no light at all upon the question of whether the forces operating to cause the adsorption were primarily capillary or chemical.

Adsorption of Solids from Solution.—The adsorption of sodium hydroxide from solution by silica gel follows the Freundlich adsorption equation, and the adsorbed sodium ions are replaceable by heavy metal cations that give insoluble oxides, in accord with ordinary stoichiometric laws.[2] Patrick considers this adsorption to be chemical adsorption in contradistinction to molecular layer or capillary adsorption. That is, he believes the molecules of sodium hydroxide combine with the colloidal particles of silica in the ordinary chemical sense, giving a product that would be a definite silicate if it were not for the magnitude of the colloidal particles. This view fails to accounts for the

---

[1] CHANEY: *Trans. Am. Electrochem. Soc.*, **36,** 91 (1919); *Trans. Am. Inst. Chem. Eng.*, **25,** Part 1, 292 (1923); CHANEY, RAY, and ST. JOHN: *Ibid.*, **25,** Part 1, 309 (1923); WILSON: *Phys. Rev.*, **16,** 8 (1920); See Coolidge [*J. Am. Chem. Soc.*, **48,** 1795 (1926)] for criticism of the capillary theory of adsorption.

[2] PATRICK and BARCLAY: *J. Phys. Chem.*, **29,** 1400 (1925).

observed increase in the ratio of alkali to silica as the concentration of alkali solution increases. To get around this difficulty,
Patrick suggests that the alkali may peptize the gel. This
seems altogether improbable with an aged gel and with alkali
concentrations of tenth normal or less, at 20°. A more probable
assumption is that the attractive forces, whatever may be their
exact nature,[1] between gel and alkali become more nearly
saturated the greater the concentration, up to a certain point.
Certainly one may get adsorption from solution where chemical
union between adsorbent and adsorbate, in the ordinary sense of
the term, is impossible or improbable. Moreover, it is possible
to have adsorption in a definite stoichiometric ratio with the
formation of a product having properties entirely different from
the definite compound of the same composition.[2]

Applications.—Silica gel has several desirable properties which
render it of value as a technical adsorbent. First of all, it
possesses a strong adsorptive capacity for vapors and liquids.[3]
Moreover, it is quite inert and the adsorbed liquids can be driven
off and recovered if desired, simply by heating the gel, leaving
the latter reactivated and ready to use over again.[4] Probably
the most important technical applications of the adsorbent are
in the refining of petroleum and in the recovery of benzine and
other volatile constituents from coal gas.

Compounds containing sulfur constitute one of the chief
undesirable impurities in crude-petroleum distillates. These
are ordinarily taken out by the sulfuric acid treatment which
has the great disadvantage of removing perfectly good unsaturated hydrocarbons. Because of its specific capacity to adsorb
the sulfur compounds, silica gel has been used with some success[5]
for removing them from gasoline, kerosene, and lubricating oils.
In the experimental plant at Baltimore, the gel powdered to
about 200 mesh is agitated with the oil and then filtered on a
continuous rotary filter. This process is carried out three times,

---

[1] *Cf.* LANGMUIR: *J. Am. Chem. Soc.*, **38**, 2221 (1916); **39**, 1848 (1917);
BARTELL: *J. Phys. Chem.*, **28**, 992 (1924).

[2] *Cf.* GILBERT: *J. Phys. Chem.*, **18**, 586 (1914).

[3] PATRICK, LOVELACE, and MILLER: U. S. Patent 1335348.

[4] *Cf.* TAYLOR: *Chem. Met. Eng.*, **28**, 805 (1923).

[5] The silica gel refinery of the Royal Dutch Shell Company at New
Orleans, La., has been running intermittently since the summer of 1924.

the gel and the oil moving in countercurrents. The spent gel containing oil and impurities passes to a multiple-hearth muffle-heated activator where the oil is driven off and condensed. The gel has to be given a further treatment to burn off all impurities, after which it is used over again.[1] Since the adsorptive capacity of the gel varies for different sulfur compounds,[2] the actual procedure will doubtless vary in different cases depending on the nature of the crude and the impurities present. It is claimed that desulfurized gasoline or kerosene, as prepared by this process, passes all specifications and has the added advantage of retaining the unsaturated hydrocarbons. The process eliminates the rerun distillation following the usual chemical treatment, increases the yield, and is said to give a superior gasoline or kerosene. I am told, however, that the process has not proved successful in the commercial refining of cracked gasoline, since there is not a complete removal of the gum-forming compounds produced by cracking.

As the adsorption process removes sulfur compounds without taking out the unsaturated hydrocarbons, it was possible to demonstrate that the former are responsible for most of the soot and smoke sometimes obtained in a kerosene flame. Gasoline purified by silica gel is said to give less carbon than ordinary gasoline; and the same is true for motor benzol.[3] Moreover, certain gel-refined lubricating oils are reported to give only about one-half as much carbon as the best ordinary oils, and about one-fifth as much as the poor grades, when used with the best grade of gasoline.

Silica gel may be used to adsorb from natural gas the low-boiling gasoline vapors[4] which are subsequently recovered and blended with refinery gasoline to increase the volatility of the latter. It may be employed also for estimating the easily condensable hydrocarbons in natural gas and coal gas. For these

---

[1] MILLER: *Trans. Am. Inst. Chem. Eng.*, **15** (1), 241 (1923); *Oil Gas J.*, **23**, 104, 151, 158 (1924); *Silica Gel Corporation, Bull.* 4 (1923); *cf.* HOLLEMAN: *Chem. Weekblad*, **21**, 187 (1924).

[2] WATERMAN, PERQUIN, BOGAERS, and GORIS: *Chem. Weekblad*, **22**, 378 (1925); WATERMAN and PERQUIN: *Bernstoff-Chem.*, **6**, 255 (1925).

[3] FIELDNER and JONES: *Bur. Mines, Serial* 2517 (1923); *Chem. Met. Eng.*, **29**, 543 (1923).

[4] BURRELL: *Chem. Met. Eng.*, **29**, 548 (1923).

purposes activated carbon appears to be a more satisfactory adsorbent.[1] Furness[2] and Williams[3] claim that silica gel is superior both to activated carbon and to oil absorbents for the recovery of benzine and motor spirit from coke-oven gas;[4] but this is disputed by Urbain[5] who reports that charcoal has great superiority over silica gel as a selective adsorbent of hydrocarbon vapors especially if they are considerably diluted, as is usually the case.

The use of silica gel has been proposed for effecting economies in the lead-chamber process for the manufacture of sulfuric acid.[6] The function of the gel is to recover sulfur dioxide and oxides of nitrogen that are ordinarily wasted. It is also recommended for use as the carrier for platinum in the contact sulfuric acid process.[7]

Adsorption by silica gel is suggested as a method for recovering the oxides of nitrogen in the arc process for the fixation of nitrogen.[8] The removal is complete from rapid air currents at low concentration, and by heating the gel the adsorbed oxides may be recovered ready for liquefaction or for adsorption in water to give concentrated nitric acid.

Because of its strong desiccating action, the gel may be employed in drying air for blast furnaces and to take up water vapor from the rapid vaporization of the liquid in the vacuum refrigeration process.[9] It is also suggested for use as a powder to adsorb perspiration. For this purpose it serves the double function of taking up the moisture and of adsorbing the odorous substances given out by the pores of the body while performing their natural functions.[9]

[1] KROCH: *Petroleum Z.*, **20**, 732 (1924); *cf.*, however, SINGER: *Ibid.*, **20**, 279 (1924); GREEN and WAW: *Colliery Guardian*, **128**, 88 (1924).

[2] *Chemistry and Industry*, **42**, 850 (1923).

[3] *J. Soc. Chem. Ind.*, **43**T, 97 (1924).

[4] LUMMIS: U. S. Patent 1336360.

[5] *Gas J.*, **167**, 449 (1924); *cf.* CHANEY: *J. Ind. Eng. Chem.*, **15**, 1244 (1923).

[6] PATRICK: U. S. Patent 1297724; MILLER: *Chem. Met. Eng.*, **23**, 1155, 1219, 1251 (1920).

[7] PATRICK: U. S. Patent 1297724; *cf.* LATSHAW and REYERSON: *J. Am. Chem. Soc.*, **47**, 610 (1925).

[8] DANIELS and McCOLLUM: *J. Ind. Eng. Chem.*, **15**, 1173 (1923).

[9] FULTON: *Chem. Age*, **31**, 521 (1923).

As a filtering agent, a refined silica known as "Filtrol" is said to be three times as good a decolorizer for vegetable oils as is the standard fuller's earth and is effective at a lower temperature. Besides its decolorizing property the silica adsorbs water, free sulfuric acid, sulfur compounds, and colloidal particles.[1] The gel is also recommended for filtering pharmaceutical preparations[2] since it gives more efficient results than an equal amount of talc, the filtering agent usually employed.

Although silica gel is a good adsorbent for various gases, it is not, in general, a good catalyzer.[3] In the esterification of acetic acid with alcohol, however, it has been found to be twice as active as titania, the best catalyst previously known for this reaction. It is also an efficient catalyst for the alkylation of aniline;[4] but its effectiveness falls off rapidly in the first hour or so owing to the formation of aldehydes which react with aniline to give easily polymerized bodies.

Since the properties of silica gel are influenced to a marked degree by the method of preparation, various attempts have been made to improve on the gel covered by Patrick's patent.[5] Briggs[6] dried the unwashed gel containing sodium chloride at 300° and plunged it while still hot into hot distilled water. After washing by decantation, the gel was dried again at 300° and the process repeated until all the chlorine was removed. The adsorption capacity of this gel for nitrogen at $-190°$ was 60 per cent greater than that of a good grade of adsorbent charcoal. Holmes[7] added dilute ferric chloride to water glass until neutrality was reached, dried the gelatinous precipitate, and then dissolved out the hydrous ferric oxide with hydrochloric acid, thereby exposing a large surface for adsorption. The product is reported to have an adsorption capacity 60 per cent greater than ordinary silica gel. Nickel chloride or other heavy metal salts may be substituted for ferric chloride.

---

[1] KELLY: *Cotton Oil Press*, **7,** 38 (1923).

[2] KRANTZ: *J. Am. Pharm. Assoc.*, **11,** 701 (1922).

[3] MULLIGAN and REID: *Science*, **53,** 576 (1921).

[4] BROWN and REID: *J. Am. Chem. Soc.*, **46,** 1836 (1924).

[5] U. S. Patent 1297724.

[6] *Proc. Roy. Soc.*, **100** A, 88 (1921); cf. FELLS and FIRTH: *J. Phys. Chem.*, **29,** 241 (1925).

[7] *J. Ind. Eng. Chem.*, **17,** 280 (1925).

SILICA SOLS

More than a century and a half ago Pott[1] reportĕd the preparation of a "semisolution" of silica; but Graham is usually credited with the discovery of silica sol. Graham[2] added to 10 per cent hydrochloric acid, two-thirds of the amount of water glass necessary for immediate gelatinization, and dialyzed the resulting mixture. Starting with highly purified chemicals, Jordis[3] obtained a pure sol containing 1.5 per cent SiO_2 by 6 weeks dialysis. Further purification in a special apparatus[4] finally led to the separation of plates of silica from a sol containing 0.6 per cent of SiO_2. If sulfuric acid instead of hydrochloric is used in preparing the sol, it is impossible to remove all the sulfate by dialysis. A sol containing 2 to 3 mols of sodium sulfate per mol of silica can be concentrated by evaporation until the silica content is 6 to 12 per cent of the entire mass.[5] Well-purified sols are quite clear colorless liquids, exhibiting but little inhomogeneity in the ultramicroscope and giving only a very slight depression of the freezing point.[6] The sols are negatively charged but are not very sensitive to the action of electrolytes.[7] Unlike colloidal ferric oxide, silica sol containing a little chloride does not prevent the appearance of turbidity on adding silver nitrate. The negative charge on the particles is decreased continuously by the addition of hydrochloric acid, becoming zero and finally positive without precipitation taking place.[8] The influence of electrolytes on the time required for silica sols to set to a jelly is determined by the magnitude of their precipitating or stabilizing action on the sol.[9]

[1] WALDEN: A History of Colloidal Silicic Acid, *Kolloid-Z.*, **9**, 145 (1911).

[2] *Phil. Trans.*, **151**, 183 (1861).

[3] *Z. anorg. Chem.*, **34**, 455; **35**, 16 (1903); **44**, 200 (1905); *Z. Elektrochem.*, **11**, 835 (1905).

[4] JORDIS: *Z. Elektrochem.*, **8**, 677 (1902).

[5] ZSIGMONDY and HEYER: *Z. anorg. Chem.*, **68**, 169 (1910).

[6] SABANEJEFF: *J. Russ. Phys-Chem. Soc.*, **21**, 515 (1889); BRUNI and PAPPADÀ: *Gazz. chim. ital.*, **31**, (1) 244 (1901).

[7] PAPPADÀ: *Gazz. chim. ital.*, **33**, 272 (1903); **35**, 78 (1905).

[8] LÖSENBECK: *Kolloidchem. Beihefte*, **16**, 27 (1922).

[9] WERNER: *J. Am. Pharm. Assoc.*, **9**, 501 (1920); KRÖGER: *Kolloid-Z.*, **30**, 18 (1922).

At the moment of its formation from water glass, Mylius and Groschuff[1] believe that silicic acid exists as such in a molecular solution which passes unchanged through a dialyzing membrane; and that the colloidal state results from polymerization of the acid with the splitting off of water. It seems more probable that the newly formed primary particles of hydrous silica are too finely divided to be stopped by the membrane. These highly dispersed particles then coalesce to form larger primary particles with the loss of adsorbed water as a result of the decrease in specific surface. This ageing process goes on continuously[2] approaching crystalline anhydrous SiO_2 as a limit.

Silica sol may be prepared by hydrolysis of methyl silicate[3] and of silicon sulfide, chloride, and fluoride.[4] It is obtained also by electrolyzing a solution of sodium silicate with a mercury cathode.[5] Recently Schwarz[1] peptized a fresh silica gel with ammonia and removed the excess peptizing agent in a vacuum desiccator containing sulfuric acid. All of these preparations are similar to the sol formed by Graham's method. Bradfield[6] obtained a sol with somewhat different properties by washing gelatinous silica with the supercentrifuge until it was practically free from electrolyte. If the washing is repeated a sufficient number of times, the hydrogen ion concentration of the sol becomes constant at pH = 6.5, whether approached from the acid or alkaline side. Hardy[7] attributes this slight acidity to the ability of certain of the adsorbed water molecules to ionize. The highly purified sol can be concentrated on the water bath to a syrupy consistency which can be brought back to the original sol condition by adding water. If the boiling is carried too far, minute crystals of hydrous silica separate from the sol.[8]   Even

---

[1] *Ber.*, **39**, 116 (1906).

[2] *Cf.* SCHWARZ and STÖWENER: *Kolloidchem. Beihefte*, **19**, 171 (1924); SCHWARZ and LEIDE: *Ber.*, **53**, 1509, 1512, 1680 (1920); SCHWARZ and LEONARD: *Kolloid-Z.*, **28**, 77 (1921); GRUNDMANN: *Kolloidchem. Beihefte*, **18**, 197 (1923).

[3] GRIMAUX: *Compt. rend.*, **98**, 1484 (1884).

[4] EBLER and FELLNER: *Ber.*, **44**, 1915 (1911).

[5] *Kolloid-Z.*, **34**, 23 (1924).

[6] *J. Am. Chem. Soc.*, **44**, 965 (1922).

[7] *J. Phys. Chem.*, **30**, 262 (1926).

[8] *Cf.* BACHMANN: *Z. anorg. Chem.*, **100**, 1 (1917); ZSIGMONDY-SPEAR: "Chemistry of Colloids," 137 (1917); SCHWARZ and STÖWENER: *Kolloidchem. Beihefte*, **19**, 171 (1924).

the most concentrated sols show no tendency to gel, probably because the secondary aggregates have been broken up by repeated centrifuging and repeptization, leaving small groups of primary particles that entangle relatively little water.

Lenher[1] prepared silica sol by grinding Ottawa sand for several days until the particles are less than 0.004 millimeter in diameter. When such finely divided silica is heated with an excess of water in a pressure bomb at 300 to 450°, gels are formed containing 15 to 18 per cent of water. Ray[2] claims that crystalline quartz is partly converted into amorphous silica by prolonged grinding; but the claim appears to be without experimental foundation.[3]

Colloidal silica has been recommended for the treatment of pulmonary tuberculosis. It is administered along with protein in the form of tablets or better by subcutaneous or intramuscular injection.[4] Great care must be taken not only in the preparation of the sol[5] but in its administration.[6] The treatment appears to be of questionable value.[7]

Kramer[8] finds that the addition of animal or vegetable oils to a 0.2 per cent solution of sodium silicate gives a fine stable emulsion in which many of the drops exhibit Brownian movement. The fatty acid of the oil combines with the alkali to form soap, liberating colloidal silica which acts as a protective colloid for the emulsion. The careful addition of dilute hydrochloric acid produces a silica gel emulsion, while the addition of lime water causes coagulation forming a cheese-like coagulum and a thin liquid. These experiments are said to reproduce synthetically the changes in the tissue which take place in tuberculosis: Alkali silicate forms a fat emulsion in the tissues. The hydrous silica in the emulsion has a strong affinity for lime which is withdrawn from the blood and causes the caseation of the emulsified

[1] *J. Am. Chem. Soc.*, **43,** 391 (1921).

[2] *Proc. Roy. Soc.*, **101***A*, 509 (1922).

[3] Sosman and Merwin: *J. Wash. Acad. Sci.*, **14,** 117 (1924).

[4] Kühn: *Münch. med. Wochschr.*, **67,** 253 (1920); *Z. Tuberk.*, **32,** 320 (1920); Kahle: *Beitr. Klin. Tuberkulose*, **47,** 296 (1921); Gonnermann: *Z. physiol. Chem.*, **99,** 255 (1917).

[5] *Chem. Ztg.*, **45,** 1249 (1921).

[6] Gye and Purdy: *Brit. J. Exptl. Path.*, **3,** 75, 86 (1922).

[7] Kalisch: *Beitr. Klin. Tuberkulose*, **53,** 111 (1922).

[8] *Kolloid-Z.*, **31,** 149 (1922).

fat as in the experiments referred to above. Carbonic acid then acts slowly on the "silica cheese," converting the lime into carbonate, a process designated by the pathologists as calcification. There remains in the tissues the small amount of hydrous silica which served originally as the protective colloid for the emulsion. In line with this, Neyland found in tubercular lymph glands of oxen, a silica content of 0.27 gram SiO_2 in 1 kilogram of dry tissue while a calcified lymph gland contained 1.54 gram SiO_2 per kilogram of tissue.[1]

SILICATE OF SODA

The commercial "silicate of soda" or water-glass solutions so widely used as an adhesive or cementing agent, are colloidal solutions containing negatively charged particles of silica and soda stabilized by preferential adsorption of hydroxyl ion.[2] When soda ash is fused with more than one equivalent of silica, a glass results. If but slightly more than one equivalent is used, the glass may crystallize partially, giving a definite sodium metasilicate. Such fusions are slowly soluble in cold water and readily soluble in hot water; but the solubility decreases as the proportion of silica increases. When the ratio is approximately $1Na_2O$ to $2SiO_2$, complete solution is obtained with difficulty; and when it reaches $1Na_2O$ to $4SiO_2$, special methods must be employed to effect solution.

The commercial "silicates of soda" are not definite chemical individuals; but are variable systems of sodium oxide, silica, and water. The solution most commonly employed in this country consists approximately of $1Na_2O$ to $3.3SiO_2$. To prepare the solution, the molten fusion of soda ash and sand is run into large revolving bins partially filled with water. By this procedure, the melt is shattered, giving a spongy mass that is fairly readily peptized by water. In a preparation containing between 18 and 35 per cent $Na_2O \cdot 3.3SiO_2$, the ultramicroscope reveals myriads of particles so clearly distinguishable that they cannot be greatly hydrated. However, the increase in viscosity with increasing concentration is typical of emulsoid colloids.

[1] KAHLE: *Beitr. Klin. Tuberkulose*, **47**, 316 (1921).
[2] STERICKER: *Chem. Met. Eng.*, **25**, 61 (1921).

The viscosity increases only slightly with the concentration for low values of the latter, but rises very rapidly when the concentration reaches a critical value. The slope of the viscosity-concentration curve is dependent on the sodium-oxide-silica ratio. Thus a change in concentration of but 1 per cent in a solution of $Na_2O \cdot 3.9SiO_2$ causes an increase in viscosity from 375 to 7000 centipoises; while an 8 per cent change in concentration is necessary for a similar increase, in a solution of $Na_2O \cdot 2SiO_2$. The rate of change of viscosity is important as a measure of the rate of set when the silicate is used as an adhesive.

Gels formed by concentrating silicate sols containing a high percentage of silica are very elastic. Stericker[1] reports that balls of the gel dropped 40 feet will rebound two-thirds of the distance; and yet, like fluids, they will take the shape of the container in which they are placed.

When a solution of water glass is neutralized by an acid, it sets to a jelly sooner or later, provided the concentration is not too low. The speed of gelation is determined by a number of factors among which may be mentioned the concentration, the excess of hydrogen or hydroxyl ions present, the impurities, the kind of acid used, and the temperature.[2] Holmes gives directions for preparing various types of jellies setting in any required time.

The addition of concentrated sodium chloride to water-glass solutions throws down a gelatinous precipitate which tends to become granular and hard; an excess of brine causes repeptization of the gel. Malcolmson[3] took advantage of this behavior to increase the volume of silicate solution without altering its viscosity appreciably. By proper adjustment of the concentration of brine, it was possible to extend the volume approximately 21 per cent. Unfortunately, the adhesive properties of the extended solution are not so good as those of the original silicate; and the cost of mixing is usually greater than that of the silicate replaced.[4]

[1] Bogue's "Colloidal Behavior," **2**, 565 (1924).
[2] FLEMMING: *Z. physik. Chem.*, **41**, 427 (1903); HOLMES: *J. Phys. Chem.*, **22**, 510 (1918).
[3] *J. Ind. Eng. Chem.*, **12**, 174 (1920).
[4] STERICKER: Bogue's "Colloidal Behavior," **2**, 569 (1924).

The addition of iron or aluminum salts to water glass yields a gelatinous precipitate of variable composition containing hydrous silica and hydrous ferric or aluminum oxide as the case may be. The action between alum and water glass is made use of in the mineral sizing of paper.[1] The gelatinous precipitate is adsorbed by the paper, giving it a smoother and harder finish than is obtained in its absence. The precipitate sizes for printers' ink which has an oil base; and it increases the resistance to aqueous inks, possibly because of an increased retention of resin in the paper.

When small crystals of various metallic salts are dropped into an 18 per cent solution of commercial water glass, growths resembling plant shoots spring up, giving rise to the so-called "artificial vegetation" or "colloidal forest."[2] The growths are colored when colored salts are used, but the water-glass solution does not become colored except in the case of manganese salts. The form of the growths is different with different metals. For example, hair-like filaments result with cadmium salts and thick fungoid growths with nickel salts. The growths are tubular and act as semipermeable membranes.

Applications.—Commercial water glass finds application in a great many branches of industry. Attention has been called to its use in paper sizing and as an adhesive. For the latter purpose it is said to be the only substance employed in the fiber-container industry for gluing together the components of both double-faced corrugated board and laminated solid fiber board.[3] It is also used for impregnating sandstone and other porous stones as a protection against weathering. This is accomplished by treating the stone with water glass followed by the application of a solution of calcium or aluminum sulfate, which precipitates an insoluble gel in the pores of the stone, greatly increasing its hardness and durability. It is also employed as a cement in the manufacture of artificial stone from sand and lime. A mixture of 2 parts fluorspar and 1 part powdered glass, made into

---

[1] VAIL: *Chem. Met. Eng.*, **25,** 823 (1921); STERICKER: *Paper Ind.*, **5,** 1398 (1923).

[2] DOLLIFIES: *Compt. rend.*, **143,** 1148 (1906); ROSS: *Proc. Roy. Soc. New South Wales*, **44,** 583 (1910); *cf. J. Chem. Soc.*, **102,** II, 49 (1912).

[3] MALCOLMSON: *J. Ind. Eng. Chem.*, **12,** 174 (1920).

a thick paste with water glass, gives a cement for glass and porcelain.

On account of its detergent properties, water glass is frequently added to cheap soap.[1]   It is employed in the calico-printing and dyeing industry and in fixing fresco colors by the process of stereochromy.   It is also used for rendering wood, paper, etc. inflammable; and to a limited extent, in preventing wood from rotting and in the preservation of eggs.

Because of its peptizing or deflocculating action, silicate of soda may be employed to produce the clay "slip" from which the casts are made in the manufacture of pottery and sanitary ware.   An undeflocculated slip containing around 20 per cent of water is a stiff plastic mass.   By working into it about 0.1 per cent each of $Na_2O \cdot 3.3SiO_2$ and sodium carbonate, the mixture becomes sufficiently fluid that it can be pumped readily through 1-inch pipes.   This casting slip is then run into plaster molds which adsorb the water and flocculate the clay.   Silicate of soda or some similar agent must also be used to prepare the slip in the electrical casting of clay.[2]

The deflocculating action of silicate of soda on siliceous and argillaceous material has been applied in concentrating ore by flotation.   Sulman[3] found that less of the gangue constituents are carried into the froth, the greater their degree of dispersion. The importance of silicate of soda solutions in flotation is due to the wide range of their deflocculating action on the gangue. On the other hand, some ores such as copper sulfide are flocculated, thereby facilitating their flotation.   Another method of ore concentration consists in deflocculating the gangue and removing it from the settled concentrate by decantation.[4]

The Hydrous Oxides of Germanium

Germanium Dioxide.—Hydrous GeO_2 is precipitated in a gelatinous form by the hydrolysis of germanium tetrachloride[5]

[1] *Cf.* RICHARDSON: *J. Ind. Eng. Chem.*, **15**, 241 (1923); STERICKER: *Ibid.*, **15**, 244 (1923).

[2] KLEEMAN: *Phys. Rev.*, **20**, 212 (1922).

[3] *Bull. Inst. Mining Met.*, **29**, 49 (1920).

[4] BORCHERDT: U. S. Patents 1446375 to 1446378; 1448514, 1448515 (1923).

[5] WINKLER: *J. prakt. Chem.*, (2) **34**, 211 (1886); DENNIS and JOHNSON: *J. Am. Chem. Soc.*, **45**, 1380 (1923).

or tetrabromide.[1] It is also obtained by passing carbon dioxide
into a solution of the oxide in alkali.[2] It forms no hydrates,[3]
but it holds on to the last trace of adsorbed water quite strongly,
complete dehydration requiring a temperature of 950°.[4] The
precipitated oxide is fairly soluble in water, giving an acid solution[5] from which microscopic rhombic crystals[6] separate on
evaporation.

Müller and Blank[7] recognize three distinct preparations: (1)
The hydrolyzed oxide obtained by hydrolysis of $GeCl_4$. This
gel forms with cold water a milky suspension which clears up on
boiling. It is readily soluble in hydrofluoric and hydrochloric
acids. (2) The "evaporated" oxide resulting from evaporation
of the aqueous solution. This preparation is but slowly soluble
in cold water but dissolves in hot water after a short time. (3)
The "insoluble" oxide prepared by heating the evaporated
oxide to any temperature between 200° and its melting point
(about 1100°) and then boiling the mass thoroughly with water
to remove the unconverted "evaporated" oxide. This preparation is insoluble in water and in boiling hydrochloric and hydrofluoric acids, alkali, and ammonia, but becomes soluble on fusion.
Analogous to the behavior of different preparation of silica and
stannic oxide, the varying properties of the three germanium
oxides might be due to differences in size of the primary particles
and physical character of the precipitates. Against this hypothesis, it was shown that the yield of "insoluble" oxide formed by
heating the evaporated oxide at different temperatures for the
same period of time increased up to 380° and then decreased to
the melting point. This suggests that 380° may represent the
temperature of maximum velocity of transformation of the
evaporated oxide into the "insoluble" form. When the time of
heating of the evaporated oxide was varied at the constant
temperature of 280°, the yield of the "insoluble" form increased

[1] DENNIS and HANCE: *J. Am. Chem. Soc.*, **44**, 299 (1922).

[2] WINKLER: *J. prakt. Chem.*, (6) **34**, 177 (1886).

[3] VAN BEMMELEN: *Rec. trav. chim.*, **6**, 205 (1887).

[4] DENNIS, TRESSLER, and HANCE: *J. Am. Chem. Soc.*, **45**, 2033 (1923).

[5] WINKLER: *J. prakt. Chem.*, (2) **34**, 211 (1886); MÜLLER and ISZARD:
J. Med. Sci., **163**, 364 (1922).

[6] HAUSHOFER: *Sitzb. Akad. München*, **1**, 133 (1887).

[7] *J. Am. Chem. Soc.*, **46**, 2358 (1924).

in such a manner as to suggest that the conversion could never reach 100 per cent. For this reason and because the yield of the insoluble form varied greatly with different preparations of evaporated oxide, Müller and Blank suggest that three allotropic forms of germanium oxide may exist, the evaporated oxide being a mixture of two of them.

Germanium dioxide is said to be of value in the treatment of secondary and pernicious anemia.[1]

Germanous Oxide.—Unlike silicon but like tin, germanium forms an "ous" oxide. This is precipitated in a gelatinous form by the action of alkalies on a solution of $GeCl_2$ or by the hydrolysis of germanium chloroform, $GeHCl_3$. When thrown down in the cold, the precipitate is yellow but it becomes yellowish red by boiling in the mother liquor. It is peptized by boiling water, giving a yellow sol. According to Hantzsch,[2] it is very slightly soluble in water, acting as a weak monobasic acid of the constitution $HGeO \cdot OH$, analogous to formic acid.

[1] LENKER: *Penn. Med. J.*, **26**, 86 (1922); KAST, CROLL, and SCHMITZ, *J. Lab. Clin. Med.*, **7**, 643 (1922); MÜLLER and ISZARD: *J. Med. Sci.*, **163**, 364 (1922); *J. Metabolic Research*, **3**, 181 (1923); *cf.*, however, MINOT and SAMPSON: *Boston Med. Surg. J.*, **189**, 629 (1923).

[2] *Z. anorg. Chem.*, **30**, 289 (1902).

CHAPTER VIII

THE HYDROUS OXIDES OF TIN AND LEAD

HYDROUS STANNIC OXIDE

As early as 1812 Berzelius[1] called attention to differences between the hydrous oxide formed by precipitation of stannic chloride with alkali and the product resulting from the action of nitric acid on tin. Berzelius thought at first that he was dealing with two degrees of oxidation; but this was disproved by subsequent investigations of Davy, Gay Lussac, and Berzelius[2] himself. Thus, Berzelius was led to conclude that the two preparations, having widely different properties, were simply modifications of the same oxide. In this way the term isomer or isomeric modification was introduced in chemistry.[3]

PRECIPITATED HYDROUS STANNIC OXIDE

Since the oxides formed by precipitation of stannic salts and by the action of nitric acid on tin both give a very slight acid reaction when shaken with water, they are commonly designated as orthostannic and metastannic acids, respectively. The earlier chemists regarded them as distinct chemical individuals and recognized the similarities and differences between the two that are listed in Table XVII. In the light of what is now known of the colloidal state of matter, the statements of earlier chemists concerning the properties of these bodies are inaccurate in many respects. Since both substances are more properly termed hydrous oxides rather than acids, I shall designate them as alpha oxide and beta oxide, respectively, instead of as orthostannic and metastannic acid.

[1] "Lehrbuch," 5th ed., **2**, 596 (1812).
[2] *Ann. chim. phys.*, [2] **5**, 149 (1817).
[3] ABEGG: "Handbuch anorg. Chemie," [2] **3**, 593 (1909).

TABLE XVII

	Orthostannic acid	Metastannic acid
Preparation.......	Precipitation from solution of stannic salt	Action of concentrated HNO_3 on tin
Formula..........	H_2SnO_3	H_2SnO_3
Action of HNO_3...	Easily soluble	Insoluble
Action of HCl.....	Easily soluble; not precipitated by excess acid	Insoluble. Product treated with concentrated acid and filtered dissolves in water but precipitates again with excess acid
Action of H_2SO_4...	Easily soluble	Insoluble but swells in concentrated acid, forming a mass that is soluble in water
Action of caustic alkalies.	Easily soluble; not precipitated by excess alkali	Soluble when freshly prepared; precipitated by excess alkali
Action of $SnCl_2$....	No action	Yellow precipitate from solution in HCl

Formation.—The typical α oxide is prepared by precipitation of $SnCl_4$ or $SnBr_4$ with alkali[1] or with an excess of the carbonate of barium or calcium;[2] and by precipitating a solution of soluble crystalline stannate having the formula $M_2Sn(OH)_6$[3] with mineral acid.[4] Rose[5] claimed to get the α oxide by hydrolysis of a dilute solution of $SnCl_4$ at the boiling point. This is unquestionably incorrect, since it has been observed repeatedly that α oxide, formed by hydrolysis of $SnCl_4$ at low temperatures, goes over to β oxide gradually on standing or very rapidly at the boiling point.[6] Similar observations have been made with $SnBr_4$[7] and with $Sn(NO_3)_4$. Lorenz[3] obtained the α oxide by

[1] BERZELIUS: "Lehrbuch," 5th ed., **2**, 1596 (1812).

[2] SCHIFF: *Liebig's Ann. Chem.*, **120**, 47 (1861).

[3] BELLUCCI and PARRAVANO: *Z. anorg. Chem.*, **45**, 142 (1902).

[4] FREMY: *Ann. chim. phys.*, (3) **12**, 463 (1844); **23**, 385 (1848); KÜHL: *Pharm. Ztg.*, **53**, 49 (1908).

[5] *Pogg. Ann.*, **75**, 1 (1848).

[6] BARFOED: *J. prakt. Chem.*, **101**, 368 (1867); ENGEL: *Compt. rend.*, **124**, 765 (1897); **125**, 464, 651, 709 (1897); ZSIGMONDY: *Liebig's Ann. Chem.*, **301**, 368 (1898).

[7] LORENZ: *Z. anorg. Chem.*, **9**, 371 (1896).

[8] *Z. anorg. Chem.*, **12**, 436 (1896).

electrolyzing an alkali chloride, nitrate, or sulfate solution using a platinum cathode and a tin anode.

The typical β oxide is prepared by the oxidation of tin with moderately concentrated HNO_3. Weber[1] claimed that acid of 1.2 sp. gr. gave both α and β oxides, while acid of 1.35 sp. gr. produced a clear solution from which β oxide was obtained by warming. Hay[2] and Scott[3] likewise observed the complete dissolution of tin in moderately dilute nitric acid (1:1) at 2°, from which β oxide precipitated by warming or by standing at ordinary temperatures. The solution contained stannous nitrate stannic nitrate,[4] and doubtless colloidal stannic oxide[5] in varying amounts depending on the concentration of acid and the temperature. As before noted, β oxide is produced whenever a dilute solution of a crystalline tin salt undergoes hydrolysis at the boiling temperature. A solution of amorphous sodium metastannate, so called, likewise precipitates β oxide when heated.

From this survey, it is evident that either oxide may be prepared by hydrolysis of stannic salts under suitable conditions. In all probability the first product of this hydrolysis is always α oxide, which subsequently goes over to β oxide quite slowly at ordinary temperatures but with increasing rapidity as the temperature is raised.

Composition.—By drying different precipitated oxides under the proper conditions, earlier investigators have reported the preparation of a wide variety of supposedly definite hydrates and hydrated acids.[6] An extensive study of the change in vapor pressure of different preparations with the temperature led van Bemmelen to conclude that such compositions were purely accidental, depending on the method of formation, the method of drying, the temperature, and the age of the sample. Van Bemmelen's observations were confirmed and extended, and his

[1] *Pogg. Ann.*, **122**, 358 (1864).
[2] *Chem. News*, **22**, 298 (1870).
[3] *Chem. News*, **22**, 322 (1870).
[4] WALKER: *J. Chem. Soc.*, **63**, 845 (1893).
[5] MECKLENBURG: *Z. anorg. Chem.*, **64**, 370 (1909).
[6] FREMY: *Ann. chim. phys.*, (3) **12**, 463 (1844); **23**, 393 (1848); *cf.* WEBER: *Pogg. Ann.*, **122**, 358 (1864); *cf.* GRAHAM: *Liebig's Ann. Chem.*, **13**, 146 (1835); SCHAFFNER: *Ibid.*, **51**, 168 (1844); CARNELLEY and WALKER: *J. Chem. Soc.*, **53**, 83 (1888).

conclusions reaffirmed by Lorenz[1] and Mecklenburg.[2] Recently, however, Willstätter and his collaborators[3] adopted the older view that the behavior of the variety of oxides could be explained best by assuming the existence of more or less stable hydrates. Willstätter claimed to remove all the adsorbed water from a compound by drying rapidly in vacuum or by leaching with acetone. The composition of a gel formed in a special way and dried by the acetone method at $-35°$ to $+10°$ was represented by the formula $Sn(OH)_4 \cdot H_2O$; but when dried at room temperature the analysis showed a composition $Sn(OH)_4$, which was regarded as the first member of a series of α stannic acids. In an aqueous medium, $Sn(OH)_4$ was supposed to go over into other less basic members of the series. Thus by suitable conditions of precipitation and drying with acetone at 0 to 10°, orthodistannic acid was supposedly formed; at 35 to 46°, orthotristannic acid; and so on. Different so-called β stannic acid were likewise prepared and many of them assigned formulas.

As proof of hydrate formation, Willstätter cites the regions of almost constant water content in the temperature-composition curves of acetone-dried preparations. Such evidence is altogether inconclusive, particularly when the nature and location of the "flats" in the curves are determined almost exclusively by the history of the sample. The same may be said of the "flats" in the temperature-vapor-pressure curves of van Bemmelen. The adsorptive capacity of a hydrous oxide for water at different stages of dehydration is determined by the physical character of the preparation; hence a "flat" corresponding to a definite hydrate is purely accidental and can be duplicated only by following a set method of procedure in precipitation, ageing, and drying. Willstätter's comparison of the behavior of hypothetical high-molecular hydrated stannic acids with their groups $Sn:O$ and $Sn \cdot OH$, to that of carbohydrates with their groups $C:O$ and $C \cdot OH$, appears highly fantastic and illusionary.

Action of Acids.—Freshly prepared α oxide is readily soluble in dilute HCl and is not precipitated by an excess of acid even at the boiling point; whereas β oxide is insoluble in both dilute and

---

[1] *Z. anorg. Chem.*, **9**, 369 (1895).

[2] *Z. anorg. Chem.*, **64**, 368 (1909); **74**, 207 (1912); **84**, 121 (1914).

[3] WILLSTÄTTER, KRAUT, and FREMERY: *Ber.*, **57** *B*, 63, 1491 (1924).

concentrated acid. However, if β oxide is treated with concentrated HCl, a gelatinous mass is formed which Engel[1] believes to be a salt, metastanyl chloride. This product is taken up by water but is reprecipitated by boiling or by adding concentrated HCl. In view of the variety of acids that are supposed to be derived from stannic oxide, it is not surprising to encounter a number of basic salts of tin. Thus Engel claims to get $SnCl_4$, $Sn_5O_8Cl_2 \cdot 4H_2O$, and $Sn_5O_9Cl_2 \cdot 2H_2O$ corresponding to his ortho, meta, and para acids.[2] While $SnCl_4$ is obtained by the action of concentrated HCl on the α oxide[3] and H_2SnCl_6[4] is formed by passing gaseous HCl into a solution of stannic chloride, there is little or no evidence to support the view that the amorphous precipitates, obtained from solutions of α and β oxide under varying conditions, are definite compounds. Van Bemmelen[5] was the first to recognize the real nature of such solutions. He proved it to be incorrect to speak of "solubility" of the oxides in acid by showing that the acid which holds the α oxide in what was thought to be a true solution may be neutralized almost entirely without the oxide precipitating; that the salt formed may be removed by dialysis without precipitation taking place; and finally, that the solutions may be boiled, converting α oxide into β, which likewise does not precipitate unless the boiling is continued too long.[6] Van Bemmelen also observed the adsorption of HCl by both oxides. Below the concentration which causes peptization, the adsorption isotherms have the usual form, indicating that the amount adsorbed depends on the concentration of acid in contact with the oxide. The adsorption was found to be less with β oxide than with α, and the older and denser the β oxide, the less was the adsorption.

The action of hydrochloric acid on the different oxides can now be explained. The newly formed oxide possesses a softer and

[1] *Compt. rend.*, **724**, 765 (1897); **125**, 464, 657, 709 (1897).

[2] *Cf.* TSCHERMAK: *J. prakt. Chem.*, **86**, 334 (1862); MALLET: *J. Chem. Soc.*, **35**, 524 (1879); SCHEURER-KESTNER: *Ann. chim. phys.* (3) **58**, 471 (1860); ORDWAY: *Am. J. Sci.*, (2) **23**, 220 (1857); *cf.* also ROSE: *Pogg. Ann.*, **75**, 1 (1848); WITTSTEIN: *Jahresber.*, 1850, 321.

[3] BARFOED: *J. prakt. Chem.*, **101**, 368 (1867).

[4] KOWALWSKY: Inaugural Dissertation, Breslau (1902).

[5] "Die Absorption," 56, 393 (1910); *Z. anorg. Chem.*, **23**, 111 (1900).

[6] GRAHAM: *Liebig's Ann. Chem.*, **121**, 1 (1861).

looser structure than the β oxide, and so the former is readily peptized by dilute acid and the colloid is stable even in the presence of a very small amount of acid. A high concentration of acid converts it into a true solution of $SnCl_4$. The coarser, denser particles of β oxide are insoluble and are not peptized by dilute HCl. Concentrated acid, on the other hand, peptizes the oxide; and if the excess of acid is poured off, the particles will go into solution in water (dilute hydrochloric acid) from which they are precipitated by excess acid or by boiling. Since α oxide changes to β even at ordinary temperatures and in contact with water, we should expect the colloidal solution of α oxide formed by hydrolysis of a dilute solution of $SnCl_4$ gradually to assume the properties of the dilute hydrochloric acid solution of β oxide, as observed by Fremy, Rose, Löwenthal,[1] and others.[2]

In the light of the experiments of van Bemmelen, it is unlikely that the amorphous masses obtained by Engel and others are definite chlorides. Further doubt is thrown on this by Biron,[3] who obtained products similar to Engel's meta and para chlorides, but found their composition to be indefinite.

Mecklenburg investigated the properties of the oxides obtained by the simultaneous action of various mixtures of hydrochloric and nitric acid on tin. The products adsorbed both acids in proportion to the relative concentrations in the original solution; the ratio, total acid:SnO_2, remaining approximately 0.5:1. The greater the hydrochloric acid content of the hydrous oxide, the more readily it was peptized by water, a circumstance which led Mecklenburg to attribute to this acid a protecting action similar to that of a protective colloid.

Collins and Wood[4] regard the various stannic oxides as salt-like complexes formed by continued condensation between molecules of stannic hydroxide acting as acid and base, respectively. The peptization by hydrochloric acid is looked upon as essentially a chemical process, although the first stage in the process is recognized as adsorption of hydrochloric acid by the

---

[1] *J. prakt. Chem.*, **77**, 321 (1859).
[2] BARFOED: *Loc. cit.*; ALLEN: *J. Chem. Soc.*, **25**, 274 (1872); LORENZ: *Z. anorg. Chem.*, **9**, 369 (1895).
[3] *J. Russ. Phys.-Chem. Soc.*, **36**, 933 (1904).
[4] *J. Chem. Soc.*, **121**, 441 (1922).

oxide particles in varying amounts, depending on the extent of surface which in turn is proportional to the degree of condensation. Following this adsorption, a reaction is thought to take place between the adsorbent and the adsorbed acid, due to neutralization of the latter by some of the basic affinities of the original stannic hydroxide still possessed by the condensed acid. The resulting salt will yield a positive complex ion and chloride ion, if the ionization is not prevented by the presence of too high a concentration of chloride ion from ionization of hydrochloric acid. While the behavior of oxides prepared in different ways has been interpreted by the aid of these assumptions, there seems to be no real justification for postulating the existence of a wide variety of condensed stannic acids and complex basic salts. It seems much more likely, particularly in the light of the recent observations of Pascal[1] and Yamada,[2] that the various products are simply hydrous stannic oxides that have adsorbed hydrogen and chloride ions, the positive charge on the colloidal particle arising from preferential adsorption of hydrogen ion.

Sulfuric acid acts on both α and β oxide in much the same way as HCl. Dilute HNO_3 peptizes α oxide quite readily when the latter is freshly prepared; but β oxide is neither dissolved nor peptized by even the most concentrated acid. However, β oxide adsorbs HNO_3 to a certain degree and the adsorbed acid can be removed only by prolonged washing.[3]

The adsorbing power of β oxide for phosphoric acid deserves special mention, since a standard analytical procedure for separating this acid from mixtures consists in adding tin foil to the nitric acid solution, the resulting β oxide carrying down the H_3PO_4.[4] For the complete precipitation of 1 mol of phosphoric acid, 6 to 7 atoms of tin must be present according to Classen;[5] 7 according to Antony and Mondolfo;[6] and about 13 according

[1] *Compt. rend.*, **175**, 1063 (1922).

[2] *J. Chem. Soc. Tokyo*, **44**, 175 (1923).

[3] Jörgensen: *Z. anorg. Chem.*, **57**, 353 (1908).

[4] Reyonoso: *J. prakt. Chem.*, **54**, 261 (1851); Roscoe and Schorlemmer: "Treatise on Chemistry," **2**, 899 (1923); Reisig: *Liebig's Ann. Chem.*, **98**, 339 (1856); Girard: *Compt. rend.*, **54**, 468 (1862).

[5] "Angew. Methoden analyt. Chem.," **2**, 555 (1903).

[6] *Gazz. chim. ital.*, (2) **38**, 145 (1898).

to Wöbling.[1] Mecklenburg[2] showed conclusively that the removal of H_3PO_4 by precipitated stannic oxide was not due to the formation of a definite stannic pyrophosphate, but to adsorption, the amount of acid carried down depending not only on its concentration but on the nature of the oxide. The adsorption isotherms for five oxides, prepared at different temperatures, showed a decreasing adsorption capacity with increasing temperature of formation.

Action of Alkalies.—Dilute caustic alkalies carry both the α and β oxides into solution. For a long time this solution was believed to taak place by virtue of the formation of definite alkali stannates and metastannates, largely because evaporation of solutions of α oxide in strong alkali yield definite crystals having the formula $M_2SnO_3 \cdot 3H_2O^3$ or $M_2Sn(OH)_6$.[4] However, if the solution of the α oxide in dilute alkali is not evaporated but treated with alcohol, a precipitate is formed, varying in composition from 5 to 17 mols of SnO_2 to 1 mol of K_2O, depending altogether on the relative amounts of the two substances in solution. In like manner, the precipitate obtained from a solution of β oxide in alkali varies very widely, depending as it does on the conditions of formation.[5]

Twenty-five years ago, van Bemmelen[6] called attention to the colloidal nature of the solutions of both α and β oxides in alkalies. He agitated the same amounts of α oxide with like volumes of cold dilute KOH of various concentrations; when the concentration of alkali was less than 8.8 mols of K_2O to 100 of SnO_2, the peptized oxide precipitated spontaneously, carrying down with it a greater part of the alkali. As is usual, the amount

---

[1] "Lehrbuch anal. Chem.," 405 (1911).

[2] *Z. anorg. Chem.*, **74**, 215 (1912).

[3] ORDWAY: *Am. J. Sci.*, (2) **40**, 173 (1865); MARIGNAC: *Ann. mines*, (3) **15**, 277 (1859); MOBERG: *J. prakt. Chem.*, **28**, 230 (1843).

[4] BELLUCCI and PARRAVANO: *Z. anorg. Chem.*, **45**, 142 (1902). Other hydrates are also known; HAEFFLEY: *Dinglers polytech. J.*, **144**, 66 (1867); JONAS: *Chem. Zentr.*, 607 (1865).

[5] FREMY: *Ann. chim. phys.*, (3) **12**, 460 (1844); **23**, 385 (1848); ROSE: *Pogg. Ann.*, **75**, 1 (1848); **105**, 564 (1858); WEBER: *Ibid.*, **122**, 358 (1864); MUSCULUS: *Compt. rend.*, **65**, 961 (1867); MOBERG: *Berzelius' Jahresber.*, **22**, 144 (1843).

[6] "Die Absorption," 57 (1910).

of KOH adsorbed by a given amount of oxide varied with the temperature and concentration, and there was no indication of the formation of definite stannates. He thus accounted for the wide variation in the composition of the precipitate thrown out by alcohol from the colloidal solution of the α oxide in alkali, as observed by Ordway and others.

Van Bemmelen obtained similar results with the more difficultly peptizable β oxide. The first action of dilute NaOH was to produce an opalescent solution that, in itself, showed the oxide to be in the colloidal state. The relative amounts of oxide and alkali in the solution were varied widely; and, as in the case of α oxide, spontaneous precipitation took place the more rapidly, the greater the relative amount of SnO_2. These colloids were coagulated by excess alkali, which was not the case with colloidal α oxide. The precipitated oxides obtained in any case, adsorbed alkali in varying amounts, depending on the alkali concentration and the physical character of the precipitate.[1]

Some observations of Heinz[2] and of Franz[3] give some idea of the relative ease of peptization of different oxides by alkali. The former prepared a colloidal solution of an α oxide in which the ratio $K_2O:SnO_2$ was 1:200; and the latter obtained colloidal β oxides in which this ratio varied from 1:25 to 1:50. As is usual, the peptizing action of potassium hydroxide is greater than that of sodium hydroxide, the precipitating power of K· ion being appreciably smaller than that of Na′ ion.[4]

Mordanting Action.—Tin salts, particularly $SnCl_4$ are sometimes used as mordants in dyeing cotton, wool, and silk. The salt is adsorbed by the dye fiber and subsequently hydrolyzes, giving hydrous stannic oxide which forms lakes with certain dyes that are distinguished by their brilliancy.[5] Vignon[6] studied the action of both β and α oxide on a basic dye, phenosafranine; with the former, a brilliant-red lake was formed, while with the latter no dye was taken up. Thus the dye is readily

---

[1] Cf. WINTGEN: Z. physik. Chem., **103**, 238 (1923).

[2] Dissertation, Göttingen (1914).

[3] Dissertation, Göttingen (1913).

[4] WEISER: J. Phys. Chem., **26**, 424–427 (1922); cf. COLLINS and WOOD: J. Chem. Soc., **121**, 2760 (1922).

[5] HERZFELD: "Das Farben und Bleichen der Textifasern," **1**, 73, (1904).

[6] Compt. rend., **112**, 580 (1891).

adsorbed by the loose finely divided particles of α oxide, while the larger denser particles of β oxide have comparatively little adsorbing power.[1] This behavior is general and has led to the statement: "The formation of metastannic acid during the preparation of tin mordants is called firing; it must be avoided, since this substance has no mordanting power and its generation involves loss of tin."[2]

The Question of Isomers.—A survey of the properties of the so-called α and β oxides discloses marked differences in their solubility, adsorbability, and ease of peptization. The typical α oxide is quite soluble in concentrated acids and alkalies forming definite salts under suitable conditions; it possesses a marked capacity for adsorption and is readily peptized. The typical β oxide, however, is very difficultly soluble, has a comparatively slight capacity for adsorption, and is not peptized by dilute acids or alkalies. If these two oxides are definite isomers, then any product having properties intermediate between the two might be looked upon as a mixture. If the difference in the properties of the two, however, is due to variation in the size of the primary particles and the compactness of the hydrous mass, then any product with intermediate properties must be a chemical individual and not a mixture.

Van Bemmelen came out definitely against the view that the difference between the two oxides is due to allotropy rather than to physical structure. He called attention to the absence of a definite inversion point at which α oxide goes over to β, and demonstrated the slow but continuous transformation at ordinary temperatures even under water. Mecklenburg[3] comes to a similar conclusion: "The α and β stannic acids are hydrous oxides that are little if at all soluble in water, and differ from each other in the size of the particles."

Mecklenburg[4] prepared five distinct oxides by hydrolysis of stannic sulfate at 0, 25, 50, 75, and 100°. These oxides were dried in the air and ground to a powder. Each product was differ-

---

[1] *Cf.* MORLEY and WOOD: *J. Soc. Dyers Colourists*, **39**, 105 (1923).

[2] KNECHT, RAWSON, and LÖWENTHAL: "A Manual of Dyeing," **1**, 272 (1916).

[3] *Z. anorg. Chem.*, **64**, 368 (1909); **74**, 207 (1912); **84**, 121 (1914).

[4] *Z. anorg. Chem.*, **74**, 207 (1912).

ent from the others, and with few exceptions, the properties approached more nearly to those usually attributed to β oxide, the higher the temperature of formation. There was no apparent connection between the compactness of the dried powder and the temperature of preparation; thus, the 100° oxide contained the least water and was most voluminous. This was possibly due to some variation in the conditions of drying and grinding of the several products, for the volume of the precipitated oxide depends on the temperature of formation in a perfectly regular fashion,[1] the oxide formed at the highest temperature being the most compact. Mecklenburg found little difference in the ease of peptization of his oxides with concentrated HCl, except the 50° oxide which appeared most difficult to peptize. It seems to me altogether unlikely that 0 and 100° oxides should be peptized with equal facility. It is more probable that the difference in peptizibility was not detectable with concentrated acid. Mecklenburg observed an increase in the precipitation concentration of sodium sulfate for the 100° oxide peptized by HCl on mixing with it the 0° oxide or one freshly prepared by hydrolysis of stannic chloride. From this he concludes that the different oxides cannot be mixtures of definite α and β isomers. While the conclusion is doubtless correct, it is certainly not justified from his precipitation experiments; on the contrary, these would seem to support the view that the oxides are mixtures. Thus, the so-called "sulfate value" of 100° oxide alone is 0.04 cubic centimeter; but when mixed with 10 to 90 per cent of a freshly prepared oxide it varies from 0.15 to 1.8 cubic centimeters. Since certain ones of his 50 and 75° oxides have sulfate values within the limits found for the mixtures, it might be argued that all of his preparations are mixtures. It should be noted in passing, that Mecklenburg's observations are exactly what one should expect. The adsorption of the sulfate ion by the fresh oxide is much greater than by the 100° oxide; hence, the initial amounts added are all taken up by the former, and the precipitation of a given amount of the latter cannot take place until a higher sulfate concentration is reached.

In order to determine the relative peptizability of hydrous stannic oxides formed at different temperatures, some experi-

---

[1] WEISER: *J. Phys. Chem.*, **26**, 667 (1922).

ments were carried out[1] on the moist instead of the dried oxides, using dilute instead of concentrated acid. In these experiments dilute nitric acid was used, since it is known that this acid peptizes α oxide, whereas it has neither a peptizing nor a solvent action on the typical β oxide. Accordingly, the behavior with dilute nitric acid of the oxides formed under different conditions should give not only a measure of the relative peptizability but should indicate whether the oxides are definite individuals

TABLE XVIII.—PEPTIZATION OF HYDROUS STANNIC OXIDES WITH NITRIC ACID

Age of samples, minutes	Temperature of precipitation, degrees	Observations
5	23	Peptized rapidly; solution cloudy after 10 minutes but clear in 15 minutes
	40	Peptized more slowly; solution very cloudy after 15 minutes, quite cloudy after 30 minutes but clear with only a slight opalescence in 45 minutes
	58	Peptized very slowly; solution very cloudy after 1 hour, clearing in 2 hours, and clear with slight opalescence after 3 hours
	100	Peptization far from complete after 8 hours
10	22	Peptized slowly; solution quite cloudy after 2 hours and slightly opalescent after 4 hours
	39	Peptized very slowly; no residue, but solution very cloudy after 5 hours; transparent but cloudy after 10 hours
	58	Most peptized in 15 hours but solution opaque
	100	But little peptized

differing in solubility, adsorbability, and peptizability, or whether they are mixtures of a definite α oxide peptizable by nitric acid with a definite β isomer not peptizable by this acid. One-gram samples of SnO_2 were precipitated at varying temperatures, the mixtures centrifuged, and the supernatant liquid discarded. The precipitates were shaken with 100 cubic centi-

[1] WEISER: *J. Phys. Chem.*, **26**, 654 (1922).

meters of 1.25 N nitric acid either 5 or 10 minutes after precipitation, as recorded in Table XVIII. It will be noted that there is a distinct difference in the peptizability of the oxides prepared at different temperatures. The loose, finely divided and highly hydrous particles of the oxide formed at room temperature are peptized readily by nitric acid; whereas the more compact, coarser and less hydrous particles formed at higher temperatures are less readily peptized. Moreover, the 40 and 60° oxides are not readily peptized by dilute HNO_3 and so would not be designated as α oxides; but they are peptized after a time, which proves them to be neither β oxide nor mixtures of α and β oxides.

Conclusions as to the relationships among the various stannic oxides, deduced from investigations of their behavior with chemical reagents, are supported in a striking way by recent studies of their physical characteristics. Thus Pascal[1] compared the theoretical values of the molecular magnetic susceptibilities for the hypothetical acids $Sn(OH)_4$ and $SnO(OH)_2$ with the values for the hydrous oxides obtained by various methods. The results show that the "acids" are not definite compounds but are mixtures of anhydrous stannic oxide with water in varying amounts, depending on their history. Quite similar conclusions were reached by Yamada[2] from x-ray analysis of natural cassiterite and of ten samples of hydrous oxides prepared by the methods of (a) Zsigmondy,[3] (b) Schneider,[4] (c) Collins and Wood,[5] from $SnCl_4$ and marble ($SnO_2 \cdot 4.2H_2O$), (d) Graham,[6] (e) Rose,[7] (f) Collins and Wood, oxidation of tin by HNO_3, (g) Engel,[8] (h) desiccating sample (f) in a vacuum, (i) drying sample (f) at 100° ($SnO_2 \cdot 1.1H_2O$), (j) heating sample (f) to redness. From the photographs were measured the distances of the lines from the center, their angles, and their intensities. All the samples, irrespective of their history, contained a similar central nucleus; hence, the physical difference among them is due not to chemi-

[1] Compt. rend., **175**, 1063 (1922).

[2] J. Chem. Soc. Japan, **44**, 210 (1923); Cf. Posnjak: J. Phys. Chem., **30**, 1073 (1926).

[3] Liebig's Ann. Chem., **301**, 361 (1898).

[4] Z. anorg. Chem., **5**, 82 (1894).

[5] J. Chem. Soc., **121**, 441 (1922).

[6] Pogg. Ann., **123**, 538 (1864).

[7] Pogg. Ann., **75**, 1 (1848).

[8] Ann. chim. phys., (3) **12**, 463 (1844).

cal differences but to the physical structure and to the manner in which water adheres to the surface of the oxide granules.

STANNIC OXIDE SOLS

Formation.—Colloidal stannic oxide almost free from electrolytes was first prepared by Graham[1] by adding alkali to stannic chloride solution or hydrochloric acid to sodium stannate solution short of precipitation and dialyzing the resulting solutions. In both cases a gel was first formed on the dialyzer, but this went into colloidal solution again as the purification was continued. The sol was negatively charged, doubtless owing to the presence of a small amount of free alkali. Excess of the latter was removed by the addition of a few drops of tincture of iodine. As noted previously, Graham was able to boil the colloid without precipitating it, thereby forming colloidal β oxide. His preparations were fairly pure and so were readily coagulated by salts and acids.

Schneider[2] dialyzed the sol formed by adding ammonia to stannic chloride short of precipitation; and Zsigmondy[3] peptized with ammonia the thoroughly washed oxide formed by hydrolysis of a dilute solution of stannic chloride. The amount of ammonia required was very small; in one experiment, a single drop containing approximately 0.03 gram of ammonia sufficed for the peptization of 1.45 grams of oxide. Any excess ammonia was removed by heating the colloid to boiling, thus doing away with the necessity for dialysis. Sols prepared in this way were negatively charged and were readily precipitated by electrolytes, particularly those having strongly adsorbed cations. The properties of the precipitated oxides lay between those of the typical α and β oxides, and Zsigmondy believed them to be mixtures of the two forms, the usual properties of each being modified by the presence of the other. This view is probably incorrect.

As previously noted, hydrous stannic oxide freshly prepared at room temperature, is readily peptized by dilute mineral acids; while the aged oxide is peptized by concentrated HCl and H_2SO_4 under suitable conditions, but not by HNO_3. The sols are posi-

[1] *Phil. Trans.*, **121**, 213 (1861).
[2] *Z. anorg. Chem.*, **5**, 82 (1894).
[3] *Liebig's Ann. Chem.*, **301**, 361 (1898).

tively charged owing to preferential adsorption of hydrogen ion,[1] as evidenced by the low precipitation value of sulfate ion in the presence of considerable excess of hydrogen ion.[2] Biltz[3] obtained a fairly pure positive sol by dialysis of stannic nitrate prepared by metathesis of stannic chloride and lead nitrate.   Metallic tin melted in an electric arc furnace and blown with air gives very finely divided SnO_2 which can be peptized by 0.02 to 0.01 N hydrochloric acid.[4]

Ageing.—Attention has been called to the transformation of α oxide peptized by dilute HCl into the β form.   This transformation has been followed in a number of ways, a few of which will be mentioned: Löwenthal[5] found that potassium ferrocyanide could be removed from solution completely by the addition of a dilute solution of stannic chloride, but that the older the tin solution, the more was necessary to precipitate a definite amount of ferrocyanide and the greater was the relative amount of tin in the precipitate.   This is shown in Table XIX.   Löwenthal's observations were confirmed by Lorenz,[6] who assumed that the ferrocyanide was removed as $SnFe(CN)_6$, and that more old stannic chloride solution was necessary on account of the lower

TABLE XIX

Age of SnCl₄ solution, days	Amount of SnCl₄ solution to precipitate 0.5 gram K₄Fe(CN)₆, cubic centimeters	Composition of precipitate, Mols of Sn(OH)₄ / mols of K₄Fe(CN)₆
0	6	1.5
7	10	2.3
14	14	3.3
81	27	6.5
126	32	7.5
162	36	0.5

[1] Cf. ZOCHER: Z. anorg. Chem., **112**, 46 (1920).

[2] LÖWENTHAL: J. prakt. Chem., **56**, 366 (1852); MECKLENBURG: Z. anorg. Chem., **74**, 207 (1912).

[3] Ber., **35**, 443 (1902).

[4] GOLDSCHMIDT and KOHLSCHÜTTER: British Patent 189706 (1922).

[5] J. prakt. Chem., **77**, 321 (1859).

[6] Z. anorg. Chem., **9**, 369 (1895).

concentration of stannic ion resulting from slow hydrolysis. This explanation is unsatisfactory[1] for two reasons: first, because the hydrolysis of inorganic salts takes place much more rapidly than Lorenz assumed; and, second, because the composition of the precipitate is not $SnFe(CN)_6$ but is variable, containing more and more tin the older the solution. The true explanation of Löwenthal's observations lies in the ageing of the colloidal hydrous oxide. The addition of $K_4Fe(CN)_6$ causes coagulation of the colloid. Since the particles of a newly formed colloid are smaller and have a greater adsorption capacity than those of an older colloid, less of the former is necessary to adsorb completely a given amount of ferrocyanide and the ratio of tin to ferrocyanide in the precipitate is relatively low. As the colloid ages, it becomes less stable; and the adsorption capacity falls off so that more colloid is necessary to adsorb a definite amount of ferrocyanide, and the ratio of tin to ferrocyanide becomes quite large.[2]

Tartaric acid was found by Löwenthal to prevent the ageing of colloidal hydrous stannic oxide. While this may be due to some specific action of tartrate ion, I am inclined to attribute it to the formation of a definite complex, obtainable in crystalline form if desired.[3]

The age of colloidal stannic oxide may be determined roughly by treating with stannous chloride. The colloid prepared from newly formed stannic oxide is not precipitated by stannous chloride,[4] whereas the aged colloid is thrown down as a yellow precipitate by this reagent. The precipitate is variable in composition,[5] consisting of hydrous stannic oxide that has adsorbed varying amounts of stannous chloride under the different conditions of precipitation.[6] Collins and Wood observed a small

---

[1] MECKLENBURG: Z. anorg. Chem., 65, 372 (1909).

[2] Cf. BARFOED: J. prakt. Chem., 101, 368 (1867).

[3] ROSENHEIM and ARON: Z. anorg. Chem., 39, 170 (1904).

[4] LÖWENTHAL: J. prakt. Chem., 77, 321 (1859); BIRON: J. Russ. Phys.-Chem. Soc., 37, 933 (1905).

[5] FREMY: Ann. chim. phys., (3) 12, 462 (1844); 23, 393 (1848); SCHIFF: Liebig's Ann. Chem., 120, 47 (1861); TSCHERMAK: J. prakt. Chem., 86, 334 (1862).

[6] WEISER: J. Phys. Chem., 26, 674 (1922); COLLINS and WOOD: J. Chem. Soc., 123, 452 (1923).

increase in adsorption with increasing β character of the hydrous oxide, indicating that some factor other than size of grain is involved. As is usual, stannic oxide shows a stronger tendency to adsorb tin ions than chloride ions. On account of the usual strong adsorption of hydrogen ion, the adsorption of stannous chloride is somewhat less in the presence of hydrochloric acid.[1]

It may be mentioned in passing that hydrogen sulfide precipitates stannous sulfide from a colloidal solution of the fresh oxide in dilute hydrochloric acid; whereas, from the aged colloid, hydrogen sulfide precipitates hydrous stannic oxide that is converted only very slowly into stannous sulfide.[2] The explanation of this behavior is evident when we consider the difference in solubility of the new and old oxide. In the new colloid prepared by peptization with hydrochloric acid there is some stannic ion, the removal of which by precipitation as stannous sulfide results in further solution and subsequent precipitation until all is thrown down as sulfide; while the aged colloid contains but a negligible amount of stannic ion and the precipitate with hydrogen sulfide is almost entirely the hydrous oxide.

It thus appears that we may have colloidal solutions of any number of hydrous stannic oxides, each differing from the others in the size of the primary hydrous particles and, hence, in their reactivity, adsorbability, and stability under given conditions. As a rule, the particles tend to agglomerate into denser and less reactive secondary aggregates on standing, but the reverse process goes on in the presence of fairly concentrated hydrochloric acid or alkali. As with the precipitated oxide, there is no ground for assuming that the different colloidal solutions are mixtures of colloidal α with colloidal β particles in varying proportions.

Behavior with Colloidal Metals.—One of the most characteristic properties of colloidal hydrous stannic oxide is its protective action on colloidal metals. It is well known that a gold solution treated with stannous chloride first gives a red coloration followed by the settling out of a purple or brown precipitate known as gold purple of Cassius from its discoverer, Andreas Cassius,

---

[1] *Cf.*, however, COLLINS and WOOD: *J. Chem. Soc.*, **123,** 452 (1923).

[2] JÖRGENSEN: *Z. anorg. Chem.*, **28,** 140 (1901); BARFOED: *J. prakt. Chem.*, **101,** 368 (1867).

of Leyden.   Because of its wide use as a pigment in the ceramic industry, a number of recipes have been given for its preparation. The substance varies in color and composition with the method of formation.   Certain earlier investigators, as Richter and Gay Lussac, believed purple of Cassius to be a mixture; but Berzelius thought it must be a definite compound.   The latter view is supported by several facts: Purple of Cassius is purple in color, while a mixture of gold and stannic oxide is brick red; gold is not separated from purple of Cassius with aqua regia, whereas it is from a mixture; mercury does not extract gold from the purple as it does from a mixture; and finally, the freshly prepared purple is dissolved by ammonia, forming a purple liquid.   In spite of this evidence we now know that Berzelius' view is incorrect. Debray[1] believed that gold forms a kind of color lake with stannic oxide, which is soluble in ammonia.   Schneider[2] emphasized the colloidal character of the purple and concludes rightly that its ammoniacal solution is a mixture of colloidal gold with colloidal hydrous stannic oxide.   Supporting Schneider's view, Zsigmondy[3] showed that a mere trace of ammonia will dissolve a large amount of freshly precipitated purple and that this purple solution will not pass through parchment during electrolysis, as electrolytes do.   He settled the question once for all by precipitating with nitric acid suitable mixtures of colloidal gold with colloidal stannic oxide, obtaining purples almost identical with those prepared in other ways.   The gold does not combine chemically with stannic oxide, but the usual properties of the former are masked by the protective action of the latter.

Colloidal gold was found by Müller[4] to impart a red coloration to a number of substances[5] and Moissan[6] obtained purples by distilling gold with tin, alumina, magnesia, zirconia, silica, and lime.   Substances similar to gold purples have been prepared with other metals.   Thus Wöhler[7] obtained silver purples similar to the gold pigment by mixing silver nitrate with stannous

[1] *Compt. rend.*, **75,** 1025 (1872).

[2] *Z. anorg. Chem.*, **5,** 80 (1894).

[3] *Liebig's Ann. Chem.*, **301,** 361 (1898).

[4] *J. prakt. Chem.*, (2) **30,** 252 (1884).

[5] ANTONY and LUCCHESI: *Gazz. chim. ital.*, (2) **26,** 195 (1896).

[6] *Compt. rend.*, **141,** 977 (1905).

[7] *Kolloid-Z.*, **7,** 248 (1910).

nitrate; and Lottermoser[1] prepared the former synthetically in the same manner as Zsigmondy prepared the latter. Wöhler[2] has also made an analogous platinum combination. All of these so-called "purples" are colloidal in nature, the composition varying with the conditions of formation. Their colloid chemistry is chiefly that of the hydrous oxide. When freshly prepared, the purples are readily peptized by ammonia or dilute hydrochloric acid; but when dried, there is little or no peptizing action even by concentrated ammonia or hydrochloric acid.

Behavior with Other Hydrous Oxides.—In analytical chemistry, the usual method of estimating tin consists in oxidizing it to insoluble stannic oxide and weighing it as such. It is well known, however, that the oxide formed in this way is always contaminated by other substances present in the solution, such as iron, bismuth, copper, and lead. Rose[3] observed that when iron is present in small amounts, the stannic oxide precipitated from nitric acid solution is contaminated by it; but that when any considerable quantity of iron is present, both the iron and tin remain in solution. Lepez and Storch[4] digested tin with nitric acid containing iron, and obtained solutions of variable stability depending on the relative amounts of the two metals present; solutions containing 2 atoms or less of tin to 1 of iron could be boiled and even evaporated to dryness in a vacuum. Concentrated nitric acid threw out of the solutions a yellowish precipitate that redissolved on dilution; sulfuric acid and sulfates caused a permanent precipitate; while acetic acid and alkali chlorides and nitrates caused no precipitation. By evaporating different solutions, the authors claimed to get compounds having such formulas as $1.8SnO_2 \cdot H_2O \cdot Fe_2O_3 \cdot 1.8N_2O_5$ and $4SnO_2 \cdot H_2O \cdot Fe_2O_3 \cdot 1.1N_2O_5$. When a mixture of hydrous ferric and stannic oxides was thrown down from the mixed nitrates by a slight excess of ammonia and the precipitate washed free from ammonium nitrate, this precipitate, still containing a trace of ammonia, dissolved in water to a clear solution. Removal of ammonia by dialysis resulted in precipitation; but the addition of a trace of

---

[1] "Anorganische Kolloide," 53 (1901).
[2] *Kolloid-Z.*, 2nd Supplement, III (1907).
[3] Rose: *Pogg. Ann.*, **112**, 164 (1861).
[4] *Monatshefte*, **10**, 283 (1889).

ammonia again caused complete solution. Chromic nitrate behaved like ferric nitrate; but aluminum, uranium, cobalt, nickel, and copper nitrates did not cause solution of stannic oxide.

The phenomena described by Lepez and Storch strongly suggest that their ferric-stannic mixtures were not salt solutions but were either colloidal solutions of hydrous ferric oxide peptized by hydrous stannic oxide or colloidal hydrous stannic oxide peptized by ferric and hydrogen ions. The real nature of the mixtures was shown by two series of experiments.[1] In the first experiments, mixtures of freshly prepared oxides were treated with 100 cubic centimeters of 0.01 N ammonium hydroxide as shown in Table XX. The results are quite conclusive: Hydrous stannic oxide is peptized by hydroxyl ion, while hydrous ferric oxide is not. However, the colloidal stannic oxide adsorbs ferric oxide and carries it into colloidal solution as long as tin is present in excess. At the same time, hydrous ferric oxide adsorbs stannic oxide and tends to take it out of colloidal solution so that no tin remains peptized when the former is present in large excess. This is quite analogous to the behavior of

TABLE XX.—PEPTIZATION OF MIXTURES OF HYDROUS STANNIC OXIDE AND HYDROUS FERRIC OXIDE WITH 0.01 N AMMONIUM HYDROXIDE

Mixed oxides prepared from N SnCl$_4$ + N FeCl$_3$, cubic centimeters		Observations
9.5	0.5	Clear colorless colloidal solution
9.0	1.0	Clear colloidal solution with yellow tinge
8.5	1.5	Clear yellow colloidal solution
8.0	2.0	Clear yellow colloidal solution
7.5	2.5	Clear reddish-yellow colloidal solution
6.0	4.0	But little ferric oxide peptized; supernatant liquid cloudy
5.0	5.0	No ferric oxide peptized; supernatant liquid clear and colorless
2.0	8.0	No peptization of either hydrous oxide

[1] WEISER: *J. Phys. Chem.*, **26**, 678 (1922).

hydrous chromic oxide with the hydrous oxides of iron, manganese, cobalt, nickel, copper, and magnesium.[1] On account of the mutual adsorption of hydrous stannic oxide and hydrous ferric oxide, we should expect the precipitate obtained by mixing positive ferric oxide sol with negative stannic oxide sol to contain appreciable amounts of both oxides. It would be interesting to know whether the precipitate obtained by mixing yellow colloidal ferric oxide[2] with colloidal stannic oxide under suitable conditions can be ignited without becoming red.[3]

In a second series of experiments, freshly prepared samples of hydrous stannic oxide were treated with mixtures of ferric nitrate and nitric acid, as shown in Table XXI. The explanation of the observations is fairly simple. As previously noted, hydrous stannic oxide peptized by nitric acid coagulates spontaneously, since the aged oxide is neither peptized nor dissolved by this acid. Ferric nitrate peptizes this oxide both when newly formed and when aged. Accordingly, if freshly prepared hydrous stannic oxide is peptized either by ferric nitrate or by a suitable mixture

TABLE XXI.—COLLOIDAL STANNIC OXIDE PEPTIZED BY $Fe(NO_3)_3$ AND HNO_3

0.38 gram $SnO_3 + xH_2O$ peptized by $N\ HNO_2 + N\ Fe(NO_3)_3 + H_2O$, cubic centimeters			Observations	
			After 1 day	After 1 week
40	0	10	All precipitated	
39	1	10	Very cloudy; partly precipitated	All precipitated
38	2	10	Slightly cloudy	Very cloudy
37	3	10	Slightly opalescent	Slightly cloudy
36	4	10	Clear	Slightly opalescent
35	5	10	Clear	Slightly opalescent
34	6	10	Clear	Clear
0	40	10	Cloudy	Clear

[1] NORTHCOTE and CHURCH: *J. Chem. Soc.*, **6**, 54 (1854); NAGEL: *J. Phys. Chem.*, **19**, 331 (1915).

[2] WEISER: *J. Phys. Chem.*, **24**, 322 (1920).

[3] KEANE: *J. Phys. Chem.*, **20**, 734 (1916); SCHEETZ: *Ibid.*, **21**, 570 (1917); YOE: *Ibid.*, **25**, 196 (1921).

of ferric nitrate and nitric acid, coagulation does not take place on standing or boiling, on account of the stabilizing action of the strongly adsorbed ferric ion; but if the concentration of ferric ion in the nitric acid solution is too low, partial coagulation takes place as shown in the table.

Stannic Oxide Jellies.—When a colloidal solution of hydrous stannic oxide is evaporated, a transparent jelly is obtained; while precipitation with electrolytes is said always to give a gelatinous precipitate and not a jelly.[1] Since hydrous stannic oxide apparently possesses the desired properties, one should expect to get stannic oxide jellies by precipitation from colloidal solution under suitable conditions. This conclusion was con-

TABLE XXII.—PRECIPITATION OF COLLOIDAL STANNIC OXIDE BY ELECTROLYTES

Electrolyte			Observations
Formula	Amount added, cubic centimeters	Concentration, milliequivalents per liter	
BaCl$_2$	3.00 N/100	3.00	Clear transparent jelly
BaCl$_2$	3.50 N/100	3.50	Clear transparent jelly; very firm
BaCl$_2$	3.75 N/100	3.75	Jelly somewhat cloudy and slightly synerized
BaCl$_2$	4.25 N/100	4.25	Gelatinous precipitate
SrCl$_2$	3.50 N/100	3.50	Clear; somewhat viscous
SrCl$_2$	4.00 N/100	4.00	Clear transparent jelly
SrCl$_2$	4.50 N/100	4.50	Clear transparent jelly; very firm
SrCl$_2$	5.00 N/100	5.00	Cloudy jelly; synerized slightly
NaCl	2.00 N/10	20.00	Clear; viscous
NaCl	2.25 N/10	22.50	Soft cloudy jelly
NaCl	2.50 N/10	25.00	Soft cloudy jelly
NaCl	2.75 N/10	27.50	Gelatinous precipitate
HCl	1.50 N/50	3.00	Clear
HCl	1.75 N/50	3.50	Clear transparent jelly
HCl	2.00 N/50	4.00	Clear transparent jelly
HCl	2.25 N/50	4.50	Cloudy jelly; synerized slightly
HCl	2.50 N/50	5.00	Gelatinous precipitate

[1] ZSIGMONDY: "Chemistry of Colloids," translated by Spear, 155 (1917).

firmed[1] by precipitating a sol prepared by Zsigmondy's method containing 28 grams SnO_2 per liter. The results as recorded in Table XXII are in accord with the general theory.[2] The jellies formed under the most favorable conditions were very firm and stable, remaining unbroken after standing several months. If just the right amount of electrolyte is added, the jelly may be converted into a sol by shaking and on standing will again set to a jelly.[3]

As might be expected, jellies are not formed by adding an excess of alkali to a stannic salt and allowing the sol to stand, the reason being that alkalies have a slight solvent action as well as a peptizing action on the hydrous oxide. This solvent action causes the precipitate which comes out spontaneously to consist of large granular particles instead of the fine chains or filaments that make up a jelly structure.

HYDROUS STANNOUS OXIDE

Hydrous stannous oxide is precipitated as a yellow highly gelatinous mass by adding alkali hydroxide or carbonate to a solution of stannous chloride. Ditte[4] assigned the formula $3SnO \cdot 2H_2O$ to the compound precipitated with alkali and dried at 110°; and Schaffner[5] claimed to get $2SnO \cdot H_2O$ by precipitating with carbonate and drying below 80°. Bury and Partington[6] prepared five different samples, using ammonia, carbonate, and alkali as precipitants, both in the air and in an atmosphere of carbon dioxide. With alkali and carbonate, the samples possessed a yellow tinge from the start; but with ammonia, they were white when first prepared, becoming yellow on drying. After drying over phosphorus pentoxide, the samples gave an analysis for tin corresponding to the compound $3SnO \cdot 2H_2O$; but the water content varied from 7.11 to 8.82 per cent, the calculated value for the compound being 8.16 per cent. These data are insufficient to establish the identity of the alleged hydrate.

---

[1] WEISER: *J. Phys. Chem.*, **26**, 681 (1922).
[2] Chap. I, p. 26.
[3] SCHALEK and SZEGVARI: *Kolloid-Z.*, **33**, 326 (1923).
[4] *Ann. chim. phys.*, (5) **27**, 145 (1882).
[5] *Liebig's Ann. Chem.*, **51**, 168 (1844).
[6] *J. Chem. Soc.*, **121**, 1998 (1922).

The gelatinous oxide is very difficult to wash free from the mother liquor, and if the washing is carried too far, the oxide passes through the filter, forming a sol. Bury and Partington observed the slow transformation of the hydrous oxide sol into a crystalline oxide, a part of which precipitated on the walls of the flask and a part remained in suspension, giving a creamy-yellow liquid that glistened on shaking.

The hydrous oxide loses water even in contact with water, going over to the anhydrous state. In the presence of alkali, the rate of dehydration is acclerated and the precipitate darkens. The effect of a trace of alkali is evidenced by the darkening of samples of hydrous oxide in contact with the walls of glass vessels and the absence of darkening in samples stored in quartz vessels.[1] The color of the anhydrous oxide varies from dark gray to black, depending on the method of preparation. It is not likely that the different shades represent different modifications. Roth[2] claims to get a red crystalline oxide by the action of an acetic acid solution of SnO_2 on the gelatinous oxide, but Bury and Partington were unable to confirm this result.

Hydrous stannic oxide is dissolved by alkali forming $NaHSnO_2$, unless the alkali is quite concentrated when Na_2SnO_2 is obtained.[3] Schneider[4] reports the preparation of a colloidal solution of Sn_2O_3 by adding a very dilute solution of stannous chloride to a sol of hydrous stannic oxide and dialyzing in the absence of air. The sol is a yellow clear neutral liquid with strong reducing properties; thus, the addition of gold chloride gives gold purple. In all probability, the sol is not Sn_2O_3 but a mixture of hydrous stannic oxide and basic stannous chloride[5] stabilized by the hydrous oxide.

HYDROUS LEAD MONOXIDE

It is somewhat surprising not to find a reference to an analysis of precipitated lead monoxide which corresponds to the formula

[1] BURY and PARTINGTON: *J. Chem. Soc.*, **121,** 1998 (1922).
[2] Abegg's "Handbuch anorg. Chem.," **4,** II, 573 (1909).
[3] HANTZSCH: *Z. anorg. Chem.*, **30,** 289 (1902); GOLDSCHMIDT and ECKARDT: *Z. physik. Chem.*, **56,** 385 (1906); KOELICHEN: *Ibid.*, **33,** 129 (1900).
[4] *Z. anorg. Chem.*, **5,** 83 (1894).
[5] CARSON: *J. Am. Chem. Soc.*, **41,** 1969 (1919).

$Pb(OH)_2$. However, it is tacitly assumed by Ditte[1] and by Wood[2] that the compound freshly precipitated from lead nitrate solution by alkali and ammonia is lead hydroxide, when, as a matter of fact, the mass is either a basic salt[3] or contains adsorbed alkali, unless it is digested repeatedly with sodium hydroxide solution which converts it to pure hydrous oxide. Hydrates having the formula $2PbO \cdot H_2O$[4] and $3PbO \cdot H_2O$[5] have been reported; but Glasstone[6] repeated the experiments of various authors and failed to get any product which could be described as either of these compounds. The water content of the oxide precipitated from lead acetate solution with alkali was lower the greater the dilution, and the higher the temperature of the reacting solutions. A variety of hydrous products were heated in a current of air at 105 to 110° until decomposition set in, as evidenced by a slight change in color, and the water content was determined. In every case the oxides contained 3.08 to 3.13 per cent of water, corresponding approximately to the composition $5PbO \cdot 2H_2O$. From this, Glasstone assumes that every form of the oxide, whether crystalline or amorphous, is the same chemical entity with varying amounts of adsorbed water; but whether the substance is a single hydrate or a solid solution of two hydrates is left undecided. Glasstone rules out the possibility of the precipitated oxide being hydrous PbO, since at 105° there is always a color change when the water content is reduced to approximately 3.18 per cent. It would seem that the cause and nature of this color change should be investigated further. If the temperature were higher, it might be ascribed to the transformation of yellow to red oxide or to the formation of minium. Glasstone quotes Winkelblech[7] as reporting a loss of

---

[1] *Compt. rend.*, **94**, 1310 (1882).

[2] Wood: *J. Chem. Soc.*, **97**, 878 (1910).

[3] Winkelblech: *Liebig's Ann. Chem.*, **21**, 21 (1837).

[4] Schaffner: *Liebig's Ann. Chem.*, **51**, 175 (1844); Lüdeking: *Am. Chem. J.*, **13**, 120 (1891); Ogata and Kaiun: *J. Pharm. Soc. Japan*, **492**, 75 (1923).

[5] Payen: *Ann. chim. phys.*, (4) **8**, 302 (1866); Mulder: Dammer's "Handbuch anorg. Chem.," **2**, II, 524; Pleissner and Auerbach: Abegg's "Handbuch anorg. Chem.," **3**, II, 677 (1909); *cf.* also Böttger: *Z. physik. Chem.*, **46**, 580 (1903); Lorenz: *Ibid.*, **12**, 436 (1897).

[6] *J. Chem. Soc.*, **121**, 58 (1922).

[7] *Liebig's Ann. Chem.*, **21**, 25 (1837).

0.6 per cent of water at 105° before decomposition started, whereas what Winkelblech actually observed was a decomposition of basic nitrate on heating to some unrecorded temperature, red fumes being evolved and minium being formed.[1]

Lead monoxide occurs in nature in two crystalline forms, litharge and massicot, which are yellow and red, respectively. Hydrous lead oxide precipitated in the cold is white, but heating with 10 per cent alkali converts it to yellow or yellowish-green oxide. If the precipitation is carried out in boiling alkali solution, red anhydrous oxide is obtained. The relationships among the various forms worked out by Ruer[2] may be represented as shown in Table XXIII.[3]

TABLE XXIII

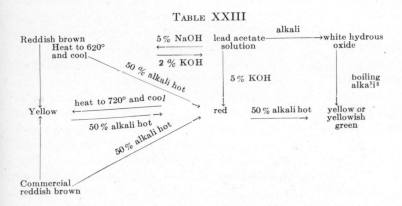

The difference between the two forms of the oxide is commonly attributed to polymorphism, the red being regarded as the more stable form at the ordinary temperature and at all temperatures up to a transition point that has not been determined.[4] This view is supported by the observed differences in crystal structure,[5] density, and solubility[6] of the two forms. The yellow crystals

[1] *Cf.* BURTON: *Dinglers polytech. J.*, **167**, 361 (1863).

[2] RUER: *Z. anorg. Chem.*, **50**, 265 (1906).

[3] GLASSTONE: *J. Chem. Soc.*, **119**, 1689 (1921).

[4] JAEGER and GERMS [*Z. anorg. Chem.*, **119**, 147 (1922)] give 587°.

[5] NORDENSKIOLD: *Pogg. Ann.*, **114**, 619 (1861); LARSEN: *U. S. Geol. Survey Bull.*, **679**, 105 (1921).

[6] GEUTHER: *Liebig's Ann. Chem.*, **219**, 56 (1883); RUER: *Z. anorg. Chem.*, **50**, 265 (1906).

are rhombic, biaxial, and positive in action on polarized light, while the red are tetragonal, uniaxial, and negative in action on polarized light.

Recently, however, Glasstone suggests a closer relationship between the two forms than that of allotropy. He calls attention to the transformation of all red forms to brownish yellow on grinding and all yellow forms to red on heating with concentrated alkali. These observations indicate a close connection between color and size of particles, the large particles appearing red and the small ones yellow. In further support of this view, Glasstone[1] made solubility determinations both gravimetric and electrometric, on eight different preparations varying in color from lemon yellow through reddish brown to red and found approximately the same value, irrespective of the color. Microscopic examinations likewise indicate that the red forms are made up of larger particles, the yellow samples being agglomerates of small particles which are almost identical with the finely divided red forms. These data are misleading, however, as Appleby and Reid[2] succeeded in making well-defined crystals of the two forms which differ not only in crystal structure but in solubility, the yellow being 1.8 times as soluble as the red. Glasstone's products were mixtures, and the constant solubility he observed was the value for the more soluble yellow form. Appleby and Reed's conclusions were confirmed by Kohlschütter and Scherrer[3] who examined the two forms with x-rays and found them structurally different. There is, therefore, no doubt of the polymorphism of lead oxide; but it is not improbable that each crystalline form should show variations in color between yellow and red by varying the size of the particles. Indeed, this is what we find with the two crystalline forms of mercuric oxide;[4] and it is known that grinding red lead oxide crystals changes them to brownish yellow, probably without changing the crystal structure.

[1] *J. Chem. Soc.*, **119**, 1689, 1914 (1921).
[2] *J. Chem. Soc.*, **121**, 2129 (1922).
[3] *Helvetica chim. Acta*, **7**, 337 (1924); *cf.* KOHLSCHÜTTER and ROESTI: *Ber.*, **56**, 275 (1923).
[4] Page 173.

Lead oxide dissolves slightly in dilute alkali but appreciably in concentrated alkali,[1] forming plumbite.[2] The alkali plumbites are strongly adsorbed by cotton. By washing the fiber thoroughly, the salts are hydrolyzed, giving alkali that dissolves out and lead oxide that is retained by the fiber and acts as a mordant.[3]

Although the compound $Pb(OH)_2$ is not known, it is an interesting fact that boiling lead sulfate or chloride with aqueous

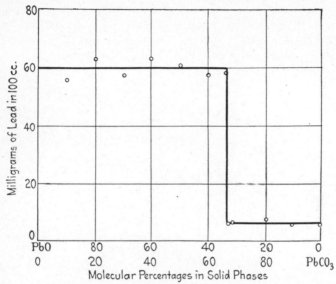

Fig. 14.—Composition of white lead.

sodium carbonate gives $Pb(OH)_2 \cdot 2PbCO_3$, basic lead carbonate or white lead.[4] The same compound is formed by bringing anhydrous PbO and lead carbonate together in a sodium acetate solution. In Fig. 14 are given the results of allowing various mixtures of PbO and $PbCO_3$ to stand in contact with 20 per cent sodium acetate solution at 75° for 12 hours and subsequently analyzing both solutions and precipitates.[5] The diagram shows

[1] BERL and AUSTERWEIL: *Z. Elektrochem.*, **13**, 165 (1907).

[2] HANTZSCH: *Z. anorg. Chem.*, **30**, 305 (1902); HERZ and FISCHER: *Ibid.*, **31**, 454 (1902).

[3] BONNET: *Compt. rend.*, **117**, 518 (1893).

[4] SALVADORI: *Gazz. chim. ital.*, **24**, I, 87 (1904).

[5] HAWLEY: *J. Phys. Chem.*, **10**, 654 (1906).

that PbO and $PbCO_3$ do not form solid solutions but a compound containing 1 mol of the former to 2 of the latter. Water determinations show the formula to be $Pb(OH)_2 \cdot 2PbCO_3$.[1]

Hydrous plumbic oxide and thorium oxide mutually adsorb each other. The former, suspended in water, is carried into colloidal solution by thorium acetate which hydrolyzes to give colloidal thorium oxide; but if an excess of hydrous lead oxide is shaken with a thorium acetate solution, thorium oxide is carried down along with the lead.[2]

HYDROUS LEAD PEROXIDE

Electrolysis of a weak alkaline solution of lead sodium tartrate gives a black lustrous compound reported to be $PbO_2 \cdot H_2O$.[3] The hydrate is also said to form during the electrolysis of a sodium chloride solution in which litharge is suspended.[4] Electrolysis of acid or neutral solutions of lead salts usually gives the anhydrous oxide;[5] but Wernicke reports the formation of lead peroxide with variable quantities of water by electrolyzing dilute solutions of lead nitrate for varying lengths of time. It is probable, therefore, that the so-called monohydrate or metaplumbic acid is really a hydrous oxide. There are well-defined metaplumbates as well as orthoplumbates, however, the latter derived from the hypothetical acid H_4PbO_4 or $PbO_2 \cdot 2H_2O$. According to Bellucci and Parravano[6] the metaplumbates such as $K_2PbO_3 \cdot 3H_2O$ should be regarded as salts of an acid $H_2Pb(OH)_6$, both because of isomerism with the corresponding potassium stannate and platinate and because they cannot be dehydrated without decomposition.

Alkali metaplumbates hydrolyze strongly in water,[7] giving colloidal hydrous lead peroxide[8] together with potassium

---

[1] *Cf.* PLEISSNER and AUERBACH: Abegg's "Handbuch anorg. Chem.," **4**, II, 726 (1909).

[2] SZILARD: *J. chim. phys.*, **5**, 645 (1907).

[3] WERNICKE: *Pogg. Ann.*, **141**, 109 (1870).

[4] Chemische Fabrik. Griesheim-Elektron, German Patent 124512; *Chem. Zentr.*, II, 1101 (1901).

[5] WÖHLER: *Liebig's Ann. Chem.*, **90**, 383 (1854); GEUTHER: *Ibid.*, **96**, 382 (1865); FEHRMANN: *Ber.*, **15**, 1882 (1882).

[6] *Z. anorg. Chem.*, **50**, 107 (1906); *Atti accad. Lincei*, **14**, I, 378, 457 (1905).

[7] PARRAVANO and CALCAGNI: *Gazz. chim. ital.*, **37**, II, 264 (1907).

[8] BELLUCCI and PARRAVANO: *Atti accad. Lincei*, **15**, II, 542, 631 (1906).

hydroxide, a great part of which can be dialysed out without precipitation taking place; but if the dialysis is carried too far, the hydrous oxide gelatinizes on the dialyzer. A sol containing 0.32 gram PbO_2 and 0.008 gram K_2O, that is, 175 mols of peroxide to 1 of alkali, is neutral in reaction and gives no depression of the freezing point of water. It possesses a chestnut-brown color, and is perfectly clear in transmitted light but cloudy by reflected light; it can be diluted, heated to boiling, frozen or evaporated on the water bath without coagulation. By evaporating off the excess water, a jelly is formed which can be repeptized by water; drying the jelly renders it non-peptizable. The sol is negatively charged and is quite sensitive to the action of certain electrolytes, particularly those having multivalent cations. The order of precipitating power of chlorides, beginning with the greatest, is: $Fe^{...}$, $Al^{...}$, $Ca^{..}$, $Sr^{..}$, $Ba^{..}$, $Mg^{..}$, $Cd^{..}$, $Hg^{..}$, $Mn^{..}$, $Ni^{..}$, $Co^{..}$, $Cu^{..}$, $NH_4^{.}$, $Cs^{.}$, $Li^{.}$, $K^{.}$, $Rb^{.}$, $Na^{.}$. The effect of stabilizing ions having the same charge as the sol is quite marked. Thus, potassium salts of AsO_4''', CO_3'', C_2O_4'' and IO_4' do not coagulate the sol; $FeCN_6'''$, ClO_4', ClO_3', MnO_4' Cr_2O_7'', Br', Cl', CNS', SO_4'', NO_3', IO_3', $C_2H_3O_2'$ precipitate it partially; and F', $C_4H_4O_6''$, $Fe(CN)_6''''$, and I' precipitate it completely. The slight stabilizing action of ferrocyanide and tartrate ions is anomalous and should be reinvestigated.

If an alkali solution of PbO_2 is treated with potassium or calcium plumbate, an amorphous orange-yellow powder is obtained which analyzes approximately for $Pb_2O_3 \cdot 2H_2O$[1] after drying over sulfuric acid. It loses only about one-third of its water at 170° but at higher temperatures it can be dried completely, apparently without decomposition. The sesquioxide can be broken up by acids into PbO and PbO_2 and is regarded as a compound of the two, $PbO \cdot PbO_2$ or $Pb(PbO_2)$, lead metaplumbate. Bellucci and Parravano consider the hydrate to be $Pb[Pb(OH)_6]$. Similarly, red lead or minium Pb_3O_4 can be decomposed by certain acids into soluble plumbous salts and PbO_2 and is, therefore, regarded as $2PbO$, PbO_2, or $Pb(PbO_2)_2$ lead orthoplumbate. No hydrate or hydrous form of Pb_3O_4 is reported.

[1] SEIDEL: *J. prakt. Chem.*, (2) **20**, 200 (1879); BELLUCCI and PARRAVANO: *Z. anorg. Chem.*, **50**, 107 (1906).

While the hydrous oxides and the alleged hydrates of lead are not important commercially, the anhydrous compounds are widely used in the arts. Thus, litharge is used in the manufacture of flint glass and as a glaze for earthenware. It is also used in making the very important pigments, white lead and minium, in the manufacture of plates for the lead accumulator, and as a "dryer" in oils. Minium, like litharge, is employed in making flint glass and battery plates, but its widest use is as a pigment. The peroxide has a strong oxidizing action and is frequently employed as an oxidizing agent. The mixture of nitrate and dioxide (oxidized red lead), obtained by heating red lead with nitric acid, is used in the manufacture of lucifer matches.

CHAPTER IX

THE HYDROUS OXIDES OF TITANIUM, ZIRCONIUM, AND THORIUM

The hydrous oxides of titanium, zirconium, and thorium are always described as existing in both an alpha or ortha and a beta or meta modification. In every case the relationship between these two forms is the same as between the so-called α and β stannic oxides whose colloid chemistry has been considered in detail in the preceding chapter. Accordingly, in this chapter will be given but a brief survey of this phase of the chemistry of the hydrous oxides under consideration.

Hydrous Titanium Dioxide

The addition of ammonia or alkali hydroxide or carbonate to a cold solution of titanium dioxide in hydrochloric or sulfuric acid throws down the so-called orthotitanic acid as a voluminous white mass easily soluble in dilute acids. The product forms no hydrates[1] but is a typical hydrous oxide whose water content is determined by the method of precipitation and drying.[2] Dried in the air, the compound gives an x-ray interference pattern indicating its crystalline character.[3] If heated rapidly, the oxide exhibits the glow phenomenon; but as usual, if the heating is slow or the temperature is held for some time below the glow temperature, there is a gradual sintering and loss of surface energy without incandescence.[4]

---

[1] Carnelley and Walker: *J. Chem. Soc.*, **53**, 81 (1888).

[2] Rose: *Pogg. Ann.*, **65**, 507 (1844); Demoly: *Compt. rend.*, **20**, 325 (1845) Merz: *Jahresber.*, 197 (1866); Tuttschew: *Liebig's Ann. Chem.*, **141**, 111 (1867).

[3] Hedvall: *Z. anorg. Chem.*, **120**, 327 (1922).

[4] See p. 79.

Heating the acid solution of titanium dioxide to boiling precipitates the typical betatitanic acid as a white powder. If obtained from hydrochloric acid solution, the oxide cannot be washed without undergoing peptization, forming a positive sol; but the oxide from sulfuric acid solution is not peptized by washing, on account of the precipitating power of sulfate ion. The typical β oxide is distinctly less hydrous than the α; it does not exhibit the glow phenomenon on heating; and it is almost insoluble in acids with the exception of concentrated sulfuric acid.

Hydrous titania is only slightly soluble in alkalies, the solubility varying from 2 milligrams per 100 cubic centimeters in 10 per cent sodium hydroxide to 120 milligrams in 100 cubic centimeters in 40 per cent potassium hydroxide. The statement that $Na_2TiO_3 \cdot 4H_2O$ and $K_2TiO_3 \cdot 4H_2O$[1] can be crystallized from alkaline solution of alkali titanate is obviously erroneous.[2]

The α and β modifications of titanic acid are not chemical individuals but are hydrous oxides differing in the size and physical character of the particles and in the amount of adsorbed water. The soluble highly gelatinous oxide ages gradually at ordinary temperatures[3] and more rapidly at higher temperatures, forming a continuous series of products that approach the character of the granular insoluble β oxide as a limit.[4] This conclusion was confirmed by Morley and Wood by observations on the varying adsorption capacity for dyes[5] and on the varying solubility and peptizability by hydrochloric acid,[6] of the hydrous oxides prepared in different ways. There seems no real justification for assuming, as Morley and Wood do, that the change in physical character of the gelatinous oxide on ageing is due to the formation of complex salt-like condensation products by the molecules of hydrous oxide functioning both as acid and base.

Titanium Dioxide Sol and Jelly.—Graham[7] obtained a sol of hydrous titanium dioxide by dialysis of a 1 per cent solution of

[1] DEMOLY: *Jahresber.*, 271 (1849).
[2] AUGER: *Compt. rend.*, **177**, 1302 (1923).
[3] WAGNER: *Ber.*, **21**, 960 (1888).
[4] LOTTERMOSER: Abegg's "Handbuch anorg. Chem.," **3**, (2), 883 (1909).
[5] *J. Soc. Dyers Colourists*, **39**, 100 (1923).
[6] *J. Chem. Soc.*, **125**, 1626 (1924).
[7] *Phil. Trans.*, **151**, 213 (1861).

the oxide in dilute hydrochloric acid. With more concentrated solutions, jellies are formed on the dialyzer during the purification process. The water in an aged jelly can be replaced by alcohol, ether, benzene, glycerin, or concentrated sulfuric acid in the same way as in the corresponding silica jelly.

More than a century ago, Rose[1] reported the formation of a soft titania jelly. He treated a fusion of titania and sodium carbonate with hydrochloric acid, filtered the solution, and allowed it to stand, whereupon the hydrous oxide aged and precipitated out as a jelly. Later, Knop[2] obtained a jelly in an interesting way: A strong hydrochloric acid solution of magnetic oxide of iron was treated with tartaric acid and then neutralized with ammonia. The iron remained in solution and the titania came down as a white precipitate. On filtering and attempting to wash the oxide, it swelled up in much the same manner as gelatin, forming a colorless transparent jelly which was transformed into a gelatinous precipitate by heating. Recently, Klosky and Marzano[3] prepared firm transparent jellies by neutralizing slowly an acid solution of titanium dioxide with the carbonates of sodium, potassium, or ammonium.

Hydrous titanium dioxide probably finds its most important use as a mordant. If leather or textile goods are immersed in a solution of titanium salt and then steamed, the hydrous dioxide is precipitated. This adsorbs certain dyes forming permanent brilliantly colored lakes. As a mordant for alizarin orange, coerulein and alizarin blue, titania is superior to chrome.[4] For delicate fabrics, titanium salts of organic acids are employed in order to avoid the injurious action of mineral acids. Both trivalent and tervalent salts are used for this purpose.

If anhydrous titanium tetrachloride is sprayed into air, it takes up moisture, giving a dense smoke composed of fine particles of the solid hydrate, $TiCl_4 \cdot 5H_2O$. The chloride was used successfully during the war for producing smoke screens. In case

[1] *Gilbert's Ann.*, **73**, 76 (1823); *cf.* PFORDTEN: *Liebig's Ann. Chem.*, **237**, 213 (1887).

[2] *Liebig's Ann. Chem.*, **123**, 351 (1862).

[3] *J. Phys. Chem.*, **29**, 1125 (1925).

[4] BARNES: *J. Soc. Dyers Colourists*, **12**, 174 (1896); **35**, 59 (1919); HAMMEL: *Ibid.*, **20**, 65 (1904).

the air is too moist, hydrolysis takes place, giving hydrochloric acid and hydrous titanium dioxide which forms a smoke, but with less obscuring power than the chloride hydrate. The cloud may be increased in moist air by the presence of ammonia which forms ammonium chloride. If the air is not quite moist, however, ammonia must be avoided, otherwise the chloride forms an ammonate, $TiCl_4 \cdot 6NH_3$, which has little obscuring power. On this account, it is usually planned to disperse the tetrachloride and ammonia separately.

Precipitated titania makes a particularly good pigment in paints on account of its permanence, great opacity, and non-poisonous nature. It has been employed with barium sulfate in place of zinc oxide, giving a titanium lithopone. Titania paints are not affected by sea water; have no saponifying action on linseed oil; and have more than a third more covering power than white lead paints.

Other Oxides of Titanium

Titanium Monoxide.—The hydrous oxide of divalent titanium is thrown down as a black precipitate by adding hydroxyl ion to a solution of titanous salt. It is very unstable in the air, oxidizing first to blue hydrous titanium sesquioxide and finally to the white dioxide.

Titanium Sesquioxide.—The hydrous oxide of trivalent titanium has been variously described as black, dark blue, cherry red and brown red, depending upon the exact conditions of formation. It is prepared by digesting a solution of dioxide in hydrochloric acid with metallic copper at 20 to 40° until the solution attains a violet-blue color, followed by the addition of ammonia. It is also thrown down directly from titanium trichloride solution with ammonia. If the hydrous oxide is shaken with milk of lime in the presence of oxygen, it is oxidized to the dioxide and at the same time an equivalent amount of hydrogen peroxide is formed. In the same way, when the sesquioxide is oxidized by a solution of chromic acid in the presence of potassium iodide, or by potassium permanganate in the presence of tartaric acid, hydrous titanium dioxide is formed, and simultaneously, oxidation of the potassium iodide or tartaric acid is brought about.[1] These are typical cases of auto-oxidation.[2]

Titanium Peroxide.—The addition of hydrogen peroxide to a neutral or acid titanium solution produces an intense yellow coloration, owing to the formation of a hexavalent titanium compound. Since the color is quite distinct, even in the presence of less than 0.01 per cent of titanium, the reaction affords a delicate test both for titanium and hydrogen peroxide.[3] If gelatinous titania is treated with an excess of hydrogen peroxide, it is converted into yellow titanium peroxide. The latter compound is best obtained by dropping titanium tetrachloride slowly into dilute alcohol; adding a large excess of hydrogen peroxide; and finally treating with ammonia, ammonium carbonate, or alkali.[4] The yellow hydrous oxide adsorbs salts very strongly, and so it is difficult to obtain pure.[5] When freshly formed, the composition can be represented by the formula $TiO_3 \cdot xH_2O$, but on drying over phosphorus pentoxide, it becomes a horny mass containing less oxygen than corresponds to a trioxide. The freshly precipitated hydrous peroxide appears to be considerably more soluble in alkali than the dioxide. This may be due in part to peptization, since the alkali peroxide solutions are instable, depositing an aged granular oxide in the course of a few days. It is usually assumed, however, that the alkali solutions contain alkali pertitanate.[6]

HYDROUS ZIRCONIUM DIOXIDE

The most gelatinous form of hydrous zirconia is obtained by precipitating a solution of a zirconium salt with ammonia or

[1] MANCHOT and RICHTER: *Ber.*, **39**, 320, 488 (1906); MANCHOT and WILHELMS: *Liebig's Ann. Chem.*, **325**, 105 (1902); HABER: *Z. Elektrochem.*, **7**, 441 (1900).

[2] SCHÖNBEIN: *J. prakt. Chem.*, **93**, 24 (1864); TRAUBE: *Ber.*, **26**, 1471 (1893); VAN'T HOFF: *Z. physik. Chem.*, **16**, 411 (1895); ENGLER: *Ber.*, **30**, 1669 (1897).

[3] RICHARZ and LONNES: *Z. physik. Chem.*, **20**, 145 (1896); HABER and GRINBERG: *Z. anorg. Chem.*, **18**, 37 (1898).

[4] LEVY: *Compt. rend.*, **110**, 1368 (1890); *Ann. chim. phys.*, (6) **25**, 433 (1892).

[5] CLASSEN: *Ber.*, **21**, 370 (1888); cf. WELLER: *Ber.*, **15**, 2592 (1882).

[6] MELIKOFF and PISSARJEWSKI: *Ber.*, **31**, 678, 953 (1898); *Z. anorg. Chem.*, **18**, 59 (1898); cf. BILLY: *Compt. rend.*, **172**, 1411 (1921).

alkali hydroxide. The latter is adsorbed so strongly that the former must be employed if a pure gel is desired. This hydrous oxide, the so-called α zirconic acid, bears a marked resemblance to alumina both in its appearance and in its capacity to adsorb water and salts. Like alumina, also, it is almost entirely insoluble in water.[1] When dried at 100°, the gel is reported to be a monohydrate, $ZrO_2 \cdot H_2O$ or $ZrO(OH)_2$;[2] but van Bemmelen[3] showed that the minimum temperature necessary for attaining this composition depends on the previous history of the sample. Thus, the water content of van Bemmelen's gels was not reduced to the point corresponding to a monohydrate until a temperature of 140° or more was reached. Between 140 and 200° the composition was approximately constant. The latter observation might be taken to mean the existence of a definite hydrate of zirconia like the crystalline hydrates of beryllia and alumina. Van Bemmelen found, however, that the adsorption capacity for water and salts, of zirconia containing 1 mol of water was similar to that of hydrous alumina and beryllia and not like that of the crystalline hydrates. He concludes, therefore, that the water in the alleged hydrate of zirconia is adsorbed in capillaries and not chemically combined in the ordinary sense. This view receives strong support from recent investigations of the structure of zirconia sols and gels, using the method of x-ray interference. Haber and his pupils[4] find that hydrous zirconia possesses no crystalline structure whatsoever either when freshly precipitated or when thoroughly dried below 400°. As has been pointed out repeatedly in these pages, hydrous oxides, amorphous when first prepared, usually assume a microcrystalline form on ageing; and all the definitely established oxide-hydrates are crystalline. If zirconia forms an amorphous hydrate, it is an outstanding exception.

When formed in the cold, the hydrous oxide is more gelatinous and more reactive than when formed in the hot. Either preparation heated to approximately 300° glows very brightly, pro-

---

[1] VENABLE and BELDEN: *J. Am. Chem. Soc.*, **20**, 273 (1898).

[2] RUER: *Z. anorg. Chem.*, **43**, 297 (1905).

[3] *Z. anorg. Chem.*, **49**, 125 (1906).

[4] HABER: *Ber.*, **55** *B*, 1717 (1922); BÖHM and NICLASSEN: *Z. anorg. Chem.*, **132**, 1 (1924).

vided the water content is not reduced below 1.9 per cent.[1] If the hydrous mass is heated rapidly above 300°, the glowing is accompanied by small explosions, caused, in all probability, by expulsion of some of the adsorbed water. It is an interesting fact that the oxide retains considerable water even after the glowing. Ruer looks upon the glow phenomenon as a manifestation of the transformation of ordinary zirconia into isomeric metazirconia; but Wöhler[2] showed it to result from a sudden diminution in surface energy accompanying the change from a gelatinous structure to a granular powder.

Ruer prepared an aged hydrous zirconia by boiling down repeatedly a solution of zirconium oxychloride. The sol obtained by this process was precipitated by hydrochloric acid giving what Ruer called a metachloride. After centrifuging out the precipitate, it was peptized in water and thrown down again with ammonia. The hydrous oxide, still containing considerable chloride, was dried over caustic alkali and then heated to 100°, where its water content corresponded approximately to $ZrO_2 \cdot \frac{2}{3}H_2O$. On account of its relatively slight solubility in acids and its failure to glow on heating, Ruer believed it to be an isomeric form of zirconic acid which he designated metazirconic acid. Van Bemmelen found, however, that oxides prepared by Ruer's method lost water continuously without any evidence of the existence of a hydrate. A composition corresponding to Ruer's 100° hydrate was obtained by van Bemmelen at 85°; and, at every observed temperature, the composition showed considerable variation with different samples. Van Bemmelen showed further that Ruer's metachloride was merely an aged zirconia with adsorbed chloride. By evaporating the oxychloride to dryness and replacing the water repeatedly, a product was obtained which retained but a trace of chloride.

Prolonged boiling of hydrous zirconia in a medium possessing a slight solvent action gives a dense structure that is not only less reactive chemically but has a much lower adsorption capacity than the gelatinous precipitated oxide. This change in structure is a gradual process, involving the formation of a continuous series of products intermediate between the typical ortho and

[1] VAN BEMMELEN: *Z. anorg. Chem.*, **45**, 83 (1905).

[2] *Kolloid-Z.*, **11**, 241 (1913).

meta oxides. It is unnecessary to start with zirconium oxychloride to prepare the so-called meta oxide. A sol of the ordinary oxide is aged by boiling, the amorphous particles gradually becoming denser and at the same time tending to orient themselves into crystals.[1]

Zirconium dioxide is the most important compound of zirconium from the technical viewpoint. Its very high melting point, low heat conductivity, low coefficient of expansion, low porosity, and high resistance to corrosion even at elevated temperatures, combine to make it an almost ideal refractory. The only difficulty is that very small amounts of certain materials modify its properties, and the removal of these is very expensive. Thus, iron, which acts as a flux, can be removed entirely only by complete solution of the oxide in hydrofluoric acid. Moreover, the oxide prepared by igniting compounds such as the hydrous oxide or nitrate is a very loose powder that shrinks enormously when highly heated. Accordingly, high-temperature utensils such as muffles, crucibles, etc. must be made from zirconia which has been fused and subsequently ground to a powder. On account of its gelatinous character, hydrous zirconia makes a good binder for holding together the particles of fused zirconia, thus giving a paste that may be molded into the desired shape.

In addition to its use as a refractory, anhydrous zirconia has been used for almost a century in connection with the problems of artificial lighting, because of the brilliant light emitted when it is heated to incandescence. The first Welsbach mantles were made largely of zirconia, but this was later replaced by thoria, since the latter oxide glows at a much lower temperature. It is also employed for coating the lime or magnesia pencils in the Drummond light where it is distinctly advantageous, not only because of the brilliant light it emits but because it does not absorb carbon dioxide or moisture from the air as do lime and magnesia. The Bleriot lamps used for automobile headlights consist of zirconia rods heated to incandescence. Nernst employed rods of pure zirconia in his early attempts to obtain a means of illumination, by use of the electric current, which would be superior to the carbon filament lamp. Later, he obtained a

---

[1] Böhm and Niclassen: *Z. anorg. Chem.*, **132**, 6 (1924).

more intense light with mixtures of the oxides of zirconium, thorium, yttrium, and sometimes cerium.

Prepared in various ways, zirconia is used as a toilet powder, as a polishing powder, and as a substitute for bismuthyl nitrate in the diagnosis of gastrointestinal disease by means of x-rays. For the latter purpose, it is distinctly advantageous because of its non-poisonous character. Zirconia is also used as an opacifying agent in enamels and a clouding agent in glass, instead of the more costly stannic oxide and the poisonous compounds of antimony and arsenic. As a pigment, it possesses good covering power, mixes readily with paint vehicles, is permanent, and is unaffected by hydrogen sulfide, acids, or alkalies.

ZIRCONIUM DIOXIDE SOLS

Hydrolysis of Zirconium Salts.—Biltz[1] dialyzed a solution of zirconium nitrate for several days, obtaining a rather impure sol of hydrous zirconium dioxide which was slightly acid and gave a distinct test for nitrate. The sol possessed a positive charge which was neutralized by the addition of negative sols, the particles of opposite sign mutually precipitating each other.

Ruer[2] dialyzed solutions of zirconium oxychloride both without heating and after heating for 2 hours. Like Biltz's preparation, the sols were clear in transmitted light but cloudy by reflected light. Addition of sodium or ammonium chloride caused precipitation, the amount required being less the more thorough the purification by dialysis. A transparent glass was obtained by evaporation on the water bath. The addition of 10 cubic centimeters of N sulfuric acid to 2.5 cubic centimeters of sol containing 0.015 gram of ZrO_2 gave a precipitate that dissolved in $\frac{1}{2}$ hour provided the solution was not heated before dialysis; the precipitate from the preheated solutions did not dissolve for approximately 6 hours under similar conditions. This decrease in solubility was the manifestation of growth of primary particles which proceeded quite gradually at ordinary temperature but more rapidly at the boiling point. As we have seen, prolonged heating of the oxychloride gave a slightly hydrous mass, insoluble

[1] *Ber.*, **35**, 4436 (1902); **37**, 1100 (1904).
[2] *Z. anorg. Chem.*, **43**, 282 (1905).

in both hydrochloric and nitric acid but readily peptized on washing with water. By dialysis of the so-called metachloride, Ruer obtained a milky white sol which left on evaporation an amorphous white residue instead of a glassy mass. The chlorine content was reduced to 0.026 atom Cl per mol of ZrO_2. On account of the relatively slight adsorption capacity of the particles, the precipitation by electrolytes with univalent anions is readily reversible.

Adolf and Pauli[1] attempted to establish the composition of equilibrium solutions of zirconium oxychloride of varying concentrations up to 0.5 N by observations of the freezing-point lowering, conductivity, and directions of migration under electrical stress, as well as the hydrogen and chloride ion concentrations using the hydrogen and calomel electrodes, respectively. The hydrolysis does not change materially with the dilution. The curves for hydrogen ion and chloride ion concentrations against the concentrations of $ZrOCl_2$ are S shaped and intersect each other at three points, so that, at very low and again at moderate concentrations, the hydrogen ion concentration appears to be greater than that of chloride, indicating the presence of complex ions containing zirconium. The osmotic concentration at the higher concentrations is less than the molar concentration of oxychloride and does not greatly exceed it even at the greatest dilutions. By subtracting from the total conductivity, the conductivity due to the hydrogen and chloride ions present, the conductivity due to the alleged complex zirconium ions is obtained. This appears to constitute a large part of the total conductivity and to vary with the concentration of oxychloride. These observations are explained by assuming the formation of complex cations and anions such as $2[Zr(OH)_4 \cdot ZrOCl_2 \cdot ZrO]^{..}$ and $2[Zr(OH)_4Cl_2]''$. Migration experiments indicate a migration of zirconium to both anode and cathode, more going to the anode than to the cathode when the hydrogen ion concentration exceeds the chloride ion concentration and *vice versa*.

It is very difficult to make head or tail of the conglomeration of facts and speculations given in the preceding paragraph. This difficulty increases when we reflect that Adolf and Pauli's conductivity and electrometric measurements do not give what

[1] *Kolloid-Z.*, **29**, 173 (1921).

they assumed them to give. Leaving out any complex ions, there are in any given solution: undecomposed oxychloride, hydrous zirconium dioxide, hydrogen ions, and chloride ions. The hydrous oxide adsorbs some undecomposed zirconium oxychloride and possibly stabilizes it to a certain degree. It also adsorbs both hydrogen ions and chloride ions in amounts depending on the experimental conditions. The conductivity is due to the unadsorbed ions and to the hydrous oxide particles which have adsorbed ions and which move with a velocity somewhat less than that of the free ions. Thus, the adsorbed ions contribute to the conductance of the solution, but they behave abnormally as regards electrometric measurements. Adsorbed chloride ion gives no test with silver nitrate, and its effect on the calomel electrode will be negligible. To assume that all the hydrogen and chloride ions which do not show up in electrometric measurements exist in complex ions will necessarily lead to erroneous conclusions. Until we know definitely what Adolf and Pauli's conductivity and electrometric measurements actually mean, it seems idle to speculate as to the real nature of solutions of zirconium oxychloride, whether dialyzed or undialyzed. Adolf and Pauli assume the existence of complex ions in sols where the ratio ZrO_2 to Cl is 3 or 4:1. This would seem to be a far-fetched assumption in a sol such as Ruer's, where the ratio is 40:1 or more.

A very satisfactory sol was prepared by Rosenheim and Hertzmann[1] by the dialysis for a week of a 1.5 per cent solution of zirconium acetate. The colloid was perfectly clear in both transmitted and reflected light and contained but a trace of acetate. Heating on the water bath converted the sol into a clear transparent jelly. It was very sensitive to the action of electrolytes, dilute potassium chloride precipitating it quantitatively.

Peptization of Hydrous Zirconia.—Müller[2] prepared sols both by adding freshly precipitated and washed zirconia to a solution of zirconium nitrate and by adding ammonia drop by drop to the nitrate solution until the precipitate first formed just failed to redissolve. Evaporating the sol to dryness gave a gummy residue that swelled in water and was then repeptized. The oftener this process was repeated, the smaller the nitrate content

[1] *Ber.*, **40**, 813 (1907).
[2] *Z. anorg. Chem.*, **52**, 316 (1907).

became. The sols were precipitated by low concentrations of electrolytes containing multivalent anions. Zirconium sulfate like the nitrate, peptizes hydrous zirconia. Hauser[1] showed conclusively that the products of the peptizations are sols and not basic salts, $ZrOSO_4$ and $ZrO(NO_3)_2$, as asummed by Berzelius[2] and Paykull.[3]

Szilard[4] added ammonia to a zirconium nitrate solution and washed the resulting gel thoroughly, using the centrifuge, until complete peptization took place. In this way, a highly purified zirconia sol was obtained which was quite sensitive to the action of electrolytes, carbon dioxide from the air being sufficient to induce coagulation. Szilard[5] also peptized the purified gelatinous oxide with the nitrates of zirconium, thorium, and uranyl, obtaining sols similar to those of Müller.

A zirconia sol of suitable concentration is converted into a jelly by adding enough electrolyte to cause slow coagulation. The jelly can be broken up by shaking, giving a sol which will set again to a jelly; but the process cannot be repeated very often without throwing down a gelatinous precipitate.[6]

ADSORPTION BY HYDROUS ZIRCONIA

On account of its highly gelatinous character, hydrous zirconia possesses a marked adsorption capacity for many substances.[7] The taking up of iodine and ammonia by the hydrous oxide carefully purified by dialysis does not follow the ordinary adsorption rule. Instead, the amount taken up increases with the concentration of the solutions without approaching a constant value, thus indicating the formation of a solid solution. Colloidal solutions of ferric oxide, molybdenum blue, zirconium, and silver are quickly decolorized by shaking with a paste of hydrous zirconia. The blue starch-iodine sol is taken up, giving a blue zirconia gel which is decolorized by heating and becomes blue

[1] Z. anorg. Chem., **54,** 208 (1907).
[2] Pogg. Ann., **4,** 117 (1825).
[3] Ber., **6,** 1467 (1873).
[4] J. chim. phys., **5,** 488 (1907).
[5] J. chim. phys., **5,** 636 (1907).
[6] SCHALEK and SZEGVARI: Kolloid-Z., **33,** 326 (1923).
[7] WEDEKIND and RHEINBOLDT: Ber., **47,** 2142 (1914).

again on cooling, just as the original sol. Colloidal Congo red is strongly adsorbed, giving a blue adsorption compound which is converted into a red salt by warming.[1] The last-mentioned phenomenon has been observed in a number of instances by Wedekind and Wilke.[2] Thus, arsenic acid is adsorbed in the cold by hydrous zirconia; but on standing or boiling, $Zr(HAsO_4)_2$ is formed. A similar thing was observed with phosphoric acid; but adsorption only takes place with the following acids: arsenious, monochloracetic, hydrochloric, and perchloric. Obviously, the tendency to form salts following adsorption is not a question of the strength of the acids. Zirconia gel rapidly catalyzes the decomposition of hydrogen peroxide, especially in concentrated solutions; but the removal of hydrogen peroxide by the gel during very short periods of contact with dilute solutions can be represented by the usual adsorption equation. After prolonged contact, the hydrogen peroxide in solution is almost completely decomposed, but large amounts remain in the gel. Not all the peroxide taken up by the gel can be titrated by permanganate in 8 per cent sulfuric acid. This is taken to indicate the formation of a complex peroxide following the initial adsorption.

The adsorption capacity of hydrous zirconia for certain dyes suggests the use of zirconium salts as mordants[3] and in the preparation of lac dyes.[4] For these purposes the hydrous oxide possesses no properties that are distinctive and so it finds but limited application.

HYDROUS ZIRCONIUM PEROXIDE

A hydrous peroxide of zirconium was first obtained by adding ammonia to a solution containing zirconium sulfate and hydrogen peroxide.[5] Such gels contain both dioxide and peroxide; but Bailey[6] added hydrogen peroxide alone to solutions of zirconium salts, obtaining gelatinous precipitates which analyzed approxi-

[1] *Cf.* BAYLISS: *Chem. Zentr.* **II**, 1095 (1911).

[2] *Kolloid-Z.*, **34**, 83, 283; **35**, 23 (1924).

[3] BARNES: *J. Soc. Chem. Ind.*, **15**, 420 (1896); WENGRAF: *Färber Ztg.*, **25**, 277 (1914).

[4] SCHEURER and BRYLIUSKI: *Bull. soc. ind. Mulhouse*, **68**, 124 (1898).

[5] CLEVE: *Bull. soc. chim.*, (2) **43**, 57 (1885).

[6] *J. Chem. Soc.*, **49**, 149, 481 (1886); *Proc. Roy. Soc.*, **46**, 74 (1890); *cf.* HERMANN: *J. prakt. Chem.*, **97**, 331 (1866).

mately for $ZrO_3 \cdot 3H_2O$ when dried over phosphorus pentoxide at ordinary temperature. The oxide loses oxygen on heating, the composition approaching Zr_2O_5 at 100°. Pissarjewsky[1] obtained hydrous ZrO_3 by electrolyzing a sodium chloride solution in which hydrous ZrO_2 was suspended. Irrespective of the method of preparation, the higher oxide behaves as a true peroxide, giving off oxygen on standing and yielding hydrogen peroxide when treated with dilute sulfuric acid. The gelatinous oxide is fairly soluble in alkali, and perzirconates are said to form.

Hydrous Thorium Dioxide

The ordinary gelatinous form of hydrous thorium dioxide is precipitated by adding ammonia or alkalies to a cold solution of thorium salt. The gel is readily soluble in mineral acids but is insoluble in alkalies. The anhydrous oxide obtained by igniting thorium nitrate, sulfate, or the hydrous oxide is not attacked by acids, whereas that prepared by ignition of the oxalate under suitable conditions is a loose insoluble powder which is rendered soluble by boiling to dryness with hydrochloric or nitric acid. As in the case of zirconia, people have assumed that the product obtained by ignition of thorium oxalate is a meta oxide and that the product of the action of hydrochloric acid, say, is a meta chloride.[2] These assumptions are erroneous, since the chlorine content of the alleged compound varies through wide limits and the solution in water is a typical case of sol formation.

Thoria Sols.—By dialyzing a 14 per cent solution of thorium nitrate for several days, Biltz[3] obtained a dilute, water-clear thoria sol containing a small amount of nitrate ion. This sol is stabilized by preferential adsorption of Th···· and H· ions and so is precipitated by suitable amounts of negatively charged sols. Under the influence of electrical stress, the colloidal particles migrate to the cathode, where they precipitate as a jelly containing bubbles of gas. Müller[4] obtained similar sols containing as much as 15 grams ThO_2 in 100 cubic centimeters by peptizing

---

[1] *Z. anorg. Chem.*, **25**, 378 (1900); **31**, 359 (1902).

[2] Cleve: *Bull. soc. chim.*, (2) **21**, 115 (1874); Stevens: *Z. anorg. Chem.*, **27**, 41 (1901).

[3] *Ber.*, **35**, 4436 (1902); **37**, 1095 (1904).

[4] *Ber.*, **39**, 2857 (1906); *Z. anorg. Chem.*, **57**, 314 (1908).

freshly precipitated and washed hydrous thoria with thorium
nitrate, hydrochloric acid, aluminum chloride, ferric chloride,
and uranyl nitrate. The sols are slightly cloudy, but they can be
boiled without precipitating. The particles in the newly formed
sols are completely amorphous; but the ageing which accom-
panies boiling, results gradually in the appearance of a crystalline structure detectable by x-ray analysis.[1] Evaporating to
dryness gives a glistening brittle varnish-like residue which
swells in water and finally is dispersed into a distinctly opalescent
sol. All of Müller's sols are quite sensitive to the action of
electrolytes, particularly those with multivalent precipitating
ions. By shaking with benzene,[2] the hydrous oxide is precipitated
at the benzene-water interface as a gel containing bubbles of air.

The amount of electrolyte required to peptize a given quantity
of hydrous oxide depends on the history of the sample. Szilard[3]
peptized the fresh oxide precipitated from thorium nitrate solution with ammonia, by thorough washing to remove the excess
of ammonium nitrate. If the oxide is allowed to age even under
water, it is not peptized by washing. As already noted, ignition
of the hydrous oxide renders it non-peptizable; and the oxide
from thorium oxalate is peptized only after boiling to dryness
with a mineral acid, such as hydrochloric. By the latter process,
Bahr[4] first prepared a so-called metachloride which was described
as forming an opalescent solution in water. By repeated evaporation and repeptization in water, Cleve[5] obtained a preparation
containing less than 1 per cent of chlorine. Cleve also observed
the instability of the supposed solutions in the presence of various
electrolytes. Stevens[6] found that the hydrous oxide, ignited
until it is completed dehydrated, no longer forms a "soluble"
chloride with hydrochloric acid. He attributed the observed
variation in the thorium-chlorine ratio in the alleged compounds
to the existence of several oxychlorides.[7] Moreover, the failure

[1] Böhm and Niclassen: *Z. anorg. Chem.*, **132**, 6 (1924).

[2] Winkelblech: *Z. angew. Chem.*, **19**, 1953 (1906).

[3] *J. chim. phys.*, **5**, 488, 636 (1907).

[4] *Liebig's Ann. Chem.*, **132**, 227 (1864).

[5] *Bull. soc. chim.*, (2) **21**, 117 (1874).

[6] *Z. anorg. Chem.*, **27**, 41 (1901).

[7] *Cf.* Wyrouboff and Verneuil: *Compt. rend.*, **127**, 863 (1898).

to obtain a test for chloride with silver nitrate was believed to furnish conclusive proof of compound formation.

All of the observations on thoria gels and sols are readily interpreted in the light of van Bemmelen's[1] investigations on hydrous zirconia. A freshly formed thoria gel is easily soluble in acids and is readily peptized by small amounts of certain acids and salts. On standing, the structure becomes more dense, and the solubility and ease of peptization fall off. Ignition of thorium oxalate under favorable conditions gives a very loose fine powder which can be peptized by acids. To get a product that is completely peptizable, the temperature of ignition of the oxalate must not exceed 700°, and the product thus formed must not be kept at temperatures above 500° for any considerable time. Ignition at very high temperatures causes sintering of the particles so that little or no peptization results, even with the strongest acids. The transformation from the easily peptized gel to the non-peptizable granules is a continuous process which does not involve the formation of definite isomers.

Kohlschütter and Frey[2] showed that peptization of the solid oxide by acids is accompanied by a decrease in the volume of the colloidal system, which is probably to be explained by the porous nature of the oxide. During peptization the electrical conductivity and the titer of the acid decrease, and the presence of thorium salts in the solution can be proved analytically; but peptization and solution do not proceed parallel to one another. The existence of the strongly adsorbed Th···· and H· ions causes the particles to be positively charged. The sol formed with hydrochloric acid is a hydrous oxide containing more or less adsorbed chloride depending on the conditions of formation. Adsorbed chloride gives no test with silver nitrate, and free chloride may not be precipitated owing to adsorption of silver chloride by the hydrous oxide, which prevents agglomeration into particles large enough to settle.[3]

Thorium dioxide finds its most important use in the manufacture of the incandescent gas mantle. For this purpose, the

[1] Z. anorg. Chem., **49,** 125 (1906).

[2] Z. Elektrochem., **22,** 145 (1916).

[3] Cf. HANTZSCH and DESCH: Liebig's Ann. Chem., **323,** 38 (1902); RUER: Z. anorg. Chem., **43,** 85 (1905).

mantle fabric is impregnated with a mixture of the nitrates of thorium and cerium which will yield the oxides in the proportion of 99 per cent thoria and 1 per cent ceria.   On ignition, thorium nitrate expands at least tenfold, but cerium oxide has approximately the same volume as the nitrate crystals from which it is prepared.   Accordingly, the mixture of oxides in the used mantle is highly porous, the ratio of ceria to thoria by volume being about 1 to 999.   The emissive power[1] of pure thoria is relatively low even though it reaches a high temperature in the flame. Ceria, on the other hand, has a high emissive power in the visible spectrum, but the energy of radiation is so great that the temperature of a pure ceria mantle does not rise sufficiently high to give the desired luminosity.   On adding ceria to pure thoria the emissive power is increased but the temperature of the mantle is lowered.[2]   The maximum luminous efficiency is reached when the rise of visible emission due to ceria is just balanced by the drop in the temperature of the mantle caused by the increased radiation.

It is an interesting coincidence that the mixture of thoria and ceria most efficient in catalyzing the combination of electrolytic gas appears to be the same as that which gives the maximum luminous efficiency in the Welsbach mantle.   This means that a higher temperature will be reached and consequently a larger radiation of visible energy by the combustion at the surface of the Welsbach mixture than at the surface of any other thoria-ceria catalyst.[3]   There is no doubt but that surface combustion takes place with the Welsbach mantle and the Drummond light. This is evidenced by the slow decay of the light in the Welsbach mantle and the much more rapid decay of the light in the Drummond light, owing to sintering.[4]   It is not known definitely whether the ceria and thoria form a solid solution as has been suggested;[5] nor is it known just what role the ceria plays in promoting the combustion of electrolytic gas.   Swan[3] suggests that

[1] RUBENS: *Ann. Physik*, (3) **20,** 583 (1906); IVES, KINGSBURY, and KARRER: *J. Franklin Inst.*, **186,** 401, 585 (1918).

[2] PODSZUS: *Z. Physik.*, **18,** 212 (1923).

[3] SWAN: *J. Chem. Soc.*, **125,** 780 (1924).

[4] STEINMETZ: "Radiation, Light, and Illumination," 92 (1909).

[5] WHITE and TRAVER: *J. Soc. Chem. Ind.*, **21,** 1012 (1902).

it may act as an oxygen carrier[1] or may increase the electron emission of thorium and thus bring about a greater ionization of the gases.

Small pencils of the Welsbach mixture of thoria and ceria become brilliantly luminous like the incandescent mantle when heated to a moderate temperature. Lamps of this kind are of use for searchlight and projection lanterns for moving pictures wherever the electric current is not available.

In addition to its use in artificial lighting and as a refractory, thoria has been employed for defining the digestive tract in clinical examinations by means of x-rays.[2] It is also used as a catalyst in the synthesis of many organic compounds. For example both symmetrical and unsymmetrical ketones are prepared directly from monocarboxylic acids;[3] alcohols are converted into ethers and olefines, depending on the temperature employed; and ammonia and alcohols yield olefines and primary amines at 360°.[4]

Hydrous Thorium Peroxide

Hydrous thorium peroxide is thrown down in a gelatinous form by adding hydrogen peroxide to a solution of thorium acetate sulfate or nitrate.[5] The gel adsorbs acids quite strongly; hence, it is very difficult to obtain in a pure state.[6] Wyrouboff and Verneuil attempted to avoid this contamination by carrying out the precipitation in the presence of an excess of ammonia; but under these conditions, the precipitate contained nitric acid resulting from the action of hydrogen peroxide on the ammonia. The peroxide is formed by the action of hydrogen peroxide on hydrous thorium dioxide and also by electrolysis of a sodium chloride solution in which the dioxide is suspended. The latter method of formation indicates that the product is a true

---

[1] Meyer and Anschütz: Ber., **40**, 2639 (1907).

[2] Kaestle: Münch. med. Wochschr., **56**, 919 (1909).

[3] Senderens: Compt. rend., **148**, 927 (1909); Kœhler: Bull. soc. chim., (4) **15**, 647 (1914).

[4] Mailhe: Chem. Ztg., **34**, 1173 (1911).

[5] Wyrouboff and Verneuil: Ann. chim. phys., (8) **6**, 441 (1906).

[6] Lecoq de Boisbaudran: Compt. rend., **100**, 605 (1885); Cleve: Bull. soc. chim., (2) **43**, 53 (1885).

peroxide and not an addition compound of hydrous thorium-dioxide and hydrogen peroxide.

The freshly prepared peroxide appears to be hydrous Th_2O_7, but this is quite unstable, going over on standing to the much stabler ThO_3.[1] Dilute sulfuric acid reacts with it, giving hydrogen peroxide; and strong sulfuric acid gives ozone. Unlike the corresponding compounds of titanium and zirconium, it is not attacked by alkalies.

[1] PISSARJEWSKY: *Z. anorg. Chem.*, **31**, 359 (1902); **25**, 378 (1900).

CHAPTER X

THE HYDROUS OXIDES OF THE RARE EARTHS

The term rare earths is applied to a group of closely related trivalent metals forming basic oxides with oxalates insoluble in dilute mineral acids. The rare-earth group includes scandium, yttrium, and lanthanum, together with all the elements between cerium, atomic number 58, and lutecium, atomic number 71, inclusive. These elements are frequently divided into three families, the basis for the arbitrary classification being the solubility of the double alkali sulfates.[1] The elements of the cerium family, scandium, lanthanum, cerium, praseodymium, neodymium, and samarium, form quite insoluble double sulfates; and the elements of the yttrium family, dysprosium, holmium, erbium, thulium, yttrium, ytterbium, and lutecium, form quite soluble double sulfates. On the border line between these two families are the terbium family elements, europium, gadolinium, and terbium, whose double sulfates are but moderately soluble. The hydrous oxides of the cerium group are the best known and will be considered separately, beginning with hydrous ceric oxide.

The Hydrous Oxides of the Cerium Family

Hydrous Ceric Oxide.—Cerium differs from all the other members of the rare-earth family in forming a definite series of ceric salts derived from the most stable oxide of cerium, CeO_2. It is only as a trivalent metal that cerium exhibits the properties of a typical rare earth.

Hydrous ceric oxide is precipitated as a yellowish highly gelatinous mass by adding ammonia or alkali to a solution of ceric salt. It is also formed by oxidizing hydrous cerous oxide suspended in water, either by the oxygen of the air or by adding an oxidizing agent such as chlorine, bromine, alkali hypochlorite,

---

[1] URBAIN: *Ann. chim. phys.*, (7) **119**, 184 (1900).

or sodium peroxide. Like most gelatinous precipitates, it adsorbs alkali salts and hydroxide strongly and so is best obtained pure by precipitating cold ceric ammonium nitrate with ammonia, allowing the washed precipitate to dry partially, and finally rewashing to remove all ammonium nitrate. The precipitate dried over potassium hydroxide has the formula $CeO_2 \cdot 1.5H_2O$,[1] but it is altogether unlikely that this is a definite hydrate. Indeed, Böhm and Niclassen[2] found the ammonia precipitated oxide to be crystalline, the x-radiogram showing it to be CeO_2. On the other hand, the hydrous gel obtained by dialysis of ceric ammonium nitrate is amorphous. The hydrous oxide gives up a great deal of adsorbed water on standing and is transformed into a fibrous or granular mass. If dried below 120°, it dissolves in acids and alkalies, but the ignited oxide is quite insoluble.[3]

Although the highly dispersed gelatinous oxide free from praseodymium,[4] is white;[5] when calcined at a high temperature, it assumes a citron-yellow color, becoming white or a lighter yellow again on cooling. The tint assumed on ignition depends on the mode of preparation; that obtained by igniting the hydrous oxide is darker than that from the sulfate; but according to Wyrouboff and Verneuil,[6] the tint of neither is definite enough to be described other than as a shade of white. Spencer[7] attributes the yellow color to polymerization, and Sterba[8] suggests that it may be due to a higher oxide. There seems to be no experimental justification for either of these assumptions, and I am inclined to believe that the color assumed on heating is due to coalescence of particles which appear white in a finer state of subdivision. It is well known that zinc oxide is yellow when hot, due to coalescence of particles; but disintegration

---

[1] WYROUBOFF and VERNEUIL: *Ann. chim. phys.*, (8) **9**, 289 (1906); RAMMELSBERG: *Pogg. Ann.*, **108**, 40 (1859); ERK: *Z. Chem.*, (2) **7**, 100 (1871); *cf.*, however, CARNELLEY and WALKER: *J. Chem. Soc.*, **53**, 59 (1888).

[2] *Z. anorg. Chem.*, **132**, 1 (1924).

[3] MENGEL: *Z. anorg. Chem.*, **19**, 71 (1899).

[4] WITT: *Chem. Ind.*, **19**, 156 (1896).

[5] *Cf.*, however, BRAUNER: *Z. anorg. Chem.*, **34**, 207 (1903).

[6] *Ann. chim. phys.*, (8) **9**, 356 (1906).

[7] *J. Chem. Soc.*, **107**, 1272 (1915); MEYER: *Z. anorg. Chem.*, **37**, 378 (1903).

[8] *Compt. rend.*, **133**, 221 (1901); *Ann. chim. phys.*, (8) **2**, 193 (1904).

takes place on cooling, accompanied by a return to the white color. However, a thoroughly sintered mass of zinc oxide remains yellow indefinitely, even on cooling.[1] Similarly, the citron-yellow color of hot hydrous ceric oxide becomes white or light yellow on cooling, depending on the time and temperature of ignition. The oxide has been suggested as a yellow opacifying agent for glass and enamel.[2]

Cerium salts may be used more or less successfully for tanning leather[3] and as a mordant in dyeing cotton.[4] In both of these processes, the hydrous oxide plays an important rôle. By far the most important use to which the oxide has been put is in the manufacture of incandescent mantels. This application has been referred to already, in connection with thorium oxide.

The precipitate of hydrous ceric oxide obtained in the cold by adding sodium peroxide to a solution of cerous salt is reddish brown in color; but on boiling, oxygen is evolved and the color disappears.[5] The red-brown color may be due to a higher oxide of cerium, possibly hydrous CeO_3[6] which is instable at $100°$.

Ceric Oxide Sols.—Hydrous ceric oxide sol is best prepared by dialysis of a solution of ceric ammonium nitrate.[7] The sol may be evaporated to dryness on the water bath, giving a gummy mass which goes into colloidal solution again on shaking with water. There is no evidence of crystal structure in the hydrous oxide formed in this way.[8]

Like hydrous chromic oxide and ferric arsenate, the sol prepared by dialysis of ceric ammonium nitrate sets to a firm jelly if the dialysis is carried too far.[9] This is particularly noticeable

[1] FARNAU: *J. Phys. Chem.*, **17**, 653 (1913).

[2] RICKMANN and RAPPE: British Patent 203773 (1908).

[3] EITNER: *Gerber*, **37**, 199, 213 (1911); GARELLI: *Collegium*, 418 (1912); PARENZO: *Ibid.*, 121 (1910).

[4] MATSCHAK: *Chem. Ind.*, **21**, 150 (1898); WITT: *Ibid.*, **19**, 156 (1896); WAEGNER and MÜLLER: *Z. Farben- u. Textil Chem.*, **15**, 290 (1903); BASKERVILLE and FOUTS: *J. Soc. Chem. Ind.*, **23**, 104 (1904).

[5] MENGEL: *Z. anorg. Chem.*, **19**, 71 (1899).

[6] LECOQ DE BOISBAUDRAN: *Compt. rend.*, **100**, 605 (1885); CLEVE: *Bull. soc. chim.*, (2) **43**, 53 (1885); KNORRE: *Z. angew. Chem.*, **11**, 687, 717 (1897).

[7] BILTZ: *Ber.*, **35**, 4431 (1902).

[8] BÖHM and NICLASSEN: *Z. anorg. Chem.*, **132**, 6 (1924).

[9] FARNAU and PAULI: *Kolloid-Z.*, **20**, 20 (1917).

if the initital concentration of the peptizing agent, nitric acid, falls below a critical value that is determined in part by the presence in the sol of the precipitating electrolyte, ammonium nitrate.[1] Thus a jelly returns to the sol conditions if shaken up with a quantity of fresh undialyzed sol; and the concentration of electrolyte necessary to precipitate the hydrous oxide as a jelly is increased by adding a small amount of nitric acid.

Kruyt and van der Made studied the effect of different electrolytes on the nature of the precipitate, obtaining stable jellies that do not contract in some instances and undergo rapid syneresis or coagulation in others. As shown,[2] this is purely a question of rate of precipitation of the sol, which in turn, is determined by the concentration of added electrolyte. Jellies with almost identical properties should result with any precipitating electrolyte that does not react with the particles, provided the concentration is such as to allow a suitable slow rate of precipitation. The order of concentration of ions necessary for jelly formation in 24 hours is: $Br > ClO_4 > Cl > NO_3 > CNS > I > SO_4 > HPO_4$. Alcohol likewise decreases the stability of the sol and in concentrations of 40 to 50 per cent precipitates it as a jelly.

Like the precipitated hydrous oxide, the primary particles in the sol condition coalesce and lose water more rapidly than is usual with sols of the hydrous oxides. This ageing is readily followed viscosimetrically, since the loss of adsorbed water by the dispersed particles is accompanied by a marked decrease in viscosity. A solution of ceric ammonium nitrate dialyzed short of the appearance of any gel on the dialyzer gives a viscosity-time curve having the general form represented in Fig. 15. This curve is for a sol containing 1.28 grams CeO_2 which was prepared by continuous dialysis for 30 hours of a 6 per cent cerium ammonium nitrate solution. The initial increase in viscosity is a manifestation of gelation; with a relatively strong sol, this may proceed to the point where the time of flow can no longer be measured, followed in the course of a few weeks by a decrease in viscosity until the value of an aged sol is reached. If gelation has already started in the dialyzer before the viscosity measurements are begun, the maximum in the viscosity curve is

---

[1] *Cf.* Kruyt and van der Made: *Rec. trav. chim.*, (4) **42**, 277 (1923).

[2] See p. 26.

missed.   Nor is it observed after the sol has been heated to 50°
which causes rapid ageing, or when the concentration of the sol is
too low to admit of marked coalescence of the hydrous particles.
Thus, the character of a hydrous ceric oxide sol is influenced
to a marked degree by relatively slight variations in the method
of dialysis, concentration, temperature, and time.   The particles
of a heated sol or one aged by long standing in the cold are no
longer sufficiently hydrous to give a jelly on precipitation, at
least in concentrations as low as 1.5 per cent CeO_2.

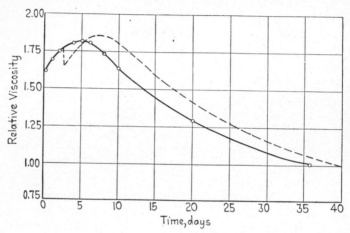

Fig. 15.—Change in viscosity of CeO_2 sols with time.

Farnau and Pauli[1] added to a fresh sol insufficient salt to produce coagulation and observed an immediate drop in the viscosity
of the sol, followed by a gradual increase in viscosity, the final
result being a jelly; with still less salt, the initial diminution in
viscosity was followed by an increase to a maximum and thereafter by a slow decrease as indicated by the dotted curve in Fig.
15. β and γ rays from radium act on the sol in much the same
manner as electrolytes.   Prolonged action produces a firm stable
jelly, while shorter action results in a viscosity-time curve readily
distinguished from the electrolyte curve by a much steeper rise
and fall on opposite sides of the maximum, as shown by the
results of observations of Farnau and Pauli represented in Fig. 16.

[1] *Kolloid-Z.*, **20,** 20 (1917).

The sols used in these experiments contained 0.96 per cent CeO_2 and had already begun to decrease in viscosity when the measurements were started. On the fifth day the sol was subjected, for 13 hours only, to the action of β rays from radium. This brought about a sharp rise in viscosity, which reached a maximum on the twentieth day, followed by a sharp fall. On the fifty-first day the

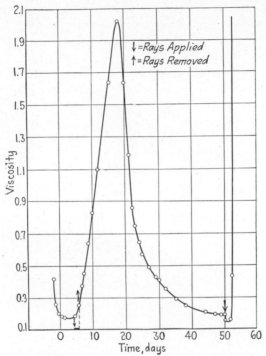

FIG. 16.—Effect of β-rays from radium on CeO_2 sol.

β rays were applied continuously until gelation took place on the fifty-fifth day.

Under the influence of a suitable amount of electrolytes or prolonged action of radiations, the charge on the particles is neutralized. This is apparently accompanied by a loss of adsorbed water and a consequent lowering of the viscosity, gradual under the influence of β and γ rays but immediately when an electrolyte is added. The subsequent increase in viscosity is due to aggregation of the electrically neutral particles forming a jelly. The attainment of a maximum viscosity and the subsequent fall, when the added electrolyte is small in amount or the time of exposure to the rays is comparatively brief, is attributed by Farnau and Pauli to the peptizing action of electrically charged particles entangled in the jelly. Since hydrogen ion is the stabilizing ion of the sol, observations of the changes in the hydrogen ion concentration might throw some light on the anomalous behavior during the ageing process.

Kruyt and van der Made[1] peptized hydrous ceric oxide with dilute hydrochloric acid; but an excess of peptizing agent was required. Wyrouboff and Verneuil[2] decomposed cerium oxalate at as low a temperature as possible and heated the oxide with 2 per cent nitric acid on the water bath. The resulting product, dried at 100°, was assigned the formula $(CeO_2)_{40} \cdot 4HNO_3$. It dissolved in water and on dialysis gave a precipitate that was represented as $(CeO_2)_{40} \cdot 10H_2O$. The soluble product was not a definite compound as Wyrouboff and Verneuil supposed, and the apparent solution was simply an aged CeO_2 sol peptized by nitric acid.

Hydrous Cerous Oxide.—This compound is obtained as a pure white,[3] gelatinous precipitate by treating a cerous salt solution with ammonia or alkali in the absence of air. It oxidizes readily in the air especially in the presence of alkali,[4] the color changing to violet and finally light yellow, owing to the formation of hydrous CeO_2. A similar color is obtained by heating ceric carbonate, nitrate, oxalate, or oxide in hydrogen. As one should not expect a mixture of two light bodies to be violet, the colored body is probably a cero-ceric oxide to which Chase[5] and Meyer[6] assign the formula C_4O_7 or $2CeO_2 \cdot Ce_2O_3$; and Wyrouboff and Verneuil[7] the formula Ce_7O_{12} or $3CeO_2 \cdot 2Ce_2O_3$. The latter

---

[1] *Rec. trav. chim.*, (4) **42**, 278 (1923).

[2] *Compt. rend.*, **124**, 1300 (1897); *Bull. soc. chim.*, (3) **17**, 679 (1897).

[3] DENNIS and MAGEE: *J. Am. Chem. Soc.*, **16**, 649 (1894); DAMIENS: *Ann. chim.*, (9) **10**, 137 (1918).

[4] SPENCER: *J. Chem. Soc.*, **107**, 1265 (1915).

[5] *J. Am. Chem. Soc.*, **39**, 1576 (1917).

[6] *Z. anorg. Chem.*, **37**, 378 (1903); *cf.* STERBA: *Ann. chim. phys.*, (8) **2**, 193 (1904).

[7] *Ann. chim. phys.*, (8) **9**, 289 (1906); *Compt. rend.*, **128**, 501 (1899).

investigators obtained the violet product directly by adding alkali to a mixed solution of cerous and ceric salts, the maximum intensity resulting when the ratio of cerous to ceric ion was 2 to 1.

Hydrous Praseodymium Oxide.—The gelatinous mass of hydrous Pr_2O_3, precipitated from a praseodymium salt by alkalies, is bright green in color and can be dried to a green powder which has, probably erroneously, been assumed to be a trihydrate.[1] If the hydrous oxide, the oxalate, or the nitrate of praseodymium is heated in air, a black powder is obtained, intermediate between Pr_2O_3 and PrO_2;[2] but the exact composition depends on the substance calcined and the temperature of calcination.[3] In the presence of a small amount of CeO_2, which appears to act as an oxygen carrier, the product approaches near the limit PrO_2.[4] It is probable that products of intermediate composition are not definite chemical individuals but are mixtures representing intermediate stages in the oxidation of the lower oxide. In the present state of our knowledge, it is, of course, open to anyone to postulate an intermediate oxide, such as seems necessary to account for the color changes accompanying the oxidation of Ce_2O_3. By adding hydrogen peroxide to a praseodymium salt before precipitating, Braesner[5] claims to get $Pr_2O_5 \cdot xH_2O$.

Hydrous Scandium Oxide.—Alkalies and ammonia precipitate hydrous Sc_2O_3 as a white voluminous mass, insoluble in excess of precipitant. Like hydrous alumina, it is amorphous when first precipitated, but after ageing for some time, an x-radiogram shows a transformation to a crystalline structure. When dried in the air at room temperature, it forms a hard horny mass which analyzes approximately for a trihydrate, $Sc_2O_3 \cdot H_2O$;[6] but there is no definite evidence that such a hydrate exists. By dialyzing a solution of $SnCl_3$ to which ammonia is added short

[1] *Cf.* DAMIENS: *Ann. chim.*, (9) **10,** 181 (1918).

[2] WELSBACH: *Monatsh.*, **6,** 477 (1885); JONES: *Am. Chem. J.*, **20,** 345 (1898); SCHOTTLÄNDER: *Ber.*, **25,** 569 (1892); MEYER: *Z. anorg. Chem.*, **41,** 97 (1904).

[3] SCHÉELE: *Ber.*, **32,** 409 (1899).

[4] JÄGER: *Proc. Acad. Sci. Amsterdam*, **16,** 1095 (1914); MARC: *Ber.*, **35,** 2382 (1902).

[5] *Proc. Chem. Soc.*, **17,** 66 (1901); *cf.* MELIKOFF and KLIMENKO: *J. Russ. Phys.-Chem. Soc.*, **33,** 663, 739 (1901).

[6] CROOKS: *Phil. Trans.*, **209**A, 15 (1909).

of precipitation, a hydrous sol results which sets to a jelly when treated with a suitable amount of electrolyte.[1] Under favorable conditions this jelly is broken up by shaking, forming a limpid sol which will set again on being allowed to stand quietly.[2]

Hydrous Lanthanum Oxide.—The oxide La_2O_3 reacts with water with the evolution of heat like lime, giving a voluminous snow-white powder which has the formula $La(OH)_3$ when dried at $100°$.[3] Although it dissolves slightly in water, the hydrous oxide thrown down by alkalies is almost as gelatinous as hydrous alumina; but the adsorption capacity of the latter for saccharose is appreciably greater.[4] The basic reaction of lanthanum hydroxide is comparable to that of ammonia;[5] hence, the gelatinous oxide absorbs CO_2 from the air and even the ignited oxide is readily soluble in acids. The basicity of the oxide would seem to preclude the formation of lanthanates, although Baskerville and Catlett[6] claim to have prepared complex compounds of this type by fusing lanthana with potassium hydroxide or by digesting the oxide with strong solutions of alkali. Undoubtedly, the products were hydrous lanthanum oxide with adsorbed alkali.[7]

A transparent sol is obtained by peptizing the freshly formed hydrous oxide with a small amount of dilute hydrochloric acid.[8]

Hydrous Neodymium Oxide.—The gelatinous oxide precipitated from a highly purified solution of a neodymium salt is blue and gives blue Nd_2O_3 on ignition. The blue color may be modified by the presence of impurities. By heating neodymium oxalate to a red heat in a stream of oxygen, Waegner[9] obtained a rose-colored product which gave a distinctly different reflection spectrum from Nd_2O_3 and which appeared to be a higher oxide of the formula Nd_4O_7. By suitable choice of conditions, mixed spectra of Nd_2O_3 and the so-called Nd_4O_7 were obtained. Similar observations were made on heating the hydrous oxide

[1] Böhm and Niclassen: Z. anorg. Chem., **132**, 6 (1924).
[2] Schalek and Szegvari: Kolloid-Z., **33**, 326 (1923).
[3] Cleve: Bull. soc. chim., (2) **21**, 196 (1874).
[4] Euler and Nilsson: Z. physiol. Chem., **131**, 107 (1923).
[5] Vesterberg: Z. anorg. Chem., **94**, 371 (1916).
[6] J. Am. Chem. Soc., **26**, 75 (1904).
[7] Cf. Zambonini and Carobbi: Gazz. chim. ital., **54**, 46, 53 (1924).
[8] Böhm and Niclassen: Z. anorg. Chem., **132**, 6 (1924).
[9] Z. anorg. Chem., **42**, 118 (1904).

and the anhydrous nitrate and carbonate. Joye and Garnier[1] claim that the different-colored products are not due to the oxygen content but to the degree of hydration of Nd_2O_3. Thus the hydrous oxide dried in air was taken to be $Nd(OH)_3$; on heating this to 320°, it has a formula corresponding to $Nd_2O_3 \cdot 1.5H_2O$ and gives a reflection spectrum corresponding to that of a similarly colored oxide described by Waegner; on further heating to 520°, the oxide has the composition $Nd_2O_3 \cdot H_2O$ and gives a reflection spectrum identical with Waegner's Nd_2O_7. These data are interpreted to establish the existence of three hydrates of Nd_2O_3 and the non-existence of a higher oxide; but they are not conclusive. Thus, Garnier claims to get the same reflection spectrum by heating the hydrous oxide that Waegner does by heating what he says is an anhydrous salt, thereby precluding the formation of a hydrate. Of course, it may be argued that Waegner's salts decomposed during dehydration, but this cannot be true, at least in the case of the carbonate which gives up all its hydrate water below 200°[2] and does not start to decompose until above 300°. Moreover, the view that the rose-colored product is a hydrate does not fit in with Waegner's observation that gentle heating in a current of hydrogen converts it into clear-blue Nd_2O_3. Obviously, the whole problem should be reinvestigated.

The blue gelatinous precipitate of the hydrous oxide is readily peptized by dilute HCl, forming a beautiful blue sol.[3]

Hydrous Samarium Oxide.—Gelatinous hydrous Sa_2O_3 is almost white with a pale-yellow tinge which is not appreciably intensified on ignition to Sa_2O_3. According to Cleve,[4] if the precipitation with ammonia is carried out in the presence of hydrogen peroxide, a hydrous oxide of the formula $Sa_4O_9 \cdot xH_2O$ results which is similar in appearance to hydrous Sa_2O_3.

THE HYDROUS OXIDES OF THE TERBIUM FAMILY

The hydrous oxides of europium, gadolinium, and terbium are obtained in the same way as the corresponding compounds of

[1] *Compt. rend.*, **134**, 510 (1912); GARNIER: *Arch. sci. phys. nat.*, (6) **40**, 93, 199 (1915).

[2] PREISS and RAINER: *Z. anorg. Chem.*, **131**, 287 (1923).

[3] BÖHM and NICLASSEN: *Z. anorg. Chem.*, **132**, 6 (1923).

[4] *Bull. soc. chim.*, (2) **43**, 53 (1885).

the cerium family, by the action of alkali or ammonia on solutions of their salts. When freshly prepared, the gelatinous oxides rapidly absorb carbon dioxide when exposed to the air. Anhydrous Gd_2O_3 and Tb_2O_3 are white solids, while Eu_2O_3 possesses a reddish-yellow tinge.[1] All of the oxides are soluble in acids; but Gd_2O_3 dissolves very slowly at the start, the velocity increasing as the action proceeds.[2] When terbium oxalate is ignited, it gives a dark-brown peroxide which approaches the composition required for TbO_2. If a mixture of air and coal gas is passed over TbO_2 or a mixture of Gd_2O_3 and TbO_2 heated almost to redness, the whole mass immediately becomes incandescent, and the gas often takes fire.[3]

The Hydrous Oxides of the Yttrium Family

Dysprosium, holmium, erbium, thulium, yttrium, ytterbium, and lutecium all form highly gelatinous oxides when thrown down from their salt solutions with ammonia. Like hydrous alumina, the gels of Er_2O_3 and Y_2O_3 become microcrystalline on standing,[4] and it is probable that the other oxides behave similarly. Ho_2O_3 has a pale-yellow color; Er_2O_3 is rose red; Tm_2O_3 is white with a greenish tinge; and Dy_2O_3, Y_2O_3, Yb_2O_3, and Lu_2O_3 are white. Hydrous peroxides of yttrium $Y_4O_9 \cdot xH_2O$ and of erbium $ErO_2 \cdot xH_2O$ are formed by adding hydrogen peroxide and ammonia to solutions of their respective salts.[5]

On account of the gelatinous character of the precipitated oxides, it is probable that all of them will form sols; but so far only two have been described. Bohm and Niclassen[6] dialyzed a solution of erbium nitrate to which ammonia was added short of precipitation. This sol set to a jelly on adding a suitable amount of precipitating electrolyte. Müller[7] peptized the hydrous oxide of yttrium with dilute hydrochloric acid, aluminum chloride, and ferric chloride; and Szilard[8] employed thorium acetate.

[1] Prandtl: *Ber.*, **55B**, 692 (1922).

[2] Benedicks: *Z. anorg. Chem.*, **22**, 392 (1900).

[3] Bissel and James: *J. Am. Chem. Soc.*, **38**, 873 (1916).

[4] Böhm and Niclassen: *Z. anorg. Chem.*, **132**, 1 (1924).

[5] Cleve: *Bull. soc. chim.*, (2) **21**, 196 (1874).

[6] *Z. anorg. Chem.*, **132**, 6 (1924).

[7] *Z. anorg. Chem.*, **57**, 314 (1908).

[8] *J. chim. phys.*, **5**, 488, 636 (1907).

CHAPTER XI

THE HYDROUS OXIDES OF THE FIFTH GROUP

The elements of the fifth group which form hydrous oxides are vanadium, columbium, tantalum, antimony, and bismuth. These will be taken up in the order named.

Hydrous Vanadium Pentoxide

The addition of a mineral acid to a concentrated solution of an alkali or alkaline earth vanadate throws down V_2O_5 as a red-brown amorphous hydrous mass, closely resembling hydrous ferric oxide. A similar precipitate results from the hydrolysis of vanadium oxychloride.[1] The gel is made up of very fine particles which cannot be washed free from the mother liquor without undergoing peptization. By drying in the air, von Hauer[2] realized a composition approaching that of a dihydrate which was taken to be pyrovanadic acid, $H_4V_2O_7$, analogous to the corresponding phosphorus compound. Continuing the drying over sulfuric acid until another molecule of water is lost, gives the correct formula for metavanadic acid, HVO_3.[3] The exact investigations of Dullberg[4] show, however, that the red-brown gel is not an acid but is hydrous vanadium pentoxide whose water content depends on the condition of drying. The so-called pyro- and metavanadic acids not only do not occur as solids but are incapable of existing in solution, although both pyro- and metavana dates are known. The stronger hexavanadic acid, $H_4V_6O_{17}$ or $6V_2O_5 \cdot 2H_2O$, does exist in dilute solution, but the solid acid is unknown.

[1] Moissan: *Bull. soc. chim.*, (3) **15**, 1278 (1896).
[2] *J. prakt. Chem.*, **80**, 324 (1860).
[3] Fritzsche: *J. prakt. Chem.*, **53**, 93 (1851); Manasse: *Liebig's Ann. Chem.*, **240**, 23 (1887).
[4] *Z. physik. Chem.*, **45**, 129 (1903).

VANADIUM PENTOXIDE SOLS

Biltz[1] treated ammonium vanadate with a dilute solution of hydrochloric acid, obtaining vanadium pentoxide as a brownish-red powder. After thorough washing to remove excess electrolyte, the oxide peptizes completely in water, giving a clear reddish-yellow sol. The colloidal particles are negatively charged and are highly hydrous. Addition of ammonium chloride to a concentrated sol causes it to set to a jelly; while a dilute sol is precipitated as reddish-yellow highly gelatinous flocs that settle very slowly. If the washed oxide is dried before being peptized, the particles in the sol are larger and are precipitated in less voluminous flocs which settle more rapidly. Wegelin[2] prepared vanadium pentoxide by hydrolysis of a boiling solution of $VOCl_3$. This was peptized by washing; but the particles are larger and less hydrous than those in the Biltz sol. When treated with electrolytes, the particles agglomerate into dense clumps that settle out rapidly. The precipitate from a boiled Biltz sol is likewise much denser and darker than from an unboiled sol.[3]

Müller[4] obtained a sol by triturating the granular mass produced by sudden cooling of molten vanadium pentoxide either by plunging the containing vessel of platinum into cold water or by pouring the melt into cold water. Sols formed in this way are reddish brown in color. The precipitation by ammonium chloride is reversible; but the dense brown residue obtained by evaporating the sol to dryness on the water bath is not repeptized by water, whereas the looser yellow mass resulting from evaporation of the Biltz sol is easily repeptized.

Freundlich and Leonhardt[5] peptized an amorphous, ocher-yellow oxide obtained by gentle ignition of ammonium vanadate. This takes up water from air saturated with moisture, the color becoming reddish yellow. The sol formed by triturating with a little water, followed by shaking with an excess of water, is

---

[1] *Ber.*, **37**, 1098 (1904).

[2] *Kolloid-Z.*, **11**, 25 (1912).

[3] Freundlich and Leonhardt: *Kolloidchem. Beihefte*, **7**, 193 (1915).

[4] *Kolloid-Z.*, **8**, 302 (1911).

[5] *Kolloidchem. Beihefte*, **7**, 187 (1915); *cf.* Ditte: *Compt. rend.*, **101**, 699 (1885).

orange yellow in color; but on standing for several days with occasional shaking, it changes to a yellowish red.

The esters of orthovanadic acid are readily hydrolyzed by water, and Prandtl and Hess[1] took advantage of this reaction to prepare "electrolyte-free" vanadium pentoxide sols. For this purpose, the tertiary butyl ester is particularly satisfactory, both because it is a stable salt and because the hydrolysis product, tertiary butyl alcohol, can be removed from the sol almost completely by boiling. The sols are orange when first prepared, but are changed to yellowish red by heating.

While two modifications of vanadium pentoxide have been described—a yellow amorphous form and a red crystalline form—the observations recorded in the preceding experiments indicate that the color is influenced to a marked extent by the degree of dispersion. The most highly dispersed oxide appears yellow, the color changing to reddish brown as the particles become larger and denser. If this view is correct, the reddish crystalline oxide should be yellow if sufficiently finely divided. As a matter of fact, Wegelin[2] prepared a canary-yellow sol by prolonged trituration, in an agate mortar, of red-brown crystals of vanadium pentoxide obtained by allowing the molten oxide to cool slowly. If this sol is coagulated by the addition of a small amount of sodium chloride, the yellow precipitate shows little change of color on keeping; but if a larger amount of sodium chloride is used in the coagulation, the resulting precipitate changes its color in the course of a few days from yellow to reddish brown. This change in color is due to growth of the particles, a process which Freundlich[3] has found to increase rapidly with increasing concentration of electrolyte in contact with a precipitate.

In vanadium pentoxide sols there is always a small amount of the oxide in molecular solution. This portion, yellow in color, passed through a dialyzing membrane and is not thrown down by electrolytes. As the sol is slightly acid, the yellow solution is a vanadic acid, possibly hexavanadic, $H_4V_6O_{17}$,[4] which yields a yellow anion, $[HV_6O_{17}]'''$. The presence of a tervalent anion

[1] *Z. anorg. Chem.*, **82**, 116 (1913); *cf.* RIEDEL: *Pharm. J.*, **92**, 643 (1914).
[2] *Kolloid-Z.*, **14**, 65 (1914).
[3] FREUNDLICH and HASE: *Z. physik. Chem.*, **89**, 446 (1915).
[4] DULLBERG: *Z. physik. Chem.*, **45**, 175 (1903).

which is likely to be strongly adsorbed accounts for the negative charge on the colloidal particles.[1] As might be expected, the solubility determinations of different investigators show wide variations owing to the influence of particle size on solubility. Moreover, the usual measurements made on the supernatant solution after agglomeration of the sol are necessarily wrong, since they fail to take into account the amount adsorbed by the hydrous particles during precipitation.

Optical Properties.—Probably the most interesting property of vanadium pentoxide sol is its double refraction on stirring, a phenomenon first observed by Freundlich and his pupils.[2] If stirred with a glass rod and viewed in reflected light, an aged sol appears to be filled with yellow glittering streaks as if there were fine crystals suspended in it. In transmitted light, the sol remains clear, but dark streaks can be observed. Viewed between crossed nicols, the field remains dark as long as the sol is not disturbed; but stirring causes the field to become bright at once. By allowing the sol to flow between crossed nicols in convergent light parallel to the line connecting the nicols, an image is obtained of a crossed axis with concentric rings. Observed with a quarter-wave mica plate, the flowing sol behaves like a positive uniaxial crystal. Freundlich pictures the sol at rest as made up of elongated particles possessing the usual unordered Brownian movement which can give no double refraction. The setting up of directed motion causes the sol to lose its isotropic nature and to become double refracting. A section cut from the sol may be looked upon as having a space lattice somewhat similar to a plate from an optically monoaxial crystal, the long axis of the sol particles coinciding in direction with the optical axis.

If the sol is rotated between two cylindrical walls and viewed between crossed nicols, four minima of brightness are seen, giving the appearance of a dark cross,[3] the arms of which form an angle with the direction of polarization. The angle is independent

[1] OSTERMAN: *Wissench. u. Ind.*, **7**, 17 (1922); *Chem. Zentr.*, **I**, 396 (1923); *cf.*, however, DUMANSKI: *Kolloid-Z.*, **33**, 147 (1923).

[2] FREUNDLICH and LEONHARDT: *Kolloidchem. Beihefte*, **7**, 207 (1915); DIESSELHORST and FREUNDLICH: *Physik. Z.*, **16**, 422 (1915); FREUNDLICH: *Z. Elektrochem.*, **22**, 27 (1916).

[3] ZOCHER: *Z. physik. Chem.*, **98**, 293 (1921).

of the concentration of sol but increases rapidly with increasing
age of sol and decreases with rise of temperature. In a slowly
moving fresh sol, the angle has the value of 45°, and in a rapidly
moving aged sol, it approaches 90°. This behavior of the
so-called vortex cross has been explained by Freundlich[1] in terms
of the elasticity of the sol.[2] In fresh, slowly moving sols the
elastic deformation of the sol elements is small; and so the sol
behaves like a rigid body and the cross-angle is 45°.[3] In an aged
rapidly moving sol, the angle is close to 90°. From this point
of view, the cross-angle is identical with the angle of maximum
deformation; and the direction of maximum deformation corresponds with the direction of the velocity gradient. Hence,
the colloidal particles do not arrange themselves along the
line of motion because of friction between adjacent liquid layers
of different velocities, but place themselves in the direction of
maximum deformation. Only in an aged sol moving with high
velocity does the direction practically coincide with the direction
of flow, giving a vortex cross with 90° angles.

The double refraction in an aged sol is so strong that it can be
demonstrated by allowing the sol to flow through a prismatic
trough with a triangular cross-section and using this as a prism
to decompose spectrum lines. In this way, the red hydrogen
line is resolved into two oppositely polarized lines. The more
strongly refracted ray vibrates parallel to the direction of flow
of the sol, and in accordance with Babinet's rule, this extraordinary ray is more strongly absorbed than the other.[4]

As already noted, the double refraction is not observed in a
freshly prepared vanadium pentoxide sol. Freundlich[5] investigated quantitatively the influence of age of sol on its double
refraction and found the velocity of ageing at constant streaming
velocity and temperature, to be given by the equation $d\Delta/dt = k\Delta$

---

[1] FREUNDLICH, STAPELFELDT, and ZOCHER: *Z. physik. Chem.*, **114**, 161,
190 (1924); *cf.*, however, MOTTSMITH and LANGMUIR: *Phys. Rev.*, (2) **20**,
95 (1922).

[2] FREUNDLICH and SEIFRITZ: *Z. physik. Chem.*, **104**, 233 (1923).

[3] SCHWESTOFF: *J. phys.*, (3) **1**, 49 (1892).

[4] *Cf.* also HUMPHREY: *Proc. Phys. Soc. London*, **35**, 217 (1923).

[5] FREUNDLICH, STAPELFELDT, and ZOCHER: *Z. physik. Chem.*, **114**, 161
(1924); *cf.* GESSNER: *Kolloidchem. Beihefte*, **19**, 283 (1924).

$(\Delta \infty - \Delta)^2$, where Δ is the double refraction. The magnitude of the velocity of ageing is very sensitive to the action of impurities which may have either a stabilizing or peptizing action on the sol. With rising temperature the anisotropy decreases in a linear fashion. The double refraction of the sol corresponds approximately to that of the vanadium pentoxide content.

Examination of an aged sol with the cardioid ultramicroscope[1] reveals rod-like structures whose length is approximately thirty times the diameter. In a slit ultramicroscope, their axis deviates by less than 30° from a line perpendiculr to the axis of the illuminating beam. Reinders[2] believes the appearance of birefringence on ageing is due to the formation of ultramicroscopic needles, since he succeeded in demonstrating a similar birefringence in sols of mercurous chloride and lead iodide which ordinarily form microscopic crystals. Later, Zocher[3] established the crystalline character of the particles in an aged vanadium pentoxide sol by means of x-radiograms. The interference lines are broad, indicating the very small size of the crystals in the sol; but the arrangement of the lines is the same as observed with crystals obtained by cooling the molten pentoxide. The effect of ageing on the dielectric constant of the sol[4] indicates that the growth of rod-shaped particles during the ageing process is not an ordinary case of crystallization.[5] Freundlich[6] attributes the appearance of double refraction, on adding electrolytes to a benzopurpurin sol, to the development of longer particles by ordered coagulation and not to the growth of needle crystals. Just why we should get ordered coagulation into rod-shaped particles only in certain cases is not obvious.

The phenomenon of streaming double refraction is not confined to sols of vanadium pentoxide, but has been observed with an aged ferric oxide sol, soap solutions, clay suspensions, silver cyanate, and a number of dyes such as benzopurpurin, alizarin,

---

[1] KRUYT: *Proc. akad. Wetenschappen*, **18**, 1625 (1916); *Kolloid-Z.*, **19**, 161 (1916).

[2] *Proc. akad. Wetenschappen*, **19**, 189 (1916).

[3] *Z. physik. Chem.*, **98**, 312 (1921).

[4] ERRERA: *Kolloid-Z.*, **31**, 59 (1922); **32**, 373 (1923).

[5] SZEGVARI and WIGNER: *Kolloid-Z.*, **33**, 218 (1923).

[6] FREUNDLICH, SCHUSTER, and ZOCHER: *Z. physik. Chem.*, **105**, 119 (1923).

and aniline blue.[1] In most of these cases, the double refraction appears to be due in large measure to the anisotropic nature of the particles themselves rather than to the lattice-like arrangement of rod-shaped isotropic particles. On the other hand, with tungsten trioxide sol, the form and size of the particles is the important factor in changing the nature of the Tyndall light, while the anisotropy of the particles is negligible.

Attention has been called to the greater adsorption of the extraordinary ray than of the ordinary ray by a streaming vanadium pentoxide sol. This gives rise to dichroism which may be termed streaming dichroism. When the intensity of transmitted polarized light whose electric victor vibrates perpendicular to the direction of flow of the sol is decreased by allowing the sol to flow, the light appears redder. As a matter of fact, the spectrum of the flowing sol extends from 710 to $582\mu\mu$; while at rest, it extends only to $558\mu\mu$. With parallel electric victor, the light appears yellower when the sol flows, the spectrum extending only to $542\mu\mu$.[2]

Coagulation of Sol. Jellies.—Vanadium pentoxide is quite sensitive to the action of most electrolytes as evidenced by the relatively low concentration necessary to cause clouding of the sol within 5 minutes, the so-called "clouding value," Table XXIV.[3] With but few exceptions the clouding value is lower, the greater the valence of the precipitating ion; but ions of the same valence show the usual large variations from a constant value. The precipitated gel is very readily repeptized by washing, provided the precipitating ions are not too strongly adsorbed.

A sol containing 5 grams V_2O_5 per liter sets to a stiff jelly when coagulated by suitable concentrations of electrolytes. This might be expected in view of the strong tendency of the oxide in mass to adsorb water and swell. A fresh sol contains smaller and more hydrous primary particles and gives a more gelatinous precipitate than an aged sol. It is probable that the relatively rapid coagulation in the presence of electrolytes gives fibrils just as the slow agglomeration during a long interval gives the

[1] ZOCHER: *Z. physik. Chem.*, **98**, 293 (1921); FREUNDLICH, SCHUSTER, and ZOCHER: *Ibid.*, **105**, 119 (1923).

[2] DIESSELHORST and FREUNDLICH: *Physik. Z.*, **16**, 419 (1925).

[3] FREUNDLICH and LEONHARDT: *Kolloidchem. Beihefte*, **7**, 195 (1915).

TABLE XXIV.—CLOUDING VALUE OF VANADIUM PENTOXIDE SOLS

Electrolyte	Clouding value, milliequivalents per liter	Electrolyte	Clouding value, milliequivalents per liter
LiCl	130.0	$Sr(NO_3)_2$	0.562
NaCl	50.0	$BaCl_2$	0.46
NH_4Cl	25.0	$ZnSO_4$	1.68
KCl	17.0	$VOSO_4$	1.26
RbCl	7.7	$Pb(C_2H_3O_2)_2$	0.62
$AgNO_3$	3.7	$CuSO_4$	0.78
Tl_2SO_4	0.51	$HgCl_2$	0.726
Guanadine nitrate	4.0	$Ce(NO_3)_3$	0.039
Strychnine nitrate	0.17	$Al_2(SO_4)_3$	0.00168
$Mg(NO_3)_2$	1.12	$Th(NO_3)_4$	0.0168
$CaCl_2$	0.50		

rod-shaped birefringent particles. Thus vanadium pentoxide appears to possess in high degree the characteristics necessary for jelly formation, and it would be interesting to know the minimum dilution of sol that could be made to form a typical jelly by coagulation.

Hydrous vanadium pentoxide prepared under suitable conditions forms a fine yellow pigment termed vanadium bronze which is employed as a substitute for gold bronze. It is obtained in the form of brilliant scales of a golden or orange color by boiling aqueous sulfurous acid with copper vanadate.[1] It is also prepared by adding a solution of ammonium vanadate to one of copper sulfate containing an excess of ammonium chloride, until a permanent precipitate forms, followed by heating gently to 75°. The slower the precipitation, the finer is the color of the bronze.

The hydrous oxide finds some application as a mordant in the dyeing of cotton and especially in fixing aniline on silk. The anhydrous oxide is an efficient catalyst for the oxidation of certain organic compounds, such as the oxidation of sugar by nitric acid and the oxidation of alcohol by atmospheric oxygen.[2] By

[1] GERLAND: *Bull. soc. chim.*, (2) **19**, 501 (1873); *Ber.*, **10**, 1515 (1877).
[2] MOSER and LINDENBAUM: *J. prakt. Chem.*, (2) **75**, 146 (1907).

heating ammonium vanadate with resin or linseed oil, the pentoxide is obtained in suitable condition to serve as a dryer for linseed oil. This drier produces a smooth tough film; but there is some darkening of the oil.[1]

LOWER OXIDES OF VANADIUM

In addition to the pentoxide, vanadium forms a suboxide, V_2O; a monoxide, VO; a sesquioxide, V_2O_3; and a dioxide, VO_2 or V_2O_4. The last two form hydrous oxides.

Vanadium Dioxide.—When a solution of vanadyl sulfate or chloride is treated cautiously with a cold solution of sodium carbonate, hydrous vanadium dioxide[2] comes down as a greyish-white precipitate soluble in excess of precipitant. The oxide takes up water from the air and must be washed in an inert atmosphere. Dried over sulfuric acid, it is a black amorphous mass exhibiting a glassy fracture when broken. It happens to analyze approximately for $V_2O_4 \cdot 7H_2O$ when dried over sulfuric acid at room temperature and for $V_2O_4 \cdot 3H_2O$ when heated at 100°. These formulas are, of course, purely accidental. Gain[3] claims to have prepared a pale-red crystalline hydrate $V_2O_4 \cdot 2H_2O$ by boiling a solution of the dioxide in sulfuric acid. When kept out of contact with the moisture of the air, it loses its red color, becoming olive green. The two compounds are said to be isomers. The dioxide is insoluble in water but dissolves in both acids and alkalies, forming vanadyl salts[4] and vanadites or hypovanadates,[5] respectively.

Vanadium Sesquioxide.—Hydrous vanadium sesquioxide comes down as a dirty-green flocculent precipitate when an aqueous solution of vanadium trichloride is treated with ammonia.[6] It is extremely unstable in the air, oxidizing to the dioxide very quickly. The hydrous oxide precipitated and washed in an inert atmosphere has been used as the starting point in the

[1] RHODES and CHEN: *J. Ind. Eng. Chem.*, **14**, 222 (1922).

[2] CROW: *J. Chem. Soc.*, **30**, 454 (1876).

[3] *Compt. rend.*, **143**, 823, 1154 (1906); **146**, 403 (1907).

[4] GUYARD: *Bull. soc. chim.*, (2) **25**, 350 (1876).

[5] KOPPEL and GOLDMANN: *Z. anorg. Chem.*, **36**, 281 (1903).

[6] LOCKE and EDWARDS: *Am. Chem. J.*, **20**, 594 (1898); PICCINI and BRIZZI: *Z. anorg. Chem.*, **19**, 394 (1899).

preparation of a number of salts of trivalent vanadium. It functions as a basic oxide only.

Hydrous Columbium Pentoxide

The hydrolysis of $CbCl_5$ or $CbOCl_3$ yields an amorphous white gelatinous mass of hydrous columbium pentoxide. It is also formed by the action of sulfuric acid on a solution of alkali columbate. When dried at room temperature, it is a horny mass; at 100°, it is a white powder which retains varying amounts of water depending on the history of the sample. The oxide is insoluble in water; hence, it must be regarded as a hydrous oxide and not as columbic acid.

Like vanadium pentoxide, the hydrous mass cannot be washed free from the mother liquor without undergoing peptization. It dissolves but slightly in hydrochloric acid, but the residue obtained after boiling with excess acid is easily peptized by water, giving a sol from which practically all the hydrochloric acid can be removed by dialysis. The sol gradually clouds up on standing and is coagulated completely by electrolytes.[1] The oxide thrown down from the hydrochloric acid sol with ammonia is an aged oxide corresponding to the so-called metatitanic acid. It is said to be a definite hydrate, $3Cb_2O_5 \cdot 4H_2O$,[2] but this is improbable.

Hauser and Lewite[3] prepared negative sols of both columbium and tantalum pentoxide by fusing the respective oxides with alkali in a silver crucible, dissolving the melt in water, and dialyzing for 10 to 12 days. Both sols are quite stable, even when heated, but are precipitated by all strong electrolytes except bases which stabilize them owing to preferential adsorption of hydroxyl ion. The two sols differ in their behavior toward carbon dioxide. If the gas is conducted into the tantalum pentoxide sol, complete coagulation takes place in a short time, whereas a sol of columbium pentoxide does not coagulate for a day under the same conditions. The Weiss-Landicker[4] method

[1] Wöhler: *Pogg. Ann.*, **48**, 93 (1839); Marignac: *Ann. chim. phys.*, (4) **13**, 20 (1868).

[2] Santesson: *Bull. soc. chim.*, (2) **24**, 52 (1875).

[3] *Z. angew. Chem.*, **20**, 100 (1912).

[4] *Z. anorg. Chem.*, **64**, 65 (1909).

of separating columbium from tantalum is based on this difference in behavior of the sols. The method is of value only for the qualitative separation and detection of the elements.

HYDROUS TANTALUM PENTOXIDE

Gelatinous tantalum pentoxide is obtained by the hydrolysis of tantalum pentachloride with an excess of water and by treating sodium tantalate with sulfurous or nitric acid. The gel exhibits the glow phenomenon when ignited, unless it has been aged by washing with hot water. A granular hydrous oxide is formed by fusing the anhydrous pentoxide with potassium bisulfate and boiling the resulting mass with water. The compounds prepared in different ways show a variable water content when dried at 100°. Formulas corresponding to hydrates have been suggested[1] for the dried oxide, but recent observations of Jander and Schulz[2] fail to establish their identity. The hydrous oxides investigated by Jander and Schulz were prepared by adding an excess of dilute nitric acid drop by drop to a solution of sodium tantalate of the composition $7Na_2O \cdot 5Ta_2O_5 \cdot 40H_2O$, at 0 and 100°. The voluminous amorphous precipitates were filtered on a membrane filter,[3] washed with large amounts of water, and dried in vacuum over sulfuric acid. The vapor-tension isotherms were determined in the vacuum apparatus described by Zsigmondy.[4] The results recorded in Fig. 17 show a continuous variation in the water content of the oxide with changing vapor pressure of the surroundings, thereby rendering the existence of hydrates improbable. The rehydration and redrying curves are similar qualitatively to those observed by van Bemmelen with the gels of stannic oxide, silica, etc. The hysteresis cycle of the 100° oxide is smaller than that of the 0° oxide and is displaced more toward the side of lower water content. The optical phenomena

[1] ROSE: *Pogg. Ann.*, **100**, 417 (1857); **106**, 141 (1839); RAMMELSBERG: *Ibid.*, **136**, 177, 325 (1869); HERMANN: *J. prakt. Chem.*, (2) **5**, 66 (1872); (1) **70**, 195 (1857).

[2] *Z. anorg. Chem.*, **144**, 225 (1925).

[3] ZSIGMONDY and BACHMANN: *Z. anorg. Chem.*, **103**, 119 (1918); ZSIGMONDY and JANDER: *Z. anal. Chem.*, **58**, 241 (1919); **63**, 673 (1923).

[4] ZSIGMONDY, BACHMANN, and STEVENSON: *Z. anorg. Chem.*, **75**, 189 (1912).

so characteristic of the hydration and dehydration of silica were lacking in the tantalum pentoxide gels; both remained white and chalky under all conditions.

Sols of hydrous tantalum pentoxide are obtained in the same way as the corresponding columbium pentoxide sols already described.   The hydrous oxide is insoluble in water but is slightly acidic in character, dissolving in alkalies with the formation of tantalate.

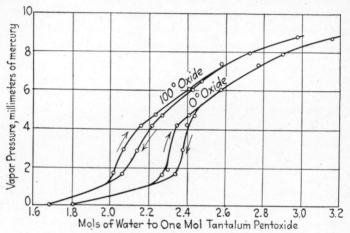

Fig. 17.—Vapor pressure diagram of tantalum pentoxide.

The Hydrous Oxides of Antimony

Antimony Pentoxide.—On account of the position of antimony in the periodic system of the elements, antimony pentoxide is usually supposed to form ortho-, pyro-, and metaantimonic acids: H_3SbO_4 or $Sb_2O_5 \cdot 3H_2O$; $H_4Sb_2O_7$ or $Sb_2O_5 \cdot 2H_2O$; and $HSbO_3$ or $Sb_2O_5 \cdot H_2O$,[1] corresponding to the acids of phosphorus. In addition to these, hydrates containing 4, 4.5, 5, and 6 mols of water per mol of pentoxide have been described.[2]   The oxide is

[1] See FREMY: *J. prakt. Chem.*, **43**, 293; **45**, 209 (1848); HEFFTNER: *Pogg. Ann.*, **86**, 419 (1852); GEUTHER: *J. prakt. Chem.*, (2) **4**, 438 (1871); DAUBRAWA: *Liebig's Ann. Chem.*, **186**, 110 (1877); CONRAD: *Chem. News*, **40**, 197 (1879); SENDERENS: *Bull. soc. chim.*, (3) **21**, 47 (1899); DELACROIX: *Ibid.*, (3) **21**, 1049 (1899).

[2] SENDERENS: *Bull. soc. chim.*, (3) **21**, 47 (1899).

thrown down in a flocculent hydrous condition by hydrolyzing antimony pentachloride in water or antimony trichloride in nitric acid solution; and by decomposition of a solution of potassium pyroantimonate with acids. A survey of the procedures that must be followed to get a composition approximating a hydrate suggests that the so-called ortho-, pyro-, and meta-antimonic acids are, in reality, hydrous antimony pentoxides dried under such conditions that the composition approaches that of the corresponding acids of phosphorus. This conclusion has been confirmed by the observations of Jander and Simon[1] on oxides prepared in a variety of ways. In Table XXV is given the composition of oxides precipitated at different tempera-

TABLE XXV.—COMPOSITION OF HYDROUS ANTIMONY PENTOXIDE

Condition of drying	Mols of water per mol of Sb_2O_5		
	0° oxide	60° oxide	100° oxide
At 15° in air..........................	30.56	9.97	7.91
Over concentrated H_2SO_4..............	3.68	2.17	0.60
At 105°............................	2.43	1.02	0.45

tures and dried under varying conditions. It is quite obvious that the composition is determined by the conditions of precipitation and the method of drying, and that a composition corresponding to a hydrate is purely accidental. This is further emphasized by the unbroken character of the dehydration-velocity-composition curves and the vapor-pressure-composition curves of various preparations. The vapor-pressure isotherms are very similar to those shown in Fig. 17 for hydrous tantalum pentoxide. All the oxides show the characteristic hysteresis region. The 100° preparation exhibits optical phenomena in this region similar to those observed by van Bemmelen with hydrous stannic oxide. At the beginning of the rehydration the oxide is a transparent glassy mass; as more water is taken up, it becomes cloudy and the color changes to brown; on complete hydration, the gel is clear and colorless once more.

Like hydrous stannic oxides, the different antimony pentoxides adsorb alkali salts and phosphoric acid, giving typical adsorption

[1] *Kolloid-Z.*, **23**, 122 (1918); *Z. anorg. Chem.*, **127**, 68 (1923).

isotherms. As would be expected, the loose finely divided 0° oxide has the highest adsorption capacity, and the dense granular 100° oxide has the lowest adsorption capacity for salts as well as water. The hydrous oxides adsorb alkalies from dilute solutions, giving amorphous masses of indefinite composition that have been mistaken for definite antimonates. More concentrated solutions dissolve the oxides, and from these solutions definite crystalline antimonates are obtained.

Alcogels of antimony pentoxide are formed by treating the hydrogels with gradually increasing amounts of alcohol. If maintained over glycerol, dealcoholation curves are obtained similar to those of dehydration.

Hydrous oxides freshly prepared by hydrolysis of antimony pentachloride are peptized by thorough washing, forming instable sols from which an aged oxide gradually separates on standing or heating. Delacroix[1] and Senderens[2] mistook these sols for molecular solutions, and so reported erroneous values for the solubility of Sb_2O_5 in water.

Antimony Trioxide.—Like phosphorus trioxide, antimony trioxide is supposed to form ortho-, pyro-, and metaantimonous acids, H_3SbO_3 or $Sb_2O_3 \cdot 3H_2O$, $H_4Sb_2O_5$ or $Sb_2O_3 \cdot 3H_2O$, and $HSbO_2$ or $Sb_2O_3 \cdot H_2O$, respectively. Clark and Stallo[3] claim to have prepared the trihydrate or ortho acid by the action of sulfuric acid on barium antimonyl tartrate. The addition of mineral acids to tartar emetic yields a hydrous product containing varying amounts of adsorbed tartaric acid and precipitating agent which are difficult to remove by washing.[4] Using alkaline carbonates, acetates, phosphates, and tungstates as precipitants, Long[5] finds the composition to be approximately $Sb_2O_3 \cdot 0.5H_2O$. Schaffner[6] reports the formation of a dihydrate, pyroantimonous acid, by treating an alkali solution of arsenious sulfide with copper sulfate until all the sulfur is removed, and then

[1] *Bull. soc. chim.*, (3) **21**, 1049 (1899); **25**, 288 (1901).
[2] *Bull. soc. chim.*, (3) **21**, 47 (1899).
[3] *Ber.*, **13**, 1792 (1880).
[4] GUNZ: *Compt. rend.*, **102**, 1472 (1886).
[5] *J. Am. Chem. Soc.*, **17**, 87 (1891).
[6] *Liebig's Ann. Chem.*, **51**, 168 (1844); *cf.*, however, SERONO: *Gazz. chim. ital.*, **24**, 274 (1894).

acidifying. Lea and Wood[1] found that the method of Clark and Stallo does not yield orthoantimonous acid but a hydrous oxide of varying composition, depending on how it is washed and dried. Long's method likewise yielded products of varying water content, depending on the temperature of precipitation. The oxide thrown down with mineral acids contains more adsorbed impurities and retains its adsorbed water more strongly than the compound precipitated with alkalies and alkali carbonates. By treating a solution of antimony trichloride in hydrochloric acid with ammonia, a very finely divided hydrous mass is first formed which goes over to the anhydrous oxide on warming. In this respect, its behavior reminds one of hydrous cupric oxide.

Antimony trioxide is insoluble in water but is amphoteric in character, giving antimonous sælts with acids and antimonate with alkalies. Heated in air, the trioxide takes on more oxygen, giving the tetraoxide, Sb_2O_4.

Hydrous Oxides of Bismuth

Bismuth Trioxide.—The most common oxide of bismuth is the trioxide, Bi_2O_3. This is thrown down quantitatively in the cold by alkalies and ammonia as a white flocculent mass, erroneously assumed to be $Bi(OH)_3$ or $Bi_2O_3 \cdot 3H_2O$. If precipitated from chloride or nitrate solution, the hydrous oxide is usually contaminated by oxychloride or nitrate; but if the solution of the oxide in alkali in the presence of glycerin[2] is acidified, the compound comes down in a highly gelatinous form free from basic salt.[3] A pure preparation is said to result also from pouring a solution of bismuth nitrate into dilute alkali[4] and by precipitating an acid solution of bismuth nitrate with concentrated ammonia.[5] The hydrous mass has a composition approximating $Bi(OH)_3$ only when dried in air. When dried at 100°, it is usually assumed to form metahydroxide, $BiOOH$ or $Bi_2O_3 \cdot 2H_2O$,[6]

---

[1] *J. Chem. Soc.*, **123**, 259 (1923).

[2] Löwe: *Z. anal. Chem.*, **22**, 498 (1883).

[3] Thibault: *J. Pharm.*, (6) **12**, 559 (1900).

[4] Prideaux and Hewis: *J. Soc. Chem. Ind.*, **41**, 167 (1922).

[5] Moles and Portillo: *Chem. Zentr.*, **I**, 33 (1924).

[6] Arppe: *Pogg. Ann.*, **64**, 237 (1845); Rupp: *Z. anal. Chem.*, **42**, 732 (1903); Moser: *Z. anorg. Chem.*, **61**, 379 (1909); Prideaux and Hewis: *J. Soc. Chem. Ind.*, **41**, 167 (1922).

but this could not be confirmed.[1]   Apparently the so-called ortho-
and metahydroxides merely represent stages in the continuous
dehydration of a hydrous gel.

A positive sol of hydrous bismuth trioxide results on dialyzing
a dilute solution of bismuth nitrate containing nitric acid.[2]
The sol is but slightly opalescent, is almost neutral, and gives
only the faintest test for nitrate.   A very stable sol is formed by
adding alkali to a solution of bismuth nitrate in glycerin containing Paal's sodium salts of lysalbinic and protalbinic acids.[3]
After purification by dialysis, this sol can be evaporated in
vacuum at 60°, giving a gel that can be repeptized in water.

The hydrous gel precipitated from antimony nitrate solution
with concentrated alkali can be peptized by thorough washing.[4]
The resulting sol is more stable in the presence of sucrose, mannite, glycerin, and lactose.[5]   The last two substances appear to
react chemically with the hydrous oxide.

While the hydrous oxide of bismuth is white, the anhydrous
oxide is yellow when cold and red when hot.   It is used for staining glass and porcelain and for neutralizing undesirable colors
in certain fluxes.

Higher Oxides of Bismuth.—If a current of chlorine is passed
into an alkali in which hydrous bismuth trioxide is suspended, a
reddish powder results which is supposed to be anhydrous or
hydrous Bi_2O_4.   Similarly, highly oxidized products are formed
by the electrolytic oxidation of the trioxide and by the action of
persulfates, hydrogen peroxide, and potassium ferricyanide on
the trioxide in the presence of alkali.[6]   According to Gutbier and
Bünz,[7] none of these reactions gives a definite homogeneous
product.

[1] CORFIELD and WOODWARD: *Pharm. J.*, **113**, 83, 128 (1924).

[2] BILTZ: *Ber.*, **35**, 4434 (1902).

[3] PAAL: *Pharm. Ztg.*, **48**, 594 (1903).

[4] KÜHN and PIRSCH: *Kolloid-Z.* (*Zsigmondy Festschrift*), **36**, 310 (1925).

[5] *Cf.* SEN and DHAR: *Kolloid-Z.*, **33**, 193 (1923).

[6] DEICHLER: *Z. anorg. Chem.*, **20**, 81 (1899); HAUSER and VANINO: *Ibid.*,
39, 381 (1904); RUFF: *Ibid.*, **57**, 220 (1908); MOSER: *Ibid.*, **50**, 33 (1906);
MUIR: *J. Chem. Soc.*, **51**, 77 (1887).

[7] *Z. anorg. Chem.*, **48**, 162, 294; **49**, 432; **50**, 210 (1907); **52**, 124 (1907);
59, 143 (1908).

Worsely and Robertson[1] claim to have obtained the tetroxide pure, by oxidizing the trioxide suspended in dilute alkali and freeing the resulting product from trioxide and alkali by triturating with glacial acetic acid. Two isomeric monohydrates are described, one brown and the other purplish black. Using concentrated alkali and chlorine, a mixture of yellow tetroxide dihydrate and red or brown pentoxide monohydrate is said to form. Ammonium persulfate is said to give some hexoxide. These observations are incomplete if not inaccurate in many respects and should be repeated. It seems altogether unlikely that the alleged hydrates are anything but indefinite hydrous oxides.

Unlike the amphoteric oxides of arsenic and antimony, the oxides of bismuth are not acid forming in character.

[1] *J. Chem. Soc.*, **117**, 63 (1920).

CHAPTER XII

THE HYDROUS OXIDES OF MOLYBDENUM, TUNGSTEN, AND URANIUM

The Hydrous Oxides of Molybdenum

Molybdenum Trioxide.—Molybdenum trioxide forms two and only two[1] crystalline hydrates, $MoO_3 \cdot 2H_2O$ and $MoO_3 \cdot H_2O$. The dihydrate separates at room temperature in yellow crusts from a nitric acid solution of ammonium molybdate such as is used in the estimation of phosphorus. By heating to 40 to 50° a solution of the dihydrate or the solid suspended in water, Rosenheim and Davidson[2] obtained what they called α $MoO_3 \cdot 2H_2O$ to distinguish it from β $MoO_3 \cdot H_2O$ which comes down at 65 to 70°. Both preparations crystallize in fine white needles, but the so-called α oxide differs from the β in forming with water a stable milky suspension or sol and in losing all its hydrate water at a lower temperature. It is probable that the differences between the two preparations are due to variations in the size and physical character of the primary particles thrown down at different temperatures, rather than to allotropy. Doubtless this could be settled by an x-ray study of the crystal structure of the two preparations such as Burger[3] used to establish the chemical individuality of $MoO_3 \cdot H_2O$ and MoO_3.

Graham[4] first recognized the existence of a sol of the trioxide which he prepared by dialysis of a 5 per cent solution of sodium molybdate acidified with a slight excess of HCl. During dialysis this sol behaves like hydrous ceric oxide in settling to a jelly which subsequently liquefies as the dialysis is continued. The sol is very stable toward electrolytes, has a yellow color and an astringent taste, and is acid to litmus. By evaporating in vac-

---

[1] Hüttig and Kurre: *Z. anorg. Chem.*, **126**, 167 (1923).

[2] *Z. anorg. Chem.*, **37**, 314 (1903).

[3] *Z. anorg. Chem.*, **121**, 240 (1922).

[4] *Liebig's Ann. Chem.*, **135**, 65 (1865).

uum over sulfuric acid, a glassy hydrous mass is obtained which is readily taken up again by water.[1] Graham's observations were confirmed by Sabanejeff,[2] Linebarger,[3] and Lottermoser;[4] but Bruni and Pappadà[5] failed to get a sol by dialysis of a nitric acid solution of ammonium molybdate having the composition of the phosphoric acid reagent. Rosenheim and Bertheim[6] likewise claimed that the solutions formed by shaking MoO_3·-$2H_2O$ with water are not colloidal since at every temperature, the oxide possesses a definite solubility. However, such solutions saturated at high temperature do not crystallize out on cooling even when stirred for a long time with crystals of dihydrate. Indeed, a solution saturated at 100° is fortyfold supersaturated on cooling to room temperature. Cryoscopic determinations on such a solution indicate a molecular weight for the trioxide in solution of approximately 600, which is of the same order as Sabanejeff obtained for the Graham sol. This fact, together with the observed high conductivity and high hydrogen ion concentration of the dihydrate solution, led to the conclusion that solutions of $MoO_3 \cdot 2H_2O$, whether prepared directly or by the method of Graham, are not colloidal. This conclusion was called in question by Wöhler and Engels,[7] who demonstrated the heterogeneity not only of Graham's sol but of the nitric acid solution of ammonium molybdate and the aqueous solutions of $MoO_3 \cdot 2H_2O$ saturated in the hot or in the cold. All of these solutions contained particles clearly visible in the ultramicroscope, which were precipitated by the addition of gelatin but not by electrolytes. In the light of their observations, Wöhler and Engels classify the solutions as semicolloidal, since they appear to lie in the borderland between true crystalloidal solutions and hydrophile sols. This disposition of the matter fails to emphasize the important fact that $MoO_3 \cdot 2H_2O$ is soluble to a certain extent and, hence, under different conditions, it may

---

[1] *Cf.* ULLICK: *Sitzb. Akad. Wiss. Wien,* **60,** 302 (1870).

[2] *Ber.,* **23,** 87 (1890).

[3] *Am. J. Sci.,* (3) **43,** 222 (1892).

[4] "Über anorg. Kolloide," Stuttgart, 11 (1901).

[5] *Gazz. chim. ital.,* **31,** I, 244 (1901).

[6] *Z. anorg. Chem.,* **34,** 427 (1903); **37,** 314 (1904).

[7] *Kolloidchem. Beihefte,* **1,** 466 (1910).

be chiefly in solution or chiefly colloidal. A newly formed solution of sodium molybdate acidified with hydrochloric acid will contain more oxide in solution than an old preparation, since ageing brings about an increase in size and a decrease in solubility of the colloidal particles. In all preparations the particles are relatively small and the solution pressure sufficiently large to make the mixture distinctly acid and a good conductor. But a part of the oxide is suspended in the liquid, and this contributes neither to the acidity nor the conductivity of the solution. The lowering of the vapor pressure of such mixtures is due in large measure to the dissolved oxide and not to the suspended particles; hence, molecular weights deduced from cryoscopic measurements under the assumption that all the oxide is dissolved are necessarily erroneous.

Rosenheim heated to 50° a solution containing hydrochloric acid and sodium molybdate in the ratio of 4:1. From this solution there precipitated gradually, a slimy hydrous mass which was readily peptized by water after thorough washing. The particles in this sol are larger and less hydrous than in the Graham sol; and, unlike the latter, it is slightly opalescent and is precipitated in flocs by the addition of solutions of neutral salts and weak acids.

Dimolybdenum Pentoxide.—The hydrous oxide of pentavalent molybdenum is thrown down by adding ammonia to a hydrochloric acid solution of MoO_3 previously reduced with metallic molybdenum[1] or with hydriodic acid.[2] At one time these were thought to be oxides of tetravalent molydenum, but Klason[3] obtained a compound with identical properties by adding ammonia to a dilute solution of $(NH_4)_2MoOCl_5$ in which the molybdenum is pentavalent. The precipitate is distinctly gelatinous; but it is said to have the composition $MoO(OH)_3$ when dried over phosphorus pentoxide. When newly formed, it is very similar in physical character and color to hydrous ferric oxide. Like the latter, it is peptized by thorough washing, forming a clear sol which varies in color from yellow to dark red depending

---

[1] Berzelius: *Pogg. Ann.*, **6**, 366, 389 (1826).

[2] Péchard: *Compt. rend.*, **118**, 804 (1894); *Ann. chim. phys.*, (6) **28**, 537 (1893).

[3] *Ber.*, **34**, 148 (1901).

on the concentration. The sol gives a gelatinous precipitate with electrolytes, but it is probable that it could be precipitated as a jelly since Berzelius obtained a transparent jelly simply by allowing a dark red sol to stand for a month in a closed vessel.

Freundlich and Leonhardt[1] studied the properties of a sol prepared by peptizing the hydrous oxide thrown down with ammonia from a very dilute solution containing pentavalent molybdenum. The precipitate as well as the sol oxidizes to molybdenum blue more readily than Berzelius' preparation, probably on account of the difference in size of the particles. The negatively charged sol agglomerates fractionally on adding electrolytes, and the last traces of sol are thrown down only by relatively high concentrations of multivalent cations that ordinarily precipitate in low concentrations. This behavior is accounted for by the wide variation in the size of the colloidal particles; the larger particles agglomerate first, leaving a very dilute, highly dispersed sol which is not readily precipitated. In this respect, it is like Péan de St. Gilles' ferric oxide sol.[2] Like the latter also, the precipitation is readily reversible when the precipitating ions are weakly adsorbed, and almost irreversible when the precipitating ions are strongly adsorbed.

Molybdenum Dioxide and Sesquioxide.—Although the oxide MoO_2 can be prepared by oxidizing molybdenum or by reducing MoO_3 under suitable conditions, it is claimed that the hydrous oxide or hydroxide of tetravalent molybdenum does not exist, the reported preparations being hydrous pentoxide.[3] Paal and his coworkers,[4] however, claim to have prepared the compound by reduction, at room temperature, of an ammonium molybdate solution with hydrogen in the presence of a little colloidal palladium. By stopping the reduction when the theoretical amount of hydrogen is used up, there is obtained a greenish-black mass which has adsorbed most of the colloidal palladium. If dried under suitable conditions, the composition can be made to approximate $MoO(OH)_2$; but there is no evidence that this is a

[1] *Kolloidchem. Beihefte*, **7**, 172 (1915).

[2] WEISER: *J. Phys. Chem.*, **25**, 672 (1921); **24**, 312 (1920).

[3] KLASON: *Ber.*, **34**, 153 (1901); GUICHARD: *Compt. rend.*, **143**, 744 (1906).

[4] PAAL and BRÜNJES: *Ber.*, **47**, 2214 (1914); PAAL and BÜTTNER: **48**, 220 (1915).

definite hydrate or that all the molybdenum is tetravalent. If the reduction is carried out in the presence of Paal's sodium protalbinate, there results a stable sol, black in reflected light and reddish brown in transmitted light. By a similar procedure Paal claimed to get the precipitated hydrous oxide and sol of trivalent molybdenum. The precipitate is an amorphous black mass[1] which cannot be dehydrated to Mo_2O_3 without oxidation taking place.[2]

Molybdenum Blue.—When a solution of MoO_3 or an acidified molybdate is reduced by hydrogen sulfide, sulfur dioxide, stannous chloride, metallic molybdenum, zinc, or other reducing agent, a deep-blue solution results, which deposits a blue hydrous precipitate known as molybdenum blue. A similar product is obtained by the oxidation of lower oxides such as MoO_2 and by adding a cold dilute solution of MoO_2 in hydrochloric acid to a solution of ammonium molybdate. The last method of formation suggests that the blue compound is a molybdenum molybdate such as $MoO_2 \cdot 2MoO_3$; but much doubt exists as to its composition. Marchetti[3] believes it to be $Mo_3O_6 \cdot 5H_2O$; Guichard,[4] $Mo_5O_{14} \cdot 6H_2O$; Junius,[5] Mo_7O_{20}; while Bailhache[6] and Klason[7] believe there are a number of blues which Klason regards as complex derivations of Mo_2O_5 and MoO_3 analogous to phosphomolybdic acid. The evidence for the existence of different compounds is based largely on analytical differences that are probably of the same order of magnitude as the experimental errors inherent in analyzing a colloidal mass; hence, whether there is an individual blue or a number of related compounds, the composition is known only approximately. Marchetti[8] claims

---

[1] MUTHMANN and NAGEL: *Ber.*, **31**, 2009 (1898); CHILESOTTI: *Atti accad. Lincei*, (5) **12**, II 22, 67 (1903); SMITH and HOSKINSON: *Am. Chem. J.*, **7**, 90 (1885).

[2] GUICHARD: *Ann. chim. phys.*, (7) **23**, 498 (1901).

[3] *Z. anorg. Chem.*, **19**, 390 (1899); MUTHMANN: *Liebig's Ann. Chem.*, **238**, 108 (1887).

[4] *Ann. chim. phys.*, (7) **23**, 498 (1901); BERZELIUS: *Pogg. Ann.*, **6**, 385 (1826).

[5] *Z. anorg. Chem.*, **46**, 428 (1905).

[6] *Compt. rend.*, **133**, 1210 (1901).

[7] *Ber.*, **34**, 153 (1901).

[8] *Z. anorg. Chem.*, **19**, 391 (1899).

to have prepared a crystalline oxide having the formula $Mo_3O_8 \cdot 5H_2O$ by the cathodic reduction of a hydrochloric acid solution of MoO_3 and subsequent evaporation to crystallization. Cryoscopic investigations on a solution of this oxide in water indicate a molecular weight of 460 as compared to 416 for Mo_3O_8. Biltz[1] was unable to confirm these observations, and Koppel[2] questions the existence of a crystalline molybdenum blue.

Biltz prepared a stable sol by reduction with hydrogen sulfide of an ammonium molybdate solution acidified with sulfuric acid, and subsequent dialysis. Dumanski made ultramicroscopic observations on a fairly pure sol prepared in this way and observed submicrons in rapid motion, if the sol was not too dilute; but on high dilution, it appeared optically empty. Dumanski also prepared an electrolyte-free solution by reducing pure MoO_3, suspended in water, with metallic molybdenum. This appeared optically empty in the ultramicroscope, and from the freezing-point lowering, the molecular weight was calculated to be $440(Mo_3O_8 = 416)$. The addition of small amounts of electrolytes caused submicrons to appear. Dumanski concludes, therefore, that very pure molybdenum blue dissolves in water forming a true solution, but the presence of a small amount of electrolyte polymerizes the molecules. Since the blue as usually prepared contains adsorbed impurities, its solutions are colloidal. These observations of Dumanski should be confirmed, for if the facts are as stated, they raise the question of the mechanism of the agglomeration of monomolecular molecules by the presence of small amounts of a variety of electrolytes.

The sol of molybdenum blue, prepared by Biltz's method, is negatively charged and so is precipitated by positively charged hydrous oxide sols of iron, aluminum, chromium, thorium, zirconium, and cerium. Particularly beautiful and stable color lakes with the hydrous oxides of aluminum, thorium, and cerium are formed by the mutual precipitation of the oppositely charged sols.

Sols of molybdenum blue act as a dye bath, imparting a blue color to various fibers. Biltz[3] studied the influence of concen-

[1] *Ber.*, **37**, 1095 (1904).

[2] Abegg's "Handbuch anorg. Chem.," **4**, (2) 626 (1921).

[3] *Ber.*, **37**, 1766 (1904); **38**, 2963 (1905).

tration of sol on the amount of blue oxide taken up by silk, cotton, and hydrous aluminum oxide. The results of these observations are given in Fig. 18. The uniform nature of the curves shows that the colored fibers and lake are "adsorption compounds," the composition of which varies continuously with the concentration of sol. The isotherms of adsorption are very similar to those obtained for organic colloidal dyestuffs such as benzidine[1] and benzopurpurine[2] and for dyes in true

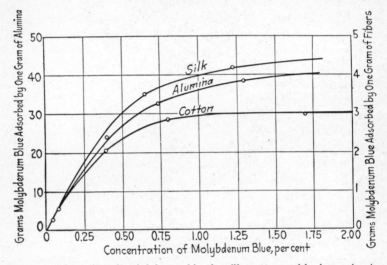

Fig. 18.—Adsorption of molybdenum blue by silk, cotton and hydrous alumina.

solution such as picric acid[3] and Congo red. In view of these observations, there is no longer any question but that dyeing by many organic and inorganic dyestuffs is essentially an adsorption process rather than a chemical process of the usual type, or a solid-solution phenomenon.

With true solutions of dyes, one is not surprised to find a continuous increase in the amount of dye taken up with increasing concentration of the dye bath, in accord with the adsorption isotherm. But in colloidal solutions of dyes, the particles con-

[1] GEORGIEVICS: *Monatshefte für Chemie*, **15**, 705 (1894); **16**, 345 (1895).

[2] FREUNDLICH and LOSEV: *Z. physik. Chem.*, **59**, 284 (1907).

[3] APPLEYARD and WALKER: *J. Chem. Soc.*, **69**, 1334 (1896).

stitute a second phase in the ordinary sense of the term; and it is
not obvious why they should fail to act like a phase of constant
composition instead of the adsorption varying continuously with
the apparent concentration of the bath.   Bancroft[1] has gotten
around this difficulty by accepting with reservations, the physicist
view that, according to the kinetic molecular theory, a suspended
particle should behave like a molecule in true solution.   If this is
true, it will account for the marked similarity in the isotherms of
adsorption for colloidal and molecular solutions.

While recognizing the value, at some times, of treating a
colloidal solution as having some of the properties of a true solution, Bancroft emphasizes the importance of distinguishing
between the two at other times.   In the same way, it is useful
to treat a solid solute as behaving in certain respects like an ideal
gas, but this does not mean either that the solute behaves in all
respects like an ideal gas or that it is an ideal gas.   In most
cases the distinction between true and colloidal solutions can be
made by applying the criterion of Gibbs.   According to Gibbs,
an apparent phase is not a one-phase system unless the properties
are definitely defined when the temperature, pressure, and concentration are fixed.   By applying this test, it may be shown
readily that most colloidal solutions are two-phase systems.
The difficulty comes with solutions of such substances as tannin
and soaps which appear to satisfy Gibbs' criterion for a one-phase
system when in reality they are two-phase systems.   A similar
situation is encountered with a mixture of two gases which in
the last analysis is neither physically nor chemically homogeneous
but which is a one-phase system, nevertheless.   To take care of
these cases, Bancroft assumes that any gas or vapor will pass
through any pore through which any other gas or vapor will
pass.   If this unproved but reasonable assumption is granted,
it leads directly to the conclusion that any substance which can
be filtered out by an ultrafilter is in colloidal solution and not
in true solution, an ultrafilter being defined as a porous membrane
which shows no marked negative adsorption, that is, specific
adsorption of the solvent.   This criterion puts soap and tannin
in the list of colloidal solutions and would undoubtedly take care
of the highly dispersed solutions of molybdenum trioxide and

[1] *J. Phys. Chem.*, **29**, 966 (1925).

molybdenum blue. It should be pointed out, however, that any apparent solution which will pass through the finest ultrafilter is not *necessarily* in true solution.

THE HYDROUS OXIDES OF TUNGSTEN

Anhydrous tungsten trioxide does not combine with water; but an insoluble monohydrate usually known as tungstic acid, H_2WO_4, is formed by precipitating a solution of a tungstate with excess mineral acid at the boiling point. The hydrate comes

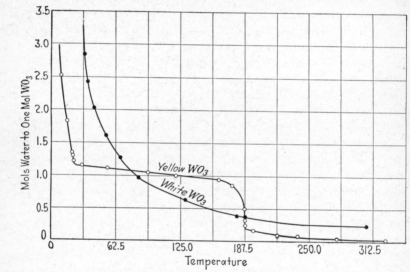

Fig. 19.—Dehydration curves of yellow and white tungsten trioxide.

down as a yellow powder possessing a definite crystalline structure distinctly different from that of WO_3.[1] By carrying out the reaction at low temperatures, the oxide comes down as a white voluminous mass that cannot be washed completely free from adsorbed salts. The white oxide was believed to be $WO_3 \cdot 2H_2O$; but this seems improbable in the light of Hüttig and Kurre's[2] recent investigations of the change in vapor pressure of different preparations with changing temperature, using a spe-

[1] BURGER: *Z. anorg. Chem.*, **121**, 240 (1922).
[2] *Z. anorg. Chem.*, **122**, 44 (1922).

cially designed tensi-eudiometer.[1] The results of observations on both yellow and white preparations are given in the temperature-composition curves reproduced in Fig. 19. The yellow oxide forms one and only one hydrate $WO_3 \cdot H_2O$, and the white voluminous compound is a hydrous oxide, the water content varying continuously with change in temperature. The curve for the yellow oxide is reproducible; but the ease with which the white compound gives up its water is determined by the size of the hydrous particles. Thus, the curve for the very highly dispersed β oxide lies above that for the coarser α oxide throughout the entire range of the investigation. The crystal structure of the white hydrous oxide is apparently different from that of the yellow monohydrate or yellow WO_3. If this be true, it means that the oxide exists in two forms and not that the white compound is a hydrate, as Burger[2] supposed. The white oxide becomes yellow on standing;[3] and the yellow oxide sometimes takes on a greenish color which has been traced to the presence of a lower oxide, possibly W_2O_5.[4]

Graham[5] first prepared a sol of tungstic acid, so called, by dialysis of a 5 per cent solution of sodium tungstate acidified with only a slight excess of dilute hydrochloric acid. On evaporating the sol to dryness, a glassy mass was obtained which could be heated to 200° without losing its sol-forming property. An 80 per cent sol with a density of 3.25 was obtained by peptizing the glassy mass with one-fourth its weight of water. The sol is less stable than the corresponding molybdenum trioxide sol and precipitates out in the form of beautiful quadratic prisms,[6] after standing several months.

The Graham sol cannot be prepared free from alkali, which led Sabanejeff[7] to conclude that it is a solution of a sodium salt of the formula $Na_2O \cdot 4WO_3$. This seems not to be the case, since Biltz and Vegesack[8] found the ratio $Na_2O : WO_3$ to be 2 : 11

[1] Hüttig: *Ibid.*, **114**, 161 (1920).
[2] *Z. anorg. Chem.*, **121**, 240 (1922).
[3] Moser and Ehrlich: *Edel-Erden u.-Erze*, **3**, 49, 65 (1922).
[4] Van Liempt: *Z. anorg. Chem.*, **119**, 310 (1921).
[5] *Pogg. Ann.*, **123**, 539 (1864).
[6] Wöhler and Engels: *Kolloidchem. Beihefte*, **1**, 472 (1910).
[7] *Z. anorg. Chem.*, **14**, 354 (1897).
[8] *Z. phys. Chem.*, **68**, 376 (1910).

in a well-dialyzed sol. Wöhler and Engels[1] confirmed Graham's observations and demonstrated the optical heterogeneity of the preparation. Unlike colloidal MoO_3, the sol is not precipitated by adding gelatin, but an adsorption complex is formed which is thrown down by the addition of a little ammonium chloride. The presence of a small amount of tungsten trioxide in colloidal molybdenum trioxide seems to act as a protective colloid,[2] preventing the precipitation of the latter by gelatin. Similarly, molybdenum trioxide seems to exert a protecting action on tungsten trioxide. As has been pointed out, molybdenum trioxide comes down only very slowly from a strongly acidified molybdate solution in the cold, whereas tungsten trioxide precipitates readily from a strongly acidified tungstate. If a mixture containing a small amount of tungstate and a large amount of molybdate is acidified, no precipitate forms for a long time unless the mixture is warmed, the time required for its appearance at a given temperature being determined by the composition of the mixture. The precipitate is an adsorption complex since the two oxides exhibit a mutual adsorption for each other. The more stable molybdenum trioxide sol adsorbs and so holds tungsten trioxide in colloidal solution until the particles of the latter grow to the point of precipitation, carrying down with them adsorbed molybdenum trioxide.

Although the nature of Graham's dialyzed solutions has been questioned, there can be no doubt as to the colloidal character of the solution of the yellow oxide formed by mechanical disintegration[3] or of the white hydrous oxide peptized by washing. The white oxide always comes down as a gelatinous precipitate when sodium tungstate is treated in the cold with excess acid. The velocity of precipitation and the nature of the precipitate depend on the hydrogen ion concentration of the acid used.[4] Contrary to von Weimarn's theory, Lottermoser[5] found the precip-

---

[1] *Kolloidchem. Beihefte*, **1**, 472 (1910); *cf.* Pappadà: *Gazz. chim. ital.*, **32**, (2), 22 (1902).

[2] *Cf.* Kröger: *Kolloid-Z.*, **30**, 18 (1922).

[3] Wegelin: *Kolloid-Z.*, **14**, 65 (1914).

[4] Lottermoser: *Kolloid-Z.*, **15**, 145 (1914); *cf.* van Liempt: *Rec. trav. chim.*, **43**, 30 (1924).

[5] Van Bemmelen's: "Gedenkboek," 152 (1910).

itate to be more voluminous the slower the rate of precipitation. On washing the gel by decantation, it gradually becomes less voluminous and yellow in color, and finally is peptized completely, forming a yellow very cloudy sol in which the particles appear rod shaped.[1] Lottermoser compares Graham's clear stable tungsten trioxide sol with the latter's clear ferric oxide sol formed in a similar way, and the cloudy tungsten trioxide sol with Péan de St. Gilles' ferric oxide sol. There is some doubt as to whether the comparison is justified. The difference between the two ferric oxide sols is due to a difference in the size and hydrous character of the particles, whereas the tungsten oxide sols may be different chemically. The x-ray investigations which indicate the chemical individuality of white and yellow tungsten trioxide should be confirmed.

Pappadà[2] prepared a very sensitive sol by peptizing the trioxide with oxalic acid and purifying by dialysis; and Müller[3] obtained a sol highly sensitive to electrolytes by diluting with water an alcohol-ether solution of the oxide.

Tungsten Blue.—The first product formed on reducing tungsten trioxide or a tungstate is a blue substance similar to molybdenum blue and known as tungsten blue. It may be formed also by partial oxidation of tungsten dioxide or of the hydrolysis product of tungsten pentachloride and pentabromide. The composition of the blue has been represented by a number of formulas ranging from W_2O_5[4] to W_5O_{14};[5] but the bulk of the evidence indicates that it is a mixture of variable composition and not a single chemical individual.[6] Depending on the method of preparation, the color varies from purple bronze to deep blue; but it is not known whether this is due to differences in composition or physical structure or both.

A sol of tungsten blue is formed by neutralization with ammonia of a solution of metatungstic acid saturated with hydrogen

[1] Diesselhorst and Freundlich: *Physik. Z.*, **17**, 117 (1916).

[2] *Gazz. chim. ital.*, **32**, II 22 (1902).

[3] Van Bemmelen's: "Gedenkboek," 416 (1910).

[4] Chaudrion: *Compt. rend.*, **170**, 1056 (1920); *Ann. chim.*, **16**, 221 (1921); van Liempt: *Z. anorg. Chem.*, **126**, 183 (1923).

[5] Allen and Gottschalk: *Am. Chem. J.*, **27**, 328 (1902).

[6] Wöhler and Balz: *Z. Elektrochem.*, **27**, 406 (1921); Reinders and Vervloet: *Rec. trav. chim.*, **42**, 625 (1923).

sulfide,[1] or by electrolytic reduction of an acidified tungstate solution.[2] In the purification by dialysis, appreciable amounts of the blue substance pass through the dialyzing membrane; the sol remaining has a deep sky-blue color in marked contrast to the slate-blue color of the corresponding molybdenum sol. Like the latter, however, it is negatively charged and is precipitated by electrolytes and positively charged sols. Freshly prepared sols dye silk, cotton, and wool directly, imparting a clear-blue color to the fiber.[3]

The Hydrous Oxides of Uranium

Uranium Trioxide.—Graham[4] first prepared a sol of uranium trioxide by adding potassium carbonate to a uranyl salt solution containing sugar, and dialyzing. The deep orange-yellow colloid was very stable but was readily agglomerated by electrolytes. It is not clear why Graham found it necessary to use sugar in the preparation of his sol, for Szilard[5] found that uranyl nitrate peptizes the oxide directly. To get the oxide in a suitable form, Szilard mixed a solution of uranyl acetate with ether and exposed the mixture to light, thereby obtaining a hydrous violet precipitate[6] analogous to molybdenum blue but having a definite composition U_3O_8. On allowing the thoroughly washed oxide to stand for a day, it oxidized to the yellow trioxide which was suspended in water and added to a hot solution of uranyl nitrate as long as it was peptized easily. The orange-yellow sol was quite stable in the presence of an appreciable excess of uranyl salt; but if too much oxide was added, it agglomerated spontaneously in a form that was not readily repeptized.

It is altogether probable that the sol is a hydrate rather than a hydrous oxide since the anhydrous oxide takes up water at

---

[1] Scheibler: *J. prakt. Chem.*, **80**, 204 (1860); **83**, 273 (1861); Biltz: *Ber.*, **37**, 1095 (1904).

[2] Leiser: *Z. Elektrochem.*, **13**, 690 (1907); Kröger: *Kolloid-Z.*, **30**, 16 (1922).

[3] Biltz: *Ber.*, **37**, 1771 (1904).

[4] *Phil. Trans.*, **151** I, 183 (1861).

[5] *J. chim. phys.*, **5**, 488, 495, 636 (1907).

[6] Aloy: *Bull. soc. chim.*, (2) **25**, 344 (1901); Aloy and Rodier: *Ibid.*, (4) **27**, 101 (1920).

room temperature,[1] forming a dihydrate that is converted into a monohydrate at a temperature of 80° and a water-vapor pressure of 15 millimeters.[2] The hydrate is usually yellow in color, but an orange compound of the same composition is obtained by electrolysis of uranyl nitrate[3] or by suspending the violet hydrous U_3O_8 in water which is subsequently boiled in the air.[4] The anhydrous oxide formed by decomposition of uranyl nitrate is yellow if the decomposition takes place slowly, but red if the decomposition is rapid.[5] It is probable that the variations in color of both the anhydrous and hydrated oxides are the result of differences in physical character of the same compound formed in different ways.

Uranium Dioxide.—Hydrous uranium dioxide is thrown down as a voluminous red-brown mass by adding alkalies or ammonia to a cold green uranous solution.[6] The gel loses water and becomes denser and darker on heating. It is probable that the newly formed hydrous mass would be peptized by washing, since Samsonow[7] obtained a sol by washing the dark hydrous dioxide precipitated during the electrolytic reduction of 50 grams of uranyl chloride in 100 cubic centimeters of 2 N hydrochloric acid. Samsonow's sol when freshly prepared contains small positively charged particles in brisk Brownian movement. The particles grow quite rapidly, however, and within 24 hours most of the oxide settles out.

It is of particular interest that colloidal uranium trioxide appears to catalyze the formation of formaldehyde by the action of sunlight on a solution of carbon dioxide in water.[8]

---

[1] Lebeau: *Compt. rend.*, **154**, 1808 (1912).

[2] Hüttig and Schroeder: *Z. anorg. Chem.*, **121**, 243 (1922).

[3] Oechsner de Coninck: *Bull. Acad. Roy. Belg.*, 222 (1901).

[4] Oechsner de Coninck: *Compt. rend.*, **132**, 204 (1901); *Bull. Acad. Roy. Belg.*, 363, 448 (1904).

[5] Aloy: *Bull. soc. chim.*, (3) **23**, 368 (1900).

[6] Aloy: *Bull. soc. chim.*, (3) **21**, 613 (1899).

[7] *Kolloid-Z.*, **8**, 96 (1911).

[8] Moore and Webster: *Proc. Roy. Soc.*, **87**B, 163 (1913); **90**B, 168 (1919).

CHAPTER XIII

THE HYDROUS OXIDES OF MANGANESE

HYDROUS MANGANESE DIOXIDE

Hydrous manganese dioxide is obtained by the oxidation of a manganous salt with such oxidizing agents as permanganate, hypochlorite, chlorate, ammonium persulfate, nitric acid, and ozone. It is also obtained by hydrolysis of a salt of tetravalent manganese and by reduction of permanganate by hydrogen peroxide, glycerin, dextrose, potassium oxalate, etc. It is difficult, if not impossible, to obtain the hydrous oxide in a pure form, partly on account of its tendency to lose a portion of its oxygen giving mixtures of MnO and MnO_2[1] and partly because of its high adsorption capacity.

While definite hydrates of precipitated manganese dioxide have been described, the composition was found by van Bemmelen[2] to be indefinite, depending on the physical character, age, and conditions of drying the sample. Two widely different preparations were studied by van Bemmelen, one the ordinary black compound precipitated from a solution of manganous salt by alkali hypochlorite, and a second red variety obtained by hydrolysis of $Mn(SO_4)_2$.[3] The red oxide is much more finely divided than the black and possesses a much higher adsorption capacity for water and dissolved electrolytes. Both oxides show a strong tendency to adsorb hydroxyl ion. This is evidenced by the fact that dilute solutions of alkali peptize the gel forming a stable negative sol. Moreover, neutral salts such as potassium sulfate, chloride, and nitrate are hydrolyzed by the gel

---

[1] WRIGHT and MENKE: *J. Chem. Soc.*, **37**, 25 (1880); GOOCH and AUSTIN: *Am. J. Sci.*, (4) **5**, 260 (1898); GORGEU: *Compt. rend.*, **110**, 1134 (1890); VON KNORRE: *Z. angew. Chem.*, **14**, 1149 (1901).

[2] *J. prakt. chem.*, (2) **23**, 324, 379 (1881).

[3] FREMY: *Compt. rend.*, **82**, 475, 1231 (1876).

owing to stronger adsorption of base than of acid, the hydrolytic decomposition being more complete when the salt solutions are dilute. Thus, 65 per cent of the potassium present in a 0.0025 N solution of potassium sulfate is adsorbed by the hydrous oxide but only 6 per cent of that from a 0.1 N solution. The total amount adsorbed, however, increases with increasing concentration of salt.[1] This behavior accounts for Gorgeu's[2] observation that solutions of both alkali and alkaline earth salts become acid when brought in contact with the hydrous oxide. In view of this marked adsorption capacity for alkalies, it is probable that the so-called manganites[3] formed by precipitating hydrous manganese dioxide in the presence of basic oxides, are not definite compounds. In favor of this conclusion, it may be pointed out that the composition is determined by such variable factors as the physical character of the hydrous mass, the concentration of alkali, and the method of washing the precipitate.

Manganese Dioxide Sols.—As previously mentioned, van Bemmelen[4] observed the ease with which hydrous manganese dioxide is peptized by dilute alkali. He also noted that the precipitated oxide is more or less completely peptized by washing out the excess of adsorbed alkali or salt. The voluminous red oxide is very readily peptized by washing, forming a clear-brown sol that is quite sensitive to the action of electrolytes.

The most satisfactory method of preparing the sol consists in reducing potassium permanganate under such conditions that the precipitation concentration of no electrolyte in the solution is exceeded. The solution becomes alkaline during the reduction; but, as already noted, an appreciable concentration of hydroxyl ion is favorable to sol formation. Reducing agents that have been employed successfully are hydrogen peroxide, sodium thiosulfate, arsenious acid, reducing sugars, and ammonia.

---

[1] HÜMMELCHEN and KAPPEN: *Z. Pflanzenernähr. Düngung*, **3A**, 289 (1924); *Chem. Abstracts*, **19**, 1800 (1925).

[2] *Ann. chim. phys.*, (3) **66**, 155 (1862).

[3] ROUSSEAU: *Compt. rend.*, **104**, 780, 1796 (1887); **114**, 72 (1892); SOLSTEIN: *Pharm. Ztg.*, **32**, 659 (1887); STINGL and MARAWSKI: *J. prakt. Chem.*, (2) **18**, 86 (1878); GLÄSER: *Monatshefte für Chemie*, **6**, 329 (1885); **7**, 651 (1886).

[4] *Cf.* also GORGEU: *Ann. chim. phys.*, (3) **66**, 154 (1862); SPRING: *Ber.*, **16**, 1142 (1883); SPRING and DE BOECK: *Bull. soc. chim.*, (2) **48**, 170 (1867).

Swiontkowski[1] first reported the formation of a coffee-colored sol of manganese dioxide by reducing a solution of $KMnO_4$ with pure neutral hydrogen peroxide. According to Bredig and Marck,[2] a satisfactory sol results if a dilute hydrogen peroxide solution is added slowly with constant shaking to a potassium permanganate solution no stronger than $M/10$ until the color of the permanganate just disappears. By dialysis with conductivity water, the conductivity of the sol may be reduced to that of ordinary distilled water. A dilute sol is clear yellow in color, changing to dark brown as the concentration increases. If not too concentrated, the sol can be kept indefinitely without precipitating; but it is very sensitive to the action of electrolytes with the exception of potassium hydroxide and permanganate.

Bredig and Marck made a quantitative study of the catalytic decomposition of hydrogen peroxide by colloidal manganese dioxide. The reaction is of the first order, but in most cases the constant increases as the decomposition progresses, possibly owing to the formation and subsequent decomposition of a hydrogen peroxide salt during the course of the reaction.[3] In alkaline solution, the velocity of decomposition increases to a maximum with increasing concentration of hydroxyl and then falls off just as Bredig found with colloidal metals. The catalytic activity of the oxide is increased by heating the sol for ½ hour, but prolonged heating causes precipitation. The presence of gelatin increases the stability of the sol and raises its catalytic activity slightly. Low concentrations of substances like hydrogen sulfide, potassium cyanide, and carbon dioxide which have a marked poisoning action on a platinum catalyst, are without effect on manganese dioxide. On the other hand, phosphorus, its oxidation products, and sodium phosphate cut down the catalytic activity of the oxide, and mercuric chloride and potassium fluoride increase it.

A mixture of perborate and permanganate may be added to bath water to make what is known as an "oxygen bath." The reaction in solution gives hydrogen peroxide and colloidal manganese dioxide, and the latter catalyzes the decomposition of

---

[1] *Liebig's Ann. Chem.*, **141**, 205 (1867).

[2] Van Bemmelen's: "Gedenkboek,"'342 (1910).

[3] *Cf.*, however, LOTTERMOSER and LEHMANN: *Kolloid-Z.*, **29**, 250 (1921).

former, setting free oxygen which forms a supersaturated solution in the water and is subsequently evolved in small bubbles on the skin of the bather. The presence of electrolytes in the bath water was found to have such a marked effect on the rate of evolution of oxygen that Lottermoser[1] investigated quantitatively the influence of various alkalies and salts on the decomposition of hydrogen peroxide by manganese dioxide. The impurity was added to the peroxide solution, after which the catalyst was prepared directly in the solution by adding permanganate and base in the order named. With salts of a common anion, different cations influenced the decomposition in the order $Ba^{..} > Sr^{..} > Ca^{..} - > Na^{.} > K^{.} > Li^{.}$, barium ion accelerating it the most and lithium ion retarding it the most. Unfortunately, Lottermoser did not inquire into the reason for the accelerating action of certain electrolytes and the inhibiting action of others; but it is probable that this is very closely related to the adsorbability of the cations and to the variation in physical character of the hydrous particles formed in the presence of different electrolytes. $Mg^{..}$ and $NH_4^{.}$ ions were found to have a marked retarding action by cutting down the concentration of hydroxyl ion. For preparing a satisfactory oxygen bath, it is obviously necessary to avoid waters containing magnesium salts.

The reduction of permanganate by arsenious acid was shown by Deisz[2] to give a very stable sol, particularly if it is not subjected to dialysis. If evaporated to dryness over sulfuric acid, a residue is obtained which is again converted into a sol by shaking with water. If a bit of sol is allowed to drop into still water, beautiful vortex rings are formed. The first ring increases to a certain size and breaks into several small rings and these in turn into others. All these rings are connected with each other by thin lines of hydrous manganese dioxide, thus giving the whole system a striking clustered or festooned appearance. If the sol is dropped into a salt solution, it is precipitated in the form of miniature rings; by using a very dilute solution, the system of rings will form before coagulation takes place. This phenomenon, first described by Thomson and Newall,[3] is not limited to col-

[1] *Kolloid-Z.*, **29**, 250 (1921).

[2] *Kolloid-Z.*, **6**, 69 (1910); *cf.* TRAVERS: *Bull. soc. chim.*, **37**, 456 (1925).

[3] *Proc. Roy. Soc.*, **39**, 417 (1886).

loids like milk, ink, blood, soap, etc., but is shown by many solutions of both electrolytes and non-electrolytes. Suitable concentrations of permanganate give strikingly beautiful rings.

A stable sol may be obtained by the oxidation of a manganous salt in the presence of a protective colloid,[1] such as albumin, dextrin, gum arabic, sodium "salts" of albuminous products and starch. Low concentrations of positive hydrous ferric oxide sols precipitate the negative manganese dioxide sol; but in high concentrations they adsorb it and hold it in the suspended form. Thus, by dissolving a manganous salt in a neutralized ferric chloride solution and treating with potassium permanganate, a dark-brown hydrosol is obtained; similarly, a ferrous chloride solution can be oxidized with a potassium permanganate solution without any precipitation taking place.

Witzemann[2] prepared colloidal manganese dioxide by incomplete oxidation of a glucose solution in the presence of a little alkali. On adding slowly 100 cubic centimeters of 6 per cent potassium permanganate to a cold solution containing 5 grams of glucose in 20 cubic centimeters, together with a few cubic centimeters of 10 per cent sodium hydroxide, the mixture rapidly became viscous and in 5 to 10 minutes set to a stiff jelly. The jelly soon started to synerize, and after standing for a few days, it was transformed completely into a stable limpid sol. The rate of transformation from the jelly to the sol stage depends on the alkali concentration. With quite low concentrations, the jelly forms slowly and does not liquefy, while with relatively high concentrations, the jelly stage is not observed, the solution merely undergoing an initial increase in viscosity, followed by a rapid transformation to the limpid sol. This behavior of colloidal manganese dioxide is very similar to that of colloidal hydrous ceric oxide[3] except that in the latter case the transformation from a hydrous sol to a jelly and again to a less hydrous sol takes place in the absence of glucose. It is obvious that the newly formed particles of manganese dioxide are in an extremely finely divided and highly hydrous form, and in rela-

[1] TRILLAT: *Compt. rend.*, **138**, 274 (1904); *Bull. soc. chim.*, (3) **31**, 811 (1904); German Patent 227491.

[2] *J. Am. Chem. Soc.*, **37**, 1079 (1915); **39**, 27 (1917).

[3] See p. 255.

tively high concentration, they adsorb and entangle all of the liquid, forming a jelly. Now, as a rule, inorganic jellies synerize, particularly in the presence of salts,[1] the hydrous particles losing water and growing until they settle out. This is particularly noticeable with barium sulfate and certain arsenate jellies. But in the case of hydrous manganese dioxide, the primary particles coalesce to form larger primary particles even though agglomeration and precipitation are prevented by the protective action of glucose and the peptizing action of adsorbed hydroxyl ion. The ageing of the primary particles in the presence of electrolytes has, however, left them relatively free from adsorbed water, the latter merely serving as the medium in which the slightly hydrous particles are suspended. Because of this irreversible change, neither an aged ceric oxide or manganese dioxide sol can be precipitated in the form of a jelly. Jellies of the hydrous oxides of iron and aluminum may be broken up by shaking, forming sols of relatively low viscosity which, on standing, set again to firm jellies. In these instances the primary particles retain their small highly hydrous character in contradistinction to the behavior of ceric oxide and manganese dioxide, and the structure broken up by shaking gradually re-forms, entangling all of the unadsorbed water.

Probably the simplest method of preparing manganese dioxide sols consists in adding concentrated ammonia, one drop every 3 minutes, to an $M/20$ solution of potassium permanganate at 90° until all the permanganate is reduced.[2] The only impurity in the sol is potassium hydroxide, which has a marked stabilizing effect.

Adsorption by Hydrous Manganese Dioxide.—Dhar and his collaborators[3] have studied the precipitation by electrolytes of a manganese dioxide sol in the presence of a protective colloid, gelatin. They have also made adsorption studies on the oxide precipitated in the presence of various salts. As a result of

---

[1] POMA and PATRONI: *Z. physik. Chem.*, **87**, 196 (1914).

[2] GUY: *J. Phys. Chem.*, **25**, 415 (1921).

[3] CHATTERJI: *Proc. Eighth Ind. Sci. Congress*, **17**, 130 (1921); GANGULY and DHAR: *J. Phys. Chem.*, **26**, 701, 836 (1922); CHATTERJI and DHAR: *Kolloid-Z.*, **33**, 18 (1923); DHAR, SEN, and GHOSH: *J. Phys. Chem.*, **28**, 457 (1924); *cf.* SPRING and DE BOECK: *Bull. soc. chim.*, (2) **48**, 170 (1887).

these observations, the conclusion is reached that an ion which has a high precipitation value for a colloid is most strongly adsorbed by the colloid and *vice versa.* "Thus, the monovalent ions—silver, sodium, and lithium—are more adsorbed (by MnO_2) than any of the bivalent, trivalent, or tetravalent ions. These facts show that ions of higher valence which in general have greater coagulating power are adsorbed the least." Dhar's observations were not made on a purified sol but on hydrous manganese dioxide formed by mixing potassium permanganate and manganous sulfate in the presence of various electrolytes. In the solution from which the oxide separated, there were the two reacting electrolytes, the salt whose adsorption was measured, together with the soluble products of the reaction, potassium acid sulfate and sulfuric acid. This makes an almost hopelessly complicated system; and it seems unsafe to draw any conclusions whatsoever from the observations until more is known of the effect of foreign electrolytes on the rate of precipitation and physical character of the precipitate, and until something is known of the influence of other salts in the system on the adsorption of the salt investigated. To cite but one example: Aluminum nitrate is adsorbed about eight times as strongly as aluminum sulfate, whereas the sulfates of cobalt, copper, and cadmium are each adsorbed somewhat more than their respective nitrates. Aluminum is not "far less adsorbed" than strontium, nickel, cobalt, zinc, barium, or cadmium if the values for the nitrates are compared. Pavlov[1] showed that the taking up of silver from nitrate solution by hydrous manganese dioxide is not a simple case of adsorption but is complicated by a chemical reaction between the adsorbent and the adsorbed salt. With colloidal manganese dioxide, as with other sols, it is probable that the most readily adsorbed ion will be found to precipitate in lowest concentrations, provided influences other than the adsorbability of the precipitating ions can be suppressed or eliminated.[2]

The adsorption of iron, nickel, and copper by hydrous manganese dioxide, formed in acid solution by the action of $(NH_4)_2S_2O_8$ on a manganese salt, follows the Freundlich adsorption iso-

[1] *Kolloid-Z.*, **35**, 375–377 (1924).
[2] *Cf.* Weiser: *J. Phys. Chem.*, **29**, 955 (1925); *cf.* Schilow: *Z. physik. Chem.*, **100**, 425 (1922).

therm, the amounts of the several ions taken up being appreciably greater at lower concentrations.[1]

Manganese compounds have been found to play an important role in many biochemical actions, and in certain instances, this may be due to colloidal oxides of manganese.[2] Thus manganese compounds stimulate alcoholic fermentation[3] and the growth of fungi.[4] The stimulating effect on the growth of plants in general[5] is evidenced by the fact that the production of wheat per acre may be increased 10 per cent by sprinkling a manganese compound on certain soils. For this purpose, manganese dioxide is one of the most effective compounds. Salts of manganese likewise appear to stimulate metabolism and to increase the hemogenetic power.[6] It is, therefore, proposed to administer manganese therapeutically along with iron to make the latter effective. Further, the addition of minute amounts of manganese increases the activity of the enzyme laccase,[7] and colloidal manganese dioxide behaves like an oxidase toward guiac tincture, hydroquinone, etc.[8] As the processes mentioned are thought to be regulated by enzymes and enzymes are colloidal, Witzemann suggests that the effect of manganese on enzymic activity is due to the effect of the hydrous oxide on the physical character of the enzyme. Thus, if the colloidal oxide keeps the colloidal enzyme dispersed under conditions which would normally be unfavorable to this effect, then it might be expected to have a positive influence on the enzymic activity.

[1] GELOSO: *Compt. rend.*, **176**, 1884 (1923); **178**, 1001 (1924); *Bull. soc. chim.*, **37**, 641 (1925).

[2] WITZEMANN: *J. Am. Chem. Soc.*, **37**, 1089 (1915).

[3] KAYSER and MARCHAND: *Compt. rend.*, **145**, 343 (1907).

[4] BERTRAND and JAVILLIER: *Bull. soc. chim.*, **11**, 212 (1912); BERTRAND: *Ibid.*, **11**, 494 (1912); WATERMAN: *J. Chem. Soc.*, **104**, I, 229 (1913).

[5] MASONI: *Staz. sper. agrar. ital.*, **44**, 85 (1911); MONTEMARTINI: *Ibid.*, **44**, 564 (1911); RICCI and BARBERA: *Ibid.*, **48**, 677 (1915); BARTMANN: *J. agr. prat.*, (2) **20**, 666 (1911); SKINNER and SULLIVAN: *U. S. Dept. Agr. Bull.* **42**, (1913); PFEIFFER and BLANCK: *Landw. Vers.-Sta.*, **77**, 33 (1912); **83**, 257 (1914).

[6] PICCININI: *Eighth Int. Cong. Applied Chem.*, **19**, 263 (1912); *Biochem. terap. sper.*, **2**, 385 (1910–1911); *Chem. Abstracts.*, **7**, 369 (1913).

[7] BERTRAND: *Bull. soc. chim.*, (3) **17**, 619, 753 (1897); *Ann. chim. phys.*, (7) **12**, 115 (1897); *cf.* also BACH: *Ber.*, **43**, 364 (1910).

[8] SJOLLEMA: *Chem. Weekblad*, **6**, 287 (1909); *Chem. Zentr.*, I, 496 (1911).

In addition to its use in the manufacture of chlorine and as a depolarizer in the Le Clanche battery, manganese dioxide in the anhydrous or slightly hydrous state finds wide application as a dryer for oils in paints. The drying is a process of oxidation and the manganese dioxide serves as an efficient oxygen carrier or catalyst. It is sometimes used also in conjunction with other oxides to produce warmer shades in colored glass and to destroy the injurious tint produced in colorless glass and white enamels by the presence of ferrous compounds. The latter greenish compounds are oxidized to the nearly colorless ferric salts while the slight pink tint imparted by the manganese still further counteracts the bluish color. The latter effect seems to be the more important, as red lead and other oxidizing agents do not have this decolorizing power. In a very finely divided state or in thin layers, manganese dioxide has a purplish-red color. The purple color of amethyst is due to a trace of MnO_2 or Mn_3O_4 as impurity in quartz crystal.

Other Hydrous Oxides of Manganese

Manganous Oxide.—By adding alkali hydroxide to a solution of manganous salt, white manganous oxide precipitates in a highly gelatinous form. The hydrous oxide adsorbs chloride slightly and sulfate strongly, so that the former is not carried down in the presence of the latter.[1]   Manganous hydroxide can be obtained in regular hexagonal prisms similar to the mineral pyrochroite, by adding manganous chloride to a boiled concentrated solution of potassium hydroxide in an atmosphere of hydrogen.[2]   By heating to 160°, all the oxide is carried into solution from which it precipitates in transparent crystals having a reddish tint. When pure, the crystalline hydroxide is fairly stable in the air, but if it contains even a small amount of alkali, it oxidizes very readily. Like magnesium hydroxide, it dissolves in excess ammonium chloride.[3]

A sol of hydrous MnO is formed by treating a solution of a manganous salt with alkali in the presence of protective colloids

---

[1] PATTEN: *J. Am. Chem. Soc.*, **25**, 192 (1903).

[2] DE SCHULTEN: *Compt. rend.*, **105**, 1265 (1887).

[3] *Cf.* HERZ: *Z. anorg. Chem.*, **21**, 242 (1899); **22**, 279 (1900).

such as gelatin,[1] Paal's "sodium protalbinate,"[2] albumin,[3] and nuclein acid.[4] Because of its fine state of subdivision, it oxidizes readily to dioxide. In the presence of certain reducing agents such as hydroquinone and gallic acid, hydrous MnO_2 will give up oxygen, again forming colloidal MnO,[5] the process coming to a standstill only when there is no further reduction to MnO by the reducing agent, that is, when the oxidation of the added substance is complete. This action as an oxidase or oxygen carrier probably accounts for the rapid drying of manganese oxide paints, varnishes, and siccatives. The drying oil, such as linseed, doubtless plays the double role of protective colloid and of oxygen-consuming reducing agent.[6]

Manganic Oxide.—Hydrous manganic oxide is best prepared by hydrolysis of manganic salts, but it is also obtained in a more or less pure condition by the partial oxidation of manganous salts. By drying at 100°, the composition is said to be represented by the formula $Mn_2O_3 \cdot H_2O$, corresponding to the mineral manganite.[7] When formed by the hydrolysis of potassium manganic cyanide, it is a black gelatinous mass which becomes less hydrous on heating with the mother liquor, changing in color from black to brown.[8] Meyer[9] suggests that the color change may be due either to the decomposition of a hydrate or to a change in the size and physical character of the particles; he leaves the matter for someone else to decide.

Mangano-manganic Oxide.—The oxide Mn_3O_4 or $MnO_2 \cdot 2MnO$ is the most stable of all the oxides of manganese when heated in the air. Accordingly, higher oxides decompose around

[1] LOBRY DE BRUYN: *Z. physik. Chem.*, **29**, 562 (1898); *Rec. trav. chim.*, **19**, 236 (1900).

[2] Kalle and Company: German Patent 180729 (1901). ,

[3] TRILLAT: *Bull. soc. chim.*, (3) **31**, 811 (1904); *Compt. rend.*, **138**, 274 (1904).

[4] SARASON: German Patent 272386 (1913).

[5] BERTRAND: *Compt. rend.*, **124**, 1032, 1355 (1897); VILLIERS: *Ibid.*, **124**, 1349 (1897).

[6] *Cf.* LEVACHE: *Compt. rend.*, **97**, 1311 (1883); **124**, 1520 (1897).

[7] FRANKE: *J. prakt. Chem.*, (2) **36**, 31, 451 (1887); MEYER: *Z. anorg. Chem.*, **81**, 385 (1913).

[8] BERTHIER: *Ann. chim. phys.*, (2) **20**, 344 (1822); HERMANN: *Pogg. Ann.*, **74**, 303 (1848); GORGEU: *Compt. rend.*, **106**, 948 (1888).

[9] *Z. anorg. Chem.*, **81**, 400 (1913).

940° and lower oxides oxidize in the air, forming Mn_3O_4. It is obtained in a hydrous condition more or less impure, by treating a mixture of manganous and manganic salts with alkali or by the oxidation of an ammonical solution of a manganous salt with oxygen. Christensen[1] obtained it by adding hydrous MnO_2 in small amounts at a time to a dilute solution of manganous chloride containing an excess of ammonium chloride. Depending on the exact condition of formation, the precipitate is yellow brown, red brown, to chocolate brown in color.

[1] *Z. anorg. Chem.*, **27**, 321 (1901).

CHAPTER XIV

THE HYDROUS OXIDES OF THE PLATINUM FAMILY

The platinum family consists of two groups of three closely related elements following iron, nickel, and cobalt in the eighth group of the periodic table. The metals of the first group— ruthenium, rhodium, and palladium—have atomic weights near 100 and densities near 12; and the metals of the second group— osmium, iridium, and platinum—have atomic weights near 200 and densities near 21. From their position in the periodic table, it is not surprising that these elements should form a number of compounds with oxygen. Some of the oxides can be obtained only in the anhydrous state while others may be precipitated as flocculent or gelatinous masses containing varying proportions of adsorbed water. The oxides of the several elements will be taken up in order, beginning with ruthenium.

HYDROUS OXIDES OF RUTHENIUM

Ruthenium Monoxide.—Hydrous RuO is thrown down by alkali from the blue solution of $RuCl_2$. The precipitate is very highly dispersed and the adsorbed alkali cannot be washed out without peptization taking place. Moreover, like hydrous ferrous oxide, the gel oxidizes very readily in the air. There seems little doubt of the chemical individuality of hydrous RuO, since the freshly precipitated oxide dissolves in hydrochloric acid, re-forming the characteristic blue solution of $RuCl_2$.[1]

Ruthenium Sesquioxide.—Hydrous Ru_2O_3 is precipitated by adding alkali to a solution of the corresponding chloride.[2] Prepared in this way, the oxide contains adsorbed alkali that

---

[1] REMY: *Z. anorg. Chem.*, **126**, 185 (1923); *cf.*, however, GUTBIER and RANSOHOFF: *Ibid.*, **45**, 243 (1905).

[2] CLAUS: *Liebig's Ann. Chem.*, **59**, 234 (1846); JOLY: *Compt. rend.*, **114**, 291 (1892); BRIZARD: *Ann. chim. phys.*, (7) **21**, 311 (1900); GUTBIER and RANSOHOFF: *Z. anorg. Chem.*, **45**, 253 (1905).

cannot be removed by prolonged washing.[1] Krauss and Küken-thal[2] obtained a chloride- and alkali-free product by evaporating the hydrochloric acid solution of $RuCl_3$ to dryness, redissolving in water, and adding just enough potassium hydroxide to the dark-brown solution to cause complete precipitation of the oxide while the colorless liquid is still acid. The black flocculent precipitate analyzed for trihydrate or hydroxide, after washing thoroughly and drying in an atmosphere of nitrogen at 120°. From these observations alone, it is impossible to say whether the compound is a true hydrate or a hydrous oxide. Since the pure preparation is soluble in acids, it furnishes a good starting point for making the most common ruthenium salts. The reddish-yellow solution of $RuCl_3$ deposits, slowly on standing but quickly when warmed, a black very finely divided precipitate said to be ruthenium oxychloride. This reaction is so delicate that 1 part of the metal imparts a distinct ink-like color to 100,000 parts of water.

Ruthenium Dioxide.—Claus[3] prepared hydrous ruthenium dioxide which he formulated $Ru(OH)_4 \cdot 3H_2O$, by evaporating a solution of $Ru(SO_4)_2$ with caustic potash. The precipitate is dark red in color and adsorbs alkali strongly. According to Gutbier, the hydrous oxide cannot be obtained pure since it goes into colloidal solution extremely readily on washing. The pure anhydrous oxide results on roasting $Ru(SO_4)_2$ in the air[4] or on burning the metal.[5] It crystallizes in small very hard tetragonal pyramids possessing a green metallic luster and a bluish or greenish iridescence.

Ruthenium Pentoxide.—Hydrous Ru_2O_5 results, according to Remy,[6] when hydrous RuO is allowed to oxidize spontaneously; but its identity has not been established with absolute certainty. Debray and Joly[7] prepared what they took to be $Ru_2O_5 \cdot 2H_2O$ by neutralizing an alkali ruthenate with nitric acid; but Gutbier

---

[1] GUTBIER: *Z. anorg. Chem.*, **95**, 185 (1916); **109**, 206 (1920).

[2] *Z. anorg. Chem.*, **132**, 315 (1923).

[3] *Liebig's Ann. Chem.*, **59**, 234 (1846).

[4] GUTBIER and RANSOHOFF: *Z. anorg. Chem.*, **45**, 243 (1905).

[5] GUTBIER, LEUCHS, WIESSMANN, and MAISCH: *Z. anorg. Chem.*, **96**, 182 (1916).

[6] *Z. anorg. Chem.*, **126**, 185 (1923).

[7] *Compt. rend.*, **106**, 328, 1494 (1888).

and Ransohoff[1] showed the alleged compound to be a mixture of hydrous Ru_2O_3 with some higher oxide.

Salts containing hexavalent and heptavalent ruthenium are known, but the oxides RuO_3 and Ru_2O_7 have not been prepared.

Ruthenium Tetroxide.—RuO_4 is not obtained in the hydrous state, but the anhydrous oxide is formed by passing chlorine into a solution of sodium ruthenate prepared by fusing ruthenium with sodium peroxide.[2] The heat of the reaction is sufficient to bring about the distillation of the oxide. The golden-yellow crystalline compound is fairly stable when dry, but decomposes quickly when moist. It dissolves slowly in water, giving a solution that is fairly stable, provided some free chlorine or hypochlorite is present. The oxide blackens organic matter readily and is reduced immediately by alcoholic potash with the separation of finely divided ruthenium. Serious explosions may occur if the solid oxide is treated with alcohol even in dilute solution.[3]

HYDROUS OXIDES OF RHODIUM

Rhodium Sesquioxide.—Hydrous Rh_2O_3 is precipitated as a black gelatinous mass by adding excess potassium hydroxide and a little alcohol to a solution of Na_3RhCl_6. If an excess of potash is not used, a sol is formed which deposits thin citron-yellow particles, said to be $Rh(OH)_3 \cdot H_2O$.[4] The gelatinous oxide is soluble in acids, forming the corresponding rhodium salts. Anhydrous Ru_2O_3 only is formed by heating the finely divided metal in the air to 600 to 1000°. According to Gutbier,[5] the alleged formation of RhO[6] in this way was the result of incomplete combustion.

Rhodium Dioxide.—Hydrous RhO_2 separates as a green powder when chlorine is passed into a solution of Rh_2O_3 in alkali. If the flow of chlorine is continued, the green precipitate dis-

[1] *Z. anorg. Chem.*, **45**, 243 (1905); **95**, 177 (1916).

[2] MYLIUS: *Ber.*, **31**, 3187 (1898); GUTBIER: *Z. angew. Chem.*, **22**, 487 (1909).

[3] DEBRAY and JOLY: *Compt. rend.*, **113**, 693 (1891).

[4] CLAUS: *J. prakt. Chem.*, **76**, 24 (1859); **80**, 282 (1860); **85**, 129 (1862).

[5] *Z. anorg. Chem.*, **95**, 225 (1916).

[6] WILM: *Ber.*, **15**, 2225 (1882).

solves, giving a deep-blue solution resembling the ammoniacal copper solution. The blue color is attributed to the alkali salt of rhodous acid, H_2RhO_4,[1] which decomposes gradually, precipitating hydrous RhO_2.

HYDROUS OXIDES OF PALLADIUM

Palladium Monoxide.—The addition of sodium carbonate to a solution of palladous salt precipitates hydrous PdO as a dark-brown mass.[2] When thrown down in the cold, the oxide is readily soluble in alkalies, but it loses this property when dried or when precipitated from boiling solution, owing to coalescence of the particles. The hydrous oxide is best obtained pure by hydrolysis of palladous nitrate. A PdO sol in paraffin oil has been introduced as a therapeutic agent under the name "Leptynol."[3] The oxide serves as a catalyst for the reduction of aldehydes to alcohols.[4]

Palladium Sesquioxide.—Hydrous Pd_2O_3 is best prepared by the electrolytic oxidation of a concentrated solution of palladous nitrate at 8° with a current density of 0.5 ampere per square centimeter. If the electrolysis is prolonged, hydrous PdO_2 is formed. This is not a direct oxidation, but the sesquioxide decomposes into dioxide and monoxide, the latter dissolving in the free acid and undergoing further oxidation.[5] The sesquioxide is formed also by the action of ozone on palladous nitrate. It is chocolate brown in color when first prepared, but on washing, it gets darker owing to agglomeration of the particles and loss of adsorbed water.

Palladium Dioxide.—An impure hydrous PdO_2 is precipitated on adding caustic soda to a solution of K_2PdCl_6. As mentioned above, it is obtained free from alkali and basic salt by the anodic oxidation of the nitrate, but is not quite free from hydrous PdO. The fresh oxide is soluble in acids, but like the monoxide, its reactivity decreases rapidly on standing. It cannot be dehy-

[1] ALVAREZ: *Compt. rend.*, **140**, 1341 (1905).
[2] WÖHLER and KÖNIG: *Z. anorg. Chem.*, **46**, 323 (1905).
[3] THORPE: "Dictionary of Chemistry," **5**, 51 (1924).
[4] SHRINER and ADAMS: *J. Am. Chem. Soc.*, **46**, 1683 (1924).
[5] WÖHLER and MARTIN: *Z. anorg. Chem.*, **57**, 398 (1908).

drated,[1] as it decomposes at the ordinary temperature under an oxygen pressure of 80 atmospheres. It is, therefore, a vigorous oxidizing agent.

HYDROUS OXIDES OF OSMIUM

Osmium Monoxide and Sesquioxide.—Claus and Jacobi prepared hydrous OsO by the action of warm concentrated alkali on $OsSO_3$ in an atmosphere of nitrogen. It is a blue-black precipitate which takes up oxygen very rapidly from the air. The same authors obtained hydrous Os_2O_3 as a brown-red precipitate on adding alkali to a solution of K_3OsCl_6.

Osmium Dioxide.—A very highly hydrous form of OsO_2 is precipitated by the addition of alkali to K_2OsCl_6, and by the action of alcohol or other reducing agent on an alkali osmate such as K_2OsO_4.[2] The hydrous mass may be converted into a fine powder by prolonged heating on the water bath in contact with the mother liquor. If the gel is dried, it forms a horny body which loses water explosively and emits flashes of light when heated above 100°. The more granular oxide aged on the water bath becomes incandescent quietly at the glow temperature. It is obvious that the primary particles of the gel are extremely small, the coalescence on ignition causing a marked decrease in surface energy with the accompanying glow. The gel is a typical hydrous oxide, the water content of which is determined by the conditions of drying. The compound formed by hydrolysis of K_2OsO_4 in the presence of alcohol and hydrogen and by the action of sulfuric acid on K_2OsO_4 is hydrous OsO_2 and not H_2OsO_4, as claimed by Moraht and Wischin.[3]

Since the gel formed by reduction of alkali osmates contains such small primary particles, it can be peptized by shaking with an excess of water[4] or by treating with a small amount of alkali

[1] WÖHLER and KÖNIG: *Z. anorg. Chem.*, **46**, 323 (1905); **48**, 203 (1906); **57**, 398 (1908); BELLUCCI: *Gazz. chim. ital.*, **35**, I, 343 (1905); *Z. anorg. Chem.*, **47**, 287 (1906).

[2] RUFF and BORNEMANN: *Z. anorg. Chem.*, **65**, 429 (1910); RUFF and RATHSBURG: *Ber.*, **50**, 484 (1917).

[3] *Z. anorg. Chem.*, **3**, 153 (1893).

[4] CLAUS and JACOBI: *J. prakt. Chem.*, **90**, 65 (1863).

or ammonia.[1] Freundlich and Baerwind[2] dissolved 1 gram of OsO_4 in 50 cubic centimeters of water, added 10 cubic centimeters of ethyl alcohol and allowed the mixture to stand 24 hours. The precipitate of the dark dioxide was washed with alcohol and then peptized by shaking for several days with 800 cubic centimeters of water. The deep-blue-black sol is fairly stable, but its stability is greater in the presence of a little alcohol or protective colloid.[3] The particles are negatively charged and are not spherical, as they appear alternately bright and dark when viewed with a cardioid ultramicroscope.

Osmium Tetroxide.—OsO_4, erroneously called osmic acid, does not form a hydrous oxide. It is obtained in transparent glistening needles by burning the metal or by the action of oxidizing agents on the lower oxides. It dissolves readily in water, forming a colorless liquid possessing a caustic or burning taste. The solution is used for staining biological preparations and also for taking finger prints,[4] the oxide being reduced to metal. The fumes of the oxide are very poisonous, attacking the lungs and eyes. It also acts violently on the skin causing painful wounds.[5] It may be employed as a catalyst for many oxidation reactions.[6]

Hydrous Oxides of Iridium

Iridium Sesquioxide.—Hydrous Ir_2O_3 is obtained in much the same way as the corresponding rhodium compound which it resembles closely. When a solution of $IrCl_3 \cdot 6NaCl \cdot 24H_2O$ is heated with alkali in a stream of carbon dioxide, an impure hydrous Ir_2O_3 separates that is greenish white to black in color, depending on the alkali concentration. The light-colored products come down from dilute alkali, while excess alkali gives

[1] Ruff and Rathsburg: *Ber.*, **50**, 484 (1917).

[2] *Kolloid-Z.*, **33**, 275 (1923).

[3] Castro: *Z. anorg. Chem.*, **41**, 126 (1904); Paal and Amberger: *Ber.*, **40**, 1392 (1907); **49**, 557 (1916); Amberger: *Kolloid-Z.*, **17**, 47 (1915).

[4] Deville and Debray: *Ann. chim. phys.* (3) **56**, 400 (1859); *Compt. rend.*, **78**, 1509 (1874).

[5] Mitchell: *Analyst*, **45**, 125 (1920).

[6] Hofmann: *Ber.*, **45**, 3329 (1913); Hofmann, Ehrhart, and Schneider: *Ibid.*, **46**, 1657 (1913).

the black oxide containing relatively little water. This recalls the behavior of cupric oxide which dehydrates and darkens very quickly in the presence of excess alkali. Wöhler and Witzmann[1] peptized the green oxide in dilute hydrochloric and sulfuric acids; concentrated acids dissolve it, giving reddish-yellow salts.

Iridium Dioxide.—Hydrous IrO_2 is best prepared by adding alkali to a hot solution of Na_2IrCl_6, the sesquioxide first formed being oxidized to dioxide in a current of oxygen.[2] The fresh preparation is fairly soluble in acids and alkalies but it loses this property on drying.[3] The oxide can be gotten almost pure by drying the hydrous mass at 400° in carbon dioxide and then boiling with alkali and subsequently with sulfuric acid.[4]

The color of the oxide varies from light blue to black, depending on the size of the particles and the structure and water content of the mass. Like the sesquioxide the precipitate is darker and less hydrous when it comes down from strong alkali solution.

The solution obtained by the action of alkali on Na_2IrCl_6 in the cold has a violet color and contains hydrous IrO_2 in suspension; after a time a violet modification of the oxide separates, which becomes blue on drying. Boiling the violet sol changes it to blue, probably owing to coalescence of the positively charged particles.[4] Dilute hydrochloric acid peptizes the desiccator-dried preparation, giving a blue sol.[5]

Iridium trioxide, IrO_3, formed by fusing finely divided iridium with sodium peroxide or by the anodic oxidation of hydrous IrO_2, is too instable to be isolated.[4]

HYDROUS OXIDES OF PLATINUM

Platinum Monoxide.—The black precipitate of hydrous PtO thrown down from $PtCl_2$ with caustic alkali cannot be washed free from chloride or alkali.[6] It is prepared in the pure state by adding the calculated amount of dilute caustic soda to

[1] Z. anorg. Chem., **57**, 323 (1908).
[2] CLAUS: J. prakt. Chem., **39**, 104 (1846).
[3] JOLY and LEIDE: Compt. rend., **120**, 1341 (1895).
[4] WÖHLER and WITZMANN: Z. anorg. Chem., **57**, 323 (1908).
[5] Cf. also PAAL, BIEHLER, and STEYER: Ber., **50**, 722 (1917).
[6] LIEBIG: Pogg. Ann., **17**, 108 (1829).

a solution of K_2PtCl_4.[1] As the fresh oxide takes up oxygen readily from the air, the precipitation, washing, and drying must be carried out in an atmosphere of carbon dioxide. When newly formed, it is readily soluble in dilute halogen acids but is insoluble in bases and in oxy acids other than sulfurous. Dried in a vacuum desiccator, the water content corresponds approximately to the formula $PtO \cdot 2H_2O$. It holds on to its water very strongly, one sample retaining 6.6 per cent water after heating several days at 400°. PtO is a stronger oxidizing agent than the dioxide and a stronger reducing agent than the metal.

Platinum Sesquioxide.—Wöhler and Martin[2] obtained hydrous Pt_2O_3 for the first time in a pure condition by adding solid $PtCl_3$ to a solution of sodium carbonate or by dissolving the chloride in concentrated potassium hydroxide and precipitating with acetic acid. The latter method yields a product containing some PtO_2. The precipitate obtained at room temperature is light brown in color and highly hydrous; by boiling with alkali, it becomes less hydrous and darker; the dried preparation is almost black. The freshly formed oxide is not oxidized by boiling with water through which a stream of oxygen is passed; but it cannot be dehydrated completely without decomposition taking place. In chemical behavior it occupies an intermediate position between hydrous PtO and PtO_2.

Platinum Dioxide.—Wöhler[3] prepared pure hydrous PtO_2 by boiling a solution of platinic chloride with caustic potash, which converts $PtCl_6''$ to $Pt(OH)_6''$. When cold, this solution is neutralized with acetic acid, and the hydrous oxide is obtained as an almost white precipitate which becomes yellow on drying. Even when dried in the air, the water content is less than corresponds to the tetrahydrate $PtO_2 \cdot 4H_2O$ or $H_2Pt(OH)_6$.[4] It loses water continuously by lowering the vapor pressure of the surroundings or by raising the temperature; and there is no evidence of the existence of any definite hydrate. The last 2.5

---

[1] THOMSEN: *J. prakt. Chem.*, (2) **15**, 299 (1877); WÖHLER: *Z. anorg. Chem.*, **40**, 456 (1904); WÖHLER and FREY: *Z. Elektrochem.*, **15**, 133 (1905).

[2] *Ber.*, **42**, 3958 (1909); *cf.*, however, DUDLEY: *Am. Chem. J.*, **28**, 59 (1902); BLONDEL: *Ann. chim. phys.*, (8) **6**, 111 (1905).

[3] *Z. anorg. Chem.*, **40**, 434 (1904); TOPSÖE: *Ber.*, **3**, 462 (1870).

[4] BELLUCCI: *Atti accad. Lincei*, (5) **12**, 635 (1903).

per cent of water cannot be removed without decomposing the oxide. The freshly precipitated product is soluble in acids and alkalies; but the thoroughly dried substance is insoluble in all dilute and concentrated acids with the exception of hydrochloric and aqua regia. It is sometimes called platinic acid, since its reactions with alkalies yields platinates such as $K_2Pt(OH)_6$ isomorphous with the stannates.[1]

Platinum Trioxide.—By the electrolysis of a solution of hydrous PtO_2 in 2 N potassium hydroxide, a brilliant golden-yellow body of the composition $K_2O \cdot 3PtO_3$ separates at the anode. When this is treated with dilute acetic acid in the cold, it yields the trioxide PtO_3, a reddish-brown substance which loses oxygen readily and evolves chlorine slowly from dilute hydrochloric acid.[2]

[1] BELLUCCI and PARRAVANO: *Atti accad. Lincei*, (5) **14,** 459 (1905).
[2] WÖHLER and MARTIN: *Ber.*, **42,** 3326 (1909).

CHAPTER XV

TANNING

Tanning is the process whereby the skin or hide of animals is converted into leather. Before subjecting hides to the tanning process, they must be treated to remove the hair, epidermis, and fat and to get the remainder of the substance in suitable condition to take up the tanning agent. The dermis or leather-producing portion of the skin consists essentially of bundles of fine connective-tissue fibers about 1μ in diameter, bound together irregularly. The fibrils consist essentially of a protein material, collagen, which is converted into gelatin by boiling with water.

To prepare the hide for tanning, it is first immersed in lime water to which is usually added sodium sulfide to "sharpen" or hasten the action of the lime. The liming process not only removes the hair and destroys the epidermis, but it swells the collagen fibers and removes the cementing material between them, thereby splitting the bundles into their constituent fibrils. Following the liming process, the alkali is neutralized with dilute acids, and the hide is subsequently "bated" by subjecting it to the action of tryptic ferments in conjunction with ammonium chloride to remove the last trace of lime. The enzymes digest off part of the remaining connecting and epidermal substance, and completely emulsify the fat. This digestive action is stopped by "drenching," that is, by treating the hide with fermenting bran infusions which bring the skins to a slightly acid state in which tryptic ferments are not active. The starchy matters of the bran are first converted into glucose, which undergoes bacterial fermentation by several types of lactic-, butyric-, and acetic-acid-forming bacteria. As these bacteria develop only in solutions of feeble acidity and are destroyed by the accumulation of their own acid products, the acidity of the drench is automatically self-regulating and tends to produce a very slight acid swelling of the skins. For chrome tanning, a similar result is brought about by "pickling" the limed or bated skins in a bath consisting of a solution of sodium chloride and sulfuric acid in amount depending on the degree of basicity of the chrome liquor employed. After all undesirable impurities are removed and the collagen fibrils are brought to a flaccid slightly swollen condition, the hide is ready for the tannage proper. In general, if the skin is soaked in infusions of barks, fruits, or galls which contain members of the class of compounds known as tannins, the process is called vegetable tanning; and if the tanning liquor is a mineral salt, it is known as mineral tanning. A consideration of the mechanism of these two processes will be taken up in order, even though any discussion of vegetable tanning might appear to be without the scope of this book.

Vegetable Tanning

It has been known for centuries that skin substance undergoes a marked change in properties when brought in contact with vegetable infusions, the active principle in which is now known to be tannin. Seguin regarded the tanning process as a reaction between hide, a base, and the tanning agent, an acid, giving leather, a salt. Berzelius and Dumas likewise considered leather to be a compound of hide and tanning agent without going into the mechanism of the process. Knapp,[1] whom Procter calls the father of leather chemistry, was the first to reason that leather could not be a definite chemical compound since the amount of material taken up by the hide is not in any definite stoichiometrical proportion but depends on the concentration of the tan liquor. Moreover, since so many chemically different substances—tannin, alum, chromic sulfate, formaldehyde, stearic acid, etc.—can be used for tanning, Knapp concludes that the process must be essentially a physical one: "The two active substances are rendered insoluble in water by means of surface attraction (adsorption)." The essential difference between hide and leather recognized by Knapp is that, in the latter, the fibers are no longer in the condition of a colloidal jelly, but may be dried without adhesion, the substance remaining porous and flexible.

[1] *Dinglers polytech. J.*, **149**, 305 (1859).

Stiasny[1] was first to call attention to the similarity in the adsorbing capacity of carbon and hide powder. Thus, both adsorb a wide variety of different substances; aromatic acids are adsorbed more strongly by both than are aliphatic acids; and with both adsorbents, acetic acid and the chloracetic acids possess approximately the same adsorbability in spite of their difference in strength. From such observations, Stiasny concludes that the taking up of tannin by hide powder is an adsorption process. Herzog and Adler[2] reached a similar conclusion from observations of adsorption by hide powder of such substances as resorcin and pyrogallol, which are closely related to tannin but differ from the latter in forming molecular solutions in water.

It remained for von Schröder[3] to demonstrate the adsorption of tannin from colloidal solution by carbon and hydrous alumina, as well as by gelatin and hide powder. Since the bacteria present in hide powder cause decomposition of tannin, giving gallic acid, more consistent results can be obtained by sterilizing the adsorbent. Within the first hour after the adsorption, there exists an adsorption equilibrium between the tannin and the adsorbent, but the amount of tannin that can be removed by washing decreases with the time of standing. The effect of acids on the adsorption of tannin is less marked than that of alkalies. Thus $0.05 \ N \ (NH_4)_2CO_3$ added to a tannin solution cut down the adsorption, expressed in millimols per gram of adsorbent, from 700 to 120.

Since the collagen of hide is converted into gelatin by boiling, von Schröder compared the adsorption of tannin by hide powder to that of gelatin. The negatively charged particles of tannin sol are adsorbed by and precipitate a slightly acid and, therefore, positively charged gelatin sol. In slightly alkaline solution the gelatin particles are negatively charged, and adsorption by tannin with the accompanying mutual precipitation does not take place. As has been mentioned, hide powder in very dilute alkali likewise adsorbs tannin but slightly. Under comparable conditions, the adsorption capacity of gelatin and hide powder for tannin is very similar. As might be expected, a longer time is required for

---

[1] *Kolloid-Z.*, **2**, 257 (1908); *Collegium*, 118 (1908).
[2] *Kolloid-Z.*, **2**, 2d Supplement, III (1908).
[3] *Kolloidchem. Beihefte*, **1**, 1 (1909).

attaining the maximum adsorption with hide powder in mass than with gelatin in the sol form where adsorption and mutual precipitation is quite rapid. Just as with hide powder, there is at first an adsorption equilibrium between gelatin and tannin, but this gradually gives way to an irreversible change in the mass.

Von Schröder's observations led him to say:

Tanning with tannin is characterized by adsorption of the tanning agent. However, the adsorption compound is not leather at first; but this results in the course of time by a change in the adsorption compound whereby the tannin is more firmly held . . .

Considering what has been said concerning the precipitation of gelatin by tannin and the parallelism in the behavior of gelatin and hide powder, one reaches the conclusion that the adsorption of tannin by hide powder is a concealed colloidal precipitation. Before the hide powder can absorb tannin, it must obviously be brought by swelling to such a condition that it can be precipitated.

Von Schröder thus comes out definitely in support of the view that the first step in the tanning process is the mutual colloidal precipitation of negatively charged tannin and positively charged hide substance. It is not obvious just wherein the Procter-Wilson theory of vegetable tanning differs from von Schröder's. It seems that Procter,[1] Wilson,[2] and others[3] were not aware of the definiteness of von Schörder's viewpoint, for Procter writes in 1924:

Knapp's theory of the purely physical nature of the combination in tanning has remained the popular one in Germany, where it has been strongly supported by Wolfgang Ostwald and others, and considered as a case of "adsorption," whatever that may be, but a view has gained ground in America and England that the change is of a colloidal character, and dependent on the opposite electric charges of the hide fiber and the tannin particles, which combine and electrically neutralize each other. Recent investigations by R. J. Browne, at the Procter Research Laboratory at Leeds, go far to prove that all vegetable tannins are colloidal in character, since they can be entirely removed from solution by ultrafiltration, and it is known from cataphoresis experiments that they are negatively charged, while hide fiber on the acid

[1] Bogue's "Colloidal Behavior," **2**, 728 (1924).
[2] "The Chemistry of Leather Manufacture," Easton, 271 (1923).
[3] THOMAS and FRIEDEN: *J. Ind. Eng. Chem.*, **15**, 839(1923).

side of its isoelectric point has a positive charge in consequence of the Donnan equilibrium. If two colloid suspensions of opposite charges come in contact, they combine, much as two oppositely charged ions would do, and, if mixed in the right proportions for complete neutralization, the precipitation is complete. The Procter-Wilson theory of tannage holds that leather is such a combination, and with regard to what may be called the first stage of vegetable tannage, there is strong evidence in its favor. Tannage only takes place when the hide fiber is slightly swollen with acid and so possesses a positive Donnan charge, and this charge will naturally vary with the difference between the hydrogen ion concentrations of the pelt and the liquor which is in equilibrium with it, which is greatest when the acidity is very small. In alkaline liquors, tannage does not take place.

So far as I can make out, von Schröder's interpretation of the mechanism of the first step in the tanning process is the same as Procter and Wilson's. What the latter have done in addition is to attempt to give the origin of the charge on the collagen of the hide. Thus it is assumed that in equilibrium with a tan liquor having a pH value lying in the range 2 to 5, collagen (represented by C) forms a compound, CHA, which is completely ionized into the positive ion $CH^{\cdot}$ and the negative ion A'. Since the hypothetical collagen cations are a part of an elastic structure which cannot diffuse, the conditions necessary for a Donnan equilibrium obtain.[1] When equilibrium is attained between the collagen and the acid:

In the tan liquor let $\quad x = [H^{\cdot}] = [A']$

and in the collagen jelly let $y = [H^{\cdot}]$

and $\quad\quad\quad\quad\quad z = [CH^{\cdot}]$

from which $\quad\quad\quad [A'] = y + z$

The equation of products may now be written:

$$x^2 = y(y + z)$$

in which the product of equals is equated to the product of unequals. It follows, therefore, that the sum of the unequals is greater than the sum of the equals, or that $2y + z$, the sum of the diffusible ions in the hide jelly, is greater than $2x$, the sum of

[1] *Cf.* Chap. I, p. 18.

the ions in the tan liquor. This gives rise to an electrical difference of potential between the jelly phase and the external solution, which may be formulated thus:

$$E = \frac{RT}{F} \log_e \frac{y}{x} = \frac{RT}{F} \log_e \frac{-z + \sqrt{4x^2 + z^2}}{2x}$$

By similar reasoning the electrical difference of potential E_1 between the surface film of the tannin particles and bulk of the solution is given by

$$E_1 = \frac{RT}{F} \log_e \frac{x}{y_1} = \frac{RT}{F} \log_e \frac{2x}{-z_1 + \sqrt{4x^2 + z_1^2}}$$

where z_1 is the concentration of the cations balancing the negative charge on the tannin particles and y_1 the concentration of the anions [A'] in the surface film. Since E and E_1 are of opposite sign, the Procter-Wilson theory assumes that the first step in the mechanism of tanning results from the tendency for E and E_1 to neutralize each other.

The equation for the difference of potential between a positive collagen jelly and the surrounding solution is deduced from the specific assumption that hydrochloric acid, say, combines with collagen, forming highly ionized collagen chloride in which the collagen is the constituent of a complex cation whose free diffusion is restricted. It should be emphasied that this does not furnish any proof whatsoever of the existence of a definite highly ionized compound, collagen chloride, yielding a collagen cation. One arrives at exactly the same equation by making the more probable assumption that collagen, like the oxides of iron, chromium, and aluminum, adsorbs hydrogen ion more strongly than chloride ion and so possesses a positive charge in dilute hydrochloric acid solution. The hydrogen ion adsorbed by the jelly is not free to diffuse, thus imposing the constraint conditions necessary for a Donnan equilibrium. As Donnan[1] puts it: "An adsorption of hydrogen ions by colloidal aggregates or micelles (constituting the units of the molecular network) would lead to the same constraint conditions and the same general equations as the ionization of the amphoteric protein molecules assumed by Procter."

[1] *Chemical Rev.*, **1**, 89 (1924).

The initial step in the tanning process would thus appear to be neutralization by adsorption of negative tannin by positive collagen, which owes its charge to preferential adsorption of hydrogen ion. The isoelectric point of collagen is claimed to be at pH = 5;[1] and the amount of tannin adsorbed by a given amount of hide powder increases with decreasing pH values, as would be expected. It caused considerable worry, however, to find an increase in the adsorption of tannin with increasing pH on the alkaline side of the alleged isoelectric point. This reaches a maximum around pH = 8, above which it falls off rapidly to zero.[2] A partial explanation of this was forthcoming when Wilson and Gallun[3] found a second isoelectric point for collagen at pH = 7.7. Two tautomeric forms of collagen are, therefore, assumed to exist: one, C_a, stable in acid solution with an isoelectric point at pH = 5; and a second, C_b, stable in alkaline solution with an isoelectric point at pH = 7.7. On increasing the pH value from 5 to 7.7, if the change from C_a to C_b proceeds at a greater rate than positive C_a changes to negative C_a, then the net result will be an increase in the amount of positive C_b and an increase in the amount of tannin adsorbed. But there is still some tannin adsorbed above pH = 7.7, more in commercial tanning extracts than in tannic acid.[4] Thomas and Kelly[5] assume the existence of some complex organic reaction to account for this.

While one cannot deny that the initial step in tanning by tannin may involve factors other than neutralization by adsorption of negatively charged tannin by positively charged hide, there seems no necessity, at least for the present, to postulate any other action to account for the fact that there appears to be some adsorption of tannin above pH = 7.7 and below pH = 2. For, if there are two modifications of collagen, C_a and C_b, with different isoelectric points in contact with each other, then each is certain to influence the other, and the values pH = 5 and

[1] PORTER: *J. Soc. Leather Trades' Chem.*, **5**, 259 (1921); **6**, 83 (1922); THOMAS and KELLY: *J. Am. Chem. Soc.*, **44**, 195 (1922).

[2] THOMAS and KELLY: *J. Ind. Eng. Chem.*, **15**, 1148 (1923).

[3] *J. Ind. Eng. Chem.*, **15**, 71 (1923).

[4] THOMAS and KELLY: *J. Ind. Eng. Chem.*, **16**, 800 (1924).

[5] *J. Ind. Eng. Chem.*, **16**, 31 (1924).

pH $= 7.7$ are not true isoelectric points at all; but each is an average or compromise value at which the mutual effect of two collagens of the same or opposite charge give a minimum. If the supposed C_b could be isolated from the influence of the supposed C_a, the isoelectric point of the former might very well be at a higher value than pH $= 7.7$.

Attention has been called to von Schröder's observation that the adsorption of tannin by hide powder is completely reversible for a short time; but on standing, the process becomes irreversible. Not only can no tannin be extracted from the hide by water, but it resists the action of dilute alkalies; that is, leather is formed. Justin-Mueller[1] believes that the second stage in the tanning process following adsorption is some chemical reaction between tannin and hide. A similar view seems to be favored by Freundlich,[2] although he does not commit himself definitely. On the other hand, a number of people[3] come out squarely in support of the view that the process is physical throughout. Thus Moeller[4] states "that the changes which tannin colloid undergoes after being taken up by hide substances were found to depend solely on irreversible colloidal changes of state. Simple chemical processes do not occur." Moeller[5] considers leather to be animal hide, the elementary particles of which are microcrystalline micelles protected from hydrolytic influences by a sheath of tan particles.

Some attempt has been made by Meunier,[6] Fahrion,[7] and others to work out a purely chemical interpretation of vegetable tanning. Thus Meunier obtained a leather of remarkable permanence by bringing skin in contact with hydroquinone. A portion of the quinone was reduced to quinol and Meunier concludes

[1] *Kolloid-Z.*, **6**, 40 (1910).

[2] "Elements of Colloid Chemistry," translated by Burger, London, 186 (1925).

[3] VON SCHRÖDER: *Kolloidchem. Beihefte*, **1**, 53 (1909); STIASNY: *Collegium*, 118 (1908); *Kolloid-Z.*, **2**, 257 (1908); **31**, 299 (1922); GOLDMANN: *Collegium*, 93 (1908).

[4] MOELLER: *Collegium*, 39 (1917).

[5] *Z. Leder-Gerberei Chem.*, **1**, 360 (1922).

[6] *Chimie & industrie*, **1**, 71, 272 (1918); *J. Am. Leather Chem. Assoc.*, **13**, 530 (1918); MEUNIER and SEYEWETZ: *Mon. sci.*, **23**, 91 (1908).

[7] *Z. angew. Chem.*, **22**, 2083, 2135, 2187 (1909).

that this reduction is accompanied by oxidation of the collagen, whereupon the oxidized collagen combines with the remaining quinone, giving leather. Meunier postulates the formation of quinones in vegetable tanning materials, which react with collagen to form leather. Powarnin[1] objects to the assumption that the quinones result from oxidation and suggests that they are formed by a tautomeric change which, for tannin, is assumed to be:

$$
\begin{array}{ccc}
& \text{CH} & \\
\text{HC} & & \text{C} - \text{OH} \\
\text{HC} & & \text{C} - \text{OH} \\
& \text{CH} & \\
\end{array}
\quad \longrightarrow \quad
\begin{array}{ccc}
& \text{CH} & \\
\text{HC} & & \text{CH} - \text{O} \\
\text{HC} & & \text{CH} - \text{O} \\
& \text{CH} & \\
\end{array}
$$

Enol form   Keto form

The enol form is supposed to be stable in alkaline solution and the keto form in acid solution. Only the latter form is assumed to have tanning properties. As yet, these views of the tanning process lack definite experimental foundation;[2] but they indicate the probable existence of a chemical as well as a physical action in vegetable tanning.

Formaldehyde has tanning properties[3] in solutions having a pH value greater than 4.8, the best practical results being obtained between pH = 5.5 to 10.0.[4] Meunier believes that a definite chemical compound is formed between the aldehyde and oxidized collagen; but this appears doubtful, as the formaldehyde can be recovered quantitatively from formaldehyde leather simply by digesting with dilute hydrochloric acid.

MINERAL TANNING

Any mineral salt may be employed for tanning leather, provided it undergoes hydrolytic dissociation forming a colloidal

[1] *Collegium*, 634 (1914).

[2] *Cf.*, however, THOMAS and KELLY: *J. Ind. Eng. Chem.*, **16**, 800 (1924); THOMAS and FOSTER: *J. Am. Chem. Soc.*, **48**, 489 (1926).

[3] British Patent 2872 (1898).

[4] HEY: *J. Soc. Leather Trades' Chem.*, **6**, 131 (1922); THOMAS and KELLY: *J. Ind. Eng. Chem.*, **16**, 925 (1924).

hydrous oxide or basic salt. Actually only the salts of iron, aluminum, and chromium have been employed, and of these the salts of chromium are by far the most important and so will be considered first.

Chrome Tanning.—As early as 1858, Knapp[1] described a process for tanning hide with solutions of salts of aluminum, iron, and chromium; but the first successful method of mineral tanning was invented by Augustus Schultz in 1884. In Schultz's two-bath process, the skins are treated with an acidified solution of potassium dichromate until the liquor penetrates them thoroughly after which they are put into a bath of acidified sodium thiosulfate which reduces the chromate in the hide to chromic salt, the tanning agent. In 1893 Dennis revived and patented Knapp's original single-bath tan liquor which consists of a partially neutralized solution of chromic chloride. Dennis prepared the bath by dissolving chromic oxide in hydrochloric acid and subsequently rendering this more basic by adding caustic soda. Later Procter[2] showed that good tanning liquors could be prepared by reducing bichromate solution with glucose in the presence of enough hydrochloric acid to leave the solution basic. Basic chromic sulfate was found to be superior to the chloride for one-bath tanning and is now almost universally employed.[3] A useful method of preparing a satisfactory bath consists in the reduction of a strong solution of sodium bichromate directly with sulfur dioxide.[4] A concentrated liquor can be obtained in this way and diluted as required. In view of the relatively weak character of sulfurous acid, the liquor is sufficiently basic for many purposes. The equation for the reduction is usually written

$$Na_2Cr_2O_7 + 3SO_2 + H_2O = Na_2SO_4 + 2CrOHSO_4$$

This merely represents the relative basicity of the final liquor, but there is no assurance of the formation of a definite basic salt like that formulated.

---

[1] "Nature and Essential Character of the Tanning Process and of Leather," J. G. Cotta Buchandlung (1858); English translation, *J. Am. Leather Chem. Assoc.*, **16**, 658 (1921).

[2] *Leather Trades' Rev.*, Jan. 12 (1897).

[3] WILSON: "The Chemistry of Leather Manufacture," Easton, 278 (1923).

[4] BALDERSTON: *Shoe & Leather Rep.*, Oct. 18 (1917); PROCTER: *J. Roy. Soc. Arts.*, **66**, 747 (1918).

That basic liquor is more satisfactory for tanning is well illustrated by some observations of Thomas, Baldwin, and Kelly[1] on the rate of taking up of chromic oxide by hide powder from a commercial tan liquor and from a solution of chromic sulfate. The chrome liquor had a basicity corresponding to the formula $Cr(OH)_{1.2}(SO_4)_{0.9}$ and contained 17 grams Cr_2O_3 per liter. The chromic sulfate contained 164 grams Cr_2O_3 per liter. The results are shown in Fig. 20. The time in hours covered by

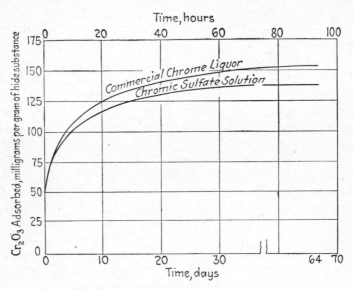

Fig. 20.—Adsorption of chromic oxide by hide substance.

the experiment with the commercial chrome liquor is plotted on the top horizontal axis and the time in days covered by the experiments with chromic sulfate solution on the bottom horizontal axis. The amount adsorbed is determined by direct analysis of the leather. It will be seen that the rate of tanning is very much less in the chromic sulfate solution which has a hydrogen ion concentration about twenty times greater than the commercial liquor. Moreover, the amount of chromic oxide taken up from

[1] J. Am. Leather Chem. Assoc., 15, 147 (1920); THOMAS and KELLY: Ibid., 15, 487 (1920).

the commercial liquor has not reached a limiting value in 4 days; but is appreciably greater than the limiting value in the case of pure chromic sulfate. Since the amount of chromic oxide taken up and the velocity of the process is greater in the more basic solutions, it is obvious why such solutions are used in practice. The basicity must be subject to careful control, however, since if too basic, the bath is rendered turbid in the presence of hide, owing to precipitation of hydrous chromic oxide. This is of importance in connection with the theory of chrome tanning, which will next be considered.

The most plausible theory of chrome tanning is that the hide fibrils adsorb from the tan liquor hydrous chromic oxide or basic salt which subsequently ages, giving a protective coating. This film not only keeps the fibrils separated and thereby prevents their coalescence on drying but protects them from the action of water and dilute alkali. As Rochelle salt dissolves even an aged hydrous chromic oxide, it is not surprising to learn that a chrome-tanned leather is detanned by soaking in a solution of this salt.[1] The detanned leather can be tanned once more by washing and soaking in fresh chrome liquor.

Davison[2] determined the amount of chromic oxide taken up in 4 hours by a constant amount of hide powder, from various concentrations up to 1.5 grams Cr_2O_3 per liter, of a single-bath chrome-tanning solution. On plotting the chromic oxide taken up against the concentration of the residual solution a continuous curve is obtained which corresponds with the ordinary adsorption formula. This supports the view that the initial step in chrome tanning consists in adsorption of hydrous chromic oxide or basic salt.[3]

Attempts have been made to interpret the chrome-tanning process as a mutual precipitation of oppositely charged particles just as in the case of vegetable tanning. The difficulty encountered is that hydrous chromic oxide in acid solution takes a positive charge just like the hide. Thompson and Atkin[4] suggest that

---

[1] PROCTER and WILSON: *J. Soc. Chem. Ind.*, **35**, 156 (1916).

[2] *J. Phys. Chem.*, **21**, 190 (1917).

[3] BENNETT: *J. Soc. Leather Trades' Chem.*, **1**, 130, 169 (1917); *cf.*, however, WILSON, THOMAS, *et al.*: *J. Am. Leather Chem. Assoc.*, **12**, 450 (1917).

[4] *J. Soc. Leather Trades' Chem.*, **6**, 207 (1922).

the active constituent of the chrome-tan liquor is a negative ion or colloidal particle having a composition such as $Cr(OH)_3 \cdot CrOCl \cdot Cl'$ which combines with positively charged collagen, forming leather. This view was called in question by Seymour-Jones[1] who found that hide was tanned in a normal fashion in a basic chromic chloride solution which showed no anodic migration of chromium whatsoever. Seymour-Jones[2] also attempted the ultrafiltration of a typical tanning bath containing 270 grams chromic oxide per liter prepared by reduction of a solution of sodium bichromate with sulfur dioxide. The solution passed unchanged through a collodion disk ultrafilter and through filter papers impregnated with 1 and 5 per cent gelatin solutions, respectively, and subsequently hardened. This was taken to mean that colloidal chromic oxide or basic salt plays no rôle in chrome tanning. There is, however, no doubt of the presence of colloidal chromic oxide in certain technical tan liquors. Thus, Wintgen and Löwenthal[3] ultrafiltered a so-called one-third basic commercial tan liquor prepared by mixing 20 grams chrome alum in 170 cubic centimeters of water with 7 grams of crystalline sodium carbonate in 20 cubic centimeters of water. Using a very thick fine hardened ultrafilter and applying a pressure of 75 atmospheres, they obtained a filtrate consisting of chromium salt in molecular solution; and a residue possessing the appearance and properties of colloidal chromic oxide. It is altogether probable that Seymour-Jones could have ultrafiltered some colloidal chromic oxide from his tan liquor had he used a sufficiently dense filter. This is, however, more or less beside the point, as one can tan leather in a chromic salt solution containing but little colloidal oxide.

If chromic sulfate is placed in solution, an equilibrium exists that may be represented thus:

$$Cr_2(SO_4)_3 + xH_2O \rightleftarrows Cr_2O_3xH_2O + 3H_2SO_4$$

or, if preferred, by

$$Cr_2(SO_4)_3 + 12H_2O \rightleftarrows [Cr(OH)_2 \cdot (H_2O)_4]_2SO_4 + 2H_2SO_4$$

[1] *J. Ind. Eng. Chem.*, **15**, 265 (1923).
[2] *J. Ind. Eng. Chem.*, **15**, 75 (1923).
[3] *Kolloid-Z.*, **34**, 294 (1924).

since Werner[1] has prepared a definite crystalline basic salt, insoluble in water, of the formula indicated. When hide is placed in such a solution, it adsorbs acid strongly, thus displacing the equilibrium to the right with the consequent precipitation of the insoluble hydrous oxide or basic salt on the surface of the particles of hide, where it is adsorbed. The amount deposited in the hide substance under these conditions is obviously small and so the tannage is relatively light. If, on the other hand, a portion of the acid is neutralized, the adsorption of acid by the hide brings about a correspondingly greater precipitation of hydrous oxide or basic salt, and the tannage is correspondingly heavy. As I have already pointed out, if the tan liquor is rendered too basic, the adsorption of acid by the hide causes precipitation of the hydrous oxide in the liquor rendering the latter cloudy. Obviously, a careful control of the conditions is necessary for successful tanning. In general, if the acidity is too high, the penetration is good, but the amount of chromic oxide deposited is slight; whereas if the basicity is too high, the bath contains hydrous chromic oxide in too coarse a state of subdivision to penetrate well.

It should be emphasized that the displacement to the right of the hydrolytic decomposition of chromic salt is occasioned not only by adsorption of sulfuric acid but by adsorption of hydrous chromic oxide as well. To illustrate, let us consider the adsorption phenomena which take place from solutions of chromate and dichromate with hydrous alumina. In such solutions, the following equilibrium exists:

$$Cr_2O_7'' + H_2O \rightleftarrows 2H^{\cdot} + 2CrO_4''$$

If a sample of highly purified "grown alumina"[2] is added to a solution of red dichromate, the solution becomes yellow. This is because hydrous alumina adsorbs hydrogen ion, strongly shifting the equilibrium to the right. But the alumina also adsorbs chromate which can be determined quantitatively and can be detected qualitatively by the color it imparts to the adsorbent. This likewise tends to displace the equilibrium to the right.

---

[1] *Ber.*, **41,** 3447 (1909).

[2] WISLICENUS: *Z. angew. Chem.*, **18,** 801 (1904); *Kolloid-Z.*, 2d Supplement, XI (1908).

If, instead of adding powdered alumina to a solution of dichromate, one adds alumina sol stabilized by preferential adsorption of hydrogen ion, the adsorption capacity of the alumina for hydrogen is partially supplied and the equilibrium is not disturbed appreciably, the solution remaining red. Under these conditions, the adsorption of chromate is relatively small; and incidentally, the amount of dichromate carried down is less than that for most multivalent ions.[1] In the same way, when hide is placed in a chromic sulfate solution containing a relatively large amount of hydrogen ion, hydrous chromic oxide or basic salt is adsorbed, as well as sulfuric acid; but the adsorption of the former is much greater from more basic solutions.

After the tannage is complete, the skin is left in a somewhat acid condition. In practice, it is rendered nearly neutral by treating with a dilute alkaline solution. Even after this treatment chrome leather is characterized by having a relatively high sulfuric acid content. Only a trace is free at any one time, but as soon as this trace is removed, more is immediately liberated. A part of this sulfuric acid is adsorbed by the hide and a part by the hydrous oxide, while some may exist in solid solution in the hydrous oxide or as a basic salt.

The addition of neutral salts to a bath cuts down the adsorption of chromic oxide by the hide. In the case of chlorides, this may be due to the observed increase in the hydrogen ion concentration;[2] but sulfates decrease the hydrogen ion concentration which should favor increased adsorption of chromic oxide. To get around this difficulty, Wilson and Gallun[3] postulate the formation of addition compounds between the chromium compounds and the added salt, which are supposed to be endowed with the property of tanning less readily than the original chromium compounds. It is probable that a great deal of the effect of neutral salts is due to their adsorption by the hide, which cuts down the adsorption of hydrous chromic oxide.

[1] WEISER and MIDDLETON: *J. Phys. Chem.*, **24,** 647 (1920).

[2] POMA: *Z. physik. Chem.*, **88,** 671 (1914); HARNED: *J. Am. Chem. Soc.*, **37,** 2460 (1915); THOMAS and BALDWIN: *J. Am. Leather Chem. Assoc.*, **13,** 248 (1918); *J. Am. Chem. Soc.*, **41,** 1981 (1919); THOMAS and FOSTER: *J. Ind. Eng. Chem.*, **14,** 132 (1922).

[2] *J. Am. Leather Chem. Assoc.*, **15,** 273 (1920).

A purely chemical theory of chrome tanning receives its most enthusiastic support from Wilson and his collaborators.[1] It is the opinion of these investigators that even in acid solution, there are some negatively charged groups in the collagen structure. In the tanning process, $Cr(OH)_2$· ions or ions of similar structure are supposed to diffuse into the jelly composing the hide and to attach themselves to negatively charged groups wherever encountered, giving salts that have been designated chromium collagenates. Attempts have been made to establish the existence of such salts by Baldwin[2] and by Thomas and Kelly.[3] Baldwin studied the fixing of chromic oxide from various liquors containing 0.38 to 66.4 grams of chromic oxide per liter and found that the amount taken up reaches a maximum in a bath containing 15 to 20 grams per liter. Davison failed to observe this maximum, as he worked with lower concentrations of tan liquor. Thomas and Kelly repeated Baldwin's experiments with concentrations varying from 0.36 to 202 grams chromic oxide per liter, and confirmed the result that the amount of chromic oxide taken up per gram of hide powder in 48 hours reached a maximum in a solution containing approximately 16 grams of chromic oxide per liter, after which the curve sloped downward, reaching a minimum when the concentration of chromic oxide in solution was approximately 150 grams per liter as shown in the lower curve, Fig. 21; the experiments were repeated, keeping the liquor in contact with the hide for 8.5 months, with the results given in the upper curve, Fig. 21. The conclusions drawn from these observations are the following: Wilson[4] found that 750 grams of a certain collagen take up 1 mol of hydrochloric acid, forming what he believes to be collagen chloride, a salt of a weak monoacid base. He, therefore, assumes the combining weight of collagen to be 750. Using this value, Thomas and Kelly calculate that 4 equivalents of chromium are combined with 1 of collagen at the maximum in the 48-hour curve which represents a definite compound, tetrachrome collagen. In the 8.5-month run, the

---

[1] WILSON: "The Chemistry of Leather Manufacturer," Easton, 278–308 (1923).

[2] *J. Am. Leather Chem. Assoc.*, **14**, 433 (1919).

[3] *J. Ind. Eng. Chem.*, **13**, 65 (1921); **14**, 621 (1922).

[4] *J. Am. Leather Chem. Assoc.*, **12**, 108 (1917).

maximum is approximately twice as high as in the 48-hour run, a circumstance that is claimed to prove the existence of octachrome collagen. The octachrome curve shows a slight bend at a higher concentration of chrome liquor where the fixation of chromic oxide is believed to be sufficiently near the theoretical for tetrachrome collagen to justify postulating its formation.

After championing the use of thermodynamic formulas to interpret tanning by tannin, one wonders why no attention what-

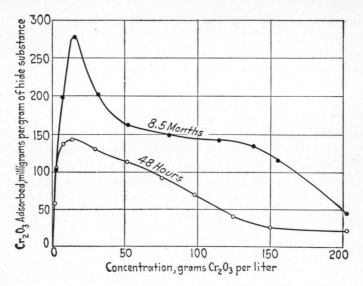

Fig. 21.—Effect of concentration of chrome liquor on the adsorption of chromic oxide by hide substance.

soever seems to have been paid to the phase rule in interpreting the results with chrome tanning. In the light of this generalization, the curves obtained by Thomas and Kelly certainly do not offer convincing proof of the formation of chromium collagenates. On the contrary, they indicate that quite the opposite is true. A maximum is observed repeatedly in the taking up of one substance from solution by another. For example, the lower curve in Fig. 22 shows the adsorption of acetic acid from toluene solution by animal charcoal[1] and the upper curve, the adsorption of

[1] Schmidt-Walter: *Kolloid-Z.*, **14**, 242 (1914).

phenol from solution in ethyl alcohol by the same adsorbent.[1] The maxima in these curves are no more indicative of compound formation than any other points on the curves. Freundlich[2] observed maxima in the adsorption of strychnine nitrate from

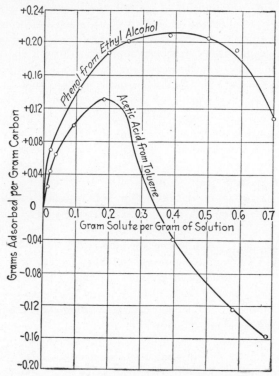

Fig. 22.—Adsorption by carbon of (1) phenol from ethyl alcohol and (2) acetic acid from toluene.

aqueous solution by carbon, wool, and arsenious sulfide; and in the adsorption of crystal violet by carbon and fibers[3]. Slmilra observations were made by Biltz and Steiner[4] in the absorption of dyes, such as night blue and Victoria blue, by wool and car-

[1] GUSTAFSON: *Z. physik. Chem.*, **91**, 397 (1916).

[2] *Z. physik. Chem.*, **73**, 400 (1910); FREUNDLICH and POSER: *Kolloidchem. Beihefte*, **6**, 295 (1914).

[3] FREUNDLICH and LOSEV: *Z. physik. Chem.*, **59**, 284 (1907).

[4] *Kolloid-Z.*, **7**, 113 (1910).

bon.   Dreyer and Douglas[1] found that the adsorption of agglu-
tinin by bacteria reached a maximum at a certain concentration
and thereafter decreased.   "In short," says Freundlich,[2] "by far
the majority of the adsorption curves that are not entirely
regular show a maximum in the adsorbed mass with increasing
concentration, followed by a falling off until the adsorption is
negative.[3]

A number of cases have been reported where a change in the
physical character of the adsorbent leads to a maximum in the
adsorption curve.   Thus Lottermoser and Rothe[4] observed a
decrease in the adsorption of potassium iodide by silver iodide
above a certain concentration of electrolyte.   This was traced
to a change in the structure of the silver iodide, which became
denser and more granular.   Freundlich and Schucht[5] noted the
spontaneous transformation of amorphous mercuric sulfide to
a crystalline form that shows a decreased power of adsorbing
dyes.   Wagner[6] showed that when salts of many of the hydrous
oxides are hydrolyzed, they absorb the free acid to some extent
and later give it up owing to a change in the physical character
of the adsorbent.   While the chromic-oxide hide-powder curves
are typical of adsorption curves showing a maximum, it is probable that the irreversible change in state which hide powder
undergoes in contact with tanning liquor is in part responsible
for this maximum.   The increasing hydrogen ion concentration
with increasing concentration of tan liquor likewise contributes
to the cutting down of the adsorption of chromic oxide at higher
concentrations.   The important thing is that the maximum in
the continuous curves should not be construed as indicating the
formation of definite chromium collagenates any more than any
other point on the curve.   At suitable points on the curve, a
whole series of definite salts from monochrome to octachrome
collagenate may be assumed to exist; but this does not indicate,
let alone prove, their existence.

[1] *Proc. Roy. Soc.*, **82***B*, 185 (1910).
[2] "Kapillarchemie," 246 (1922).
[3] *Cf.* WILLIAMS: *Med. fr. K. Vet. Akad. Nobelinst.*, (2) No. 27 (1913).
[4] *Z. physik. Chem.*, **62**, 359 (1908).
[5] *Z. physik. Chem.*, **85**, 660 (1913).
[6] *Monatshefte für Chemie*, **34**, 95, 931 (1913).

Alumina Tanning.—An alumina tan bath consists of basic aluminum sulfate together with enough sodium chloride to prevent undue swelling of the skin. The hydrous oxide or basic salt appears to be adsorbed less strongly than in the case of chrome tanning, and the freshly treated hide cannot be washed without swelling. Moreover, hydrous chromic oxide ages much more rapidly than hydrous alumina, and so it is necessary to keep the alumina-treated skins in the dried state for weeks or months before a satisfactory leather is obtained. Even at best, alumina-tanned leather is not so permanent as chrome-tanned leather, probably because hydrous alumina becomes crystalline on ageing and so does not afford such good protection to the hide particles as does the amorphous film of hydrous chromic oxide which never assumes the crystalline form.

Iron Tanning.—Ferric salts may be employed as tanning agents, but attempts to manufacture iron-tanned leathers have not met with success. According to Procter,[1] a part of the difficulty arises from the fact that ferric oxide acts as an oxygen carrier, causing slow oxidation of the hide and consequent deterioration. Moreover, difficulty is encountered in neutralizing the excess sulfuric acid after tanning. When the leather is treated with a dilute alkali solution, the adsorbed hydrous oxide is displaced, and any normal or basic salt is converted into colloidal hydrous oxide and washed out of the skin.[2] Jackson and How[3] claim to have prepared a fairly good leather by adjusting the acidity so as to give a tan liquor in which the ratio of equivalents of hydroxide groups to equivalents of acid radical is never less than 1:5 nor more than 1:3. After tanning, the neutralization is effected very gradually.

Silica Tanning.—Graham[4] pointed out in 1862 that gelatin was precipitated by colloidal silica. The precipitate was insoluble in water and was not decomposed by washing; in other words, the gelatin was tanned. Hough[5] found that purified colloidal silica is much too instable to serve as a tanning agent. As would

---

[1] "The Principles of Leather Manufacture," 2d ed., p. 275.

[2] JETTMAR: *Cuir*, **8**, 74, 106 (1919).

[3] *J. Am. Leather Chem. Assoc.*, **16**, 63, 139, 202, 229 (1921).

[4] *J. Chem. Soc.*, **15**, 246 (1862).

[5] *Cuir*, **8**, 209, 257, 314 (1919).

be expected, the sol agglomerates before it has a chance to diffuse into the hide substance. By adding a 30 per cent solution of sodium silicate to a 30 per cent solution of hydrochloric acid until the concentration of free acid is reduced to tenth normal, a bath is obtained which diffuses into the hide and deposits a protecting layer of hydrous silica. A fully tanned leather usually contains from 17 to 24 per cent of silica. One of the difficulties of the process is to prevent too great an adsorption of silica by the hide.

The most serious fault with silica-tanned leather is that it tears very easily after keeping for a few months.[1] This is probably due to a change in the physical character of the hydrous silica on ageing.

Miscellaneous Tanning Agents.—Basic ceric chloride[2] can be used for a tan bath, giving a fairly good leather; but salts of bismuth have not proved satisfactory.[3]

It is a remarkable fact that freshly precipitated finely divided sulfur is adsorbed by hide substance, giving a white leather[4] which does not swell when left for 24 hours in water and can be dried without losing its stability. Apostolo claims that the sulfur is not extracted by carbon bisulfide; but this is disputed by Thomas[5] who finds that sulfur is not a true tanning agent.

Colloidally dispersed insoluble sulfides, silicates, oxides, and phosphates of many metals appear to act as tanning agents.[6] Indeed, Procter[7] reports that finely divided insoluble powders, such as ultramarine, can convert hide into leather by mere mechanical drumming. There is no doubt of the essential physical nature of the latter process. At the opposite extreme is the tanning action of chlorine and bromine but not iodine, where the change is doubtless of a purely chemical nature.[8] The leather obtained with halogens is imputrescible and resists the action of cold water but not boiling water.

[1] Thuau: *Cuir*, **9,** 10, 80, 102 (1921).

[2] Garelli: *Collegium*, 418 (1912).

[3] Garelli and Apostolo: *Collegium*, 422 (1913).

[4] Apostolo: *Collegium*, 420 (1913).

[5] *J. Ind. Eng. Chem.*, **18,** 259 (1926).

[6] Sommerhoff: *Collegium*, 381 (1913).

[7] Bogue's "Colloidal Behavior," **2,** 718 (1924).

[8] Meunier and Seyewetz: *Collegium*, 289, 373 (1911).

From this survey it is obvious that the term "tanning" has been applied to a wide variety of processes whereby hide fiber is converted into what is called "leather." It would be more proper to speak of "leathers," for the commercial article shows marked variations in properties, depending on the method of manufacture. Procter[1] distinguishes the following general methods of tanning:

1. By mere dehydration of the separated fibrils in such a way that they can be dried without adhesion.

2. By actual changes in the chemical nature of the fibrils, which destroy their adhesive character.

3. By coating the fibers with fine powders or precipitates or, perhaps, fatty matters, which mechanically separate them.

[1] Bogue's "Colloidal Behavior," **2,** 730 (1924).

CHAPTER XVI

MORDANTS

The adsorption of many dyes by wool, silk, and cotton is so weak that they are of value to the practical dyer only when used in conjunction with mordants. The term mordant (from mordre, to bite or to corrode) was first applied by the French to metallic salts which were supposed to act by biting or opening a passage into the fibers of the cloth, giving access to the color. Thus, alum was believed to be effective in fixing certain dyes, owing to the solvent or corrosive action of sulfuric acid.[1] It is now known that the real mordant is the hydrous oxide and not the acid derived from the salt.

In general, a mordant may be defined as any substance that is adsorbed strongly by the cloth and, in turn, adsorbs the dye strongly. In dyeing a mordanted cloth, it is the mordant rather than the fiber which adsorbs the dye in most cases. When a mordant adsorbs a dye in the absence of a fiber, the product is called a lake. The lakes employed as pigments are usually prepared in contact with what are termed lake bases, such as barium sulfate, china clay, red lead, and lead sulfate, which modify the physical properties of the lakes in some desired way.

In order to appreciate the importance of mordants in the art of dyeing, one needs but to recall that the first so-called direct or substantive dye, Congo red, was not discovered until 1884. Before this date it was impossible to dye cotton with acid and basic dyes except by the use of mordants. Moreover, substantive dyes on cotton are in general much less fast to light and washing than are the mordant colors.

A typical example of a mordant dye is alizarin, the important coloring matter of the roots of *rubia tinctorium*, or madder, a plant of Indian origin which was cultivated largely in France and

---

[1] BANCROFT: "Philosophy of Permanent Colors," **1,** 341 (1813); NAPIER: "A Manual of Dyeing," 186 (1875).

Holland before the synthesis of alizarin from anthracene was accomplished in 1868. If a piece of cotton is dipped into an aqueous solution of alizarin, it assumes a yellow color that is easily removed by washing with soap and water; but if the cloth is first mordanted, it is dyed a fast color: red with alumina, reddish brown with chrome, orange with tin, and purple or black with iron. By treating the fiber with the so-called sulfonated oils before mordanting with alumina, there results the brilliant Turkey red, a color remarkable for its fastness to light and to the action of soap and water. The dyeing of Turkey red is a very ancient process having been carried out centuries ago in India, using milk as fatty matter and munjeet, the Indian madder plant. The plant itself with its earthy incrustations furnished enough alumina to give the color lake. The art spread from the East through Persia and Turkey, reaching France and England in the latter part of the eighteenth century.

Wool like cotton can be dyed with madder only by the aid of mordants. The scarlet trousers of the French soldiers, introduced by Louis Philippe to encourage madder culture, and the scarlet uniform of the British soldier of Revolutionary war days were made possible by the use of the mordant alumina.

Two classes of mordants are generally recognized: acid and basic or metallic. The acid mordants are the tannins, the fatty acids, albumin, hydrous silica, arsenic acid, and phosphoric acid; while the basic mordants are the hydrous oxides of the heavy metals.

The most important metallic mordants are the hydrous oxides of chromium, aluminum, iron, tin and copper, in the order named. Alumina was the first mordant used, and years ago, alumina and stannic oxide were the most important because people were interested in getting the bright colors which these mordants yield. As might be expected, the mordanting action of nearly all the possible oxides has been investigated. Liebermann[1] reports that the oxides of yttrium, beryllium, thorium, cerium, zirconium, and copper hold dyes most tenaciously; while the oxides of zinc, cadmium, manganese, antimony, bismuth, lead, tin, and thallium are much less satisfactory; and the oxides of iron, aluminum, chromium, and uranium occupy an intermediate position. Such

[1] *Ber.*, **35**, 1493 (1902).

a classification is not generally applicable; thus Wingraf[1] finds zirconia to be a stronger mordant for certain dyes than alumina; while the reverse is true in other cases. In any event, oxides of metals other than aluminum, chromium, iron, and tin are used only in special cases. For example, titania is reported to be a particularly good mordant to use with leather.[2] The more important mordants will be taken up in some detail.

ALUMINA

If an aluminum salt which we shall represent by AlA_3 is dissolved in water, hydrolysis takes place in accord with the following equation:

$$2AlA_3 + xH_2O \rightleftarrows Al_2O_3 \cdot xH_2O + 6HA$$

The reaction proceeds further to the right, the more dilute the solution, the weaker the acid formed, and the higher the temperature. Whether the insoluble hydrous oxide precipitates out on heating or remains in colloidal solution depends on the concentration of the solution and the precipitating power of the anion. Crum[3] prepared a positive sol of hydrous alumina by hydrolyzing the acetate and boiling off the excess acetic acid; and Neidle[4] obtained a sol by dialysis of a solution of aluminum chloride at elevated temperatures. A sol cannot be prepared by dialysis of the sulfate on account of the high precipitating power of sulfate ion. The amount of hydrous oxide formed in a given case is increased by removing hydrogen ion with alkali; but the range of hydrogen ion concentration in which the oxide precipitates is much wider in the case of salts with strongly adsorbed multivalent ions, such as sulfate, than with salts of univalent ions.

While the non-existence of definite basic salts of aluminum has not been established with certainty, it is probable that no definite basic compounds are formed by the hydrolysis of aluminum salts either alone or on the addition of alkali. Certainly, the vast majority of the alleged basic acetates described by Crum and of the basic nitrates, chlorides, sulfates, acetates, and sulfoacetates

[1] *Färber-Ztg.*, **25**, 277 (1914).
[2] BARNES: *J. Soc. Dyers Colourists*, **35**, 59 (1919).
[3] *Liebig's Ann. Chem.*, **89**, 168 (1854).
[4] *J. Am. Chem. Soc.*, **39**, 71 (1917).

formulated by Liechti and Suida[1] are wholly without experimental foundation. By adding alkali to aluminum sulfate, a phase separates below pH = 5.5 having approximately the composition $5Al_2O_3 \cdot 3SO_3$;[2] but the ease with which the sulfate can be displaced by a wide variety of inorganic and dye cations argues against its being a definite compound.[3]

In view of the fact that aluminum salts hydrolyze of themselves, one should expect the hydrolysis in a given case to proceed further in the presence of a fiber which adsorbs hydrous aluminum oxide. This is actually the case, as will be shown in the subsequent paragraphs.

Mordanting of Wool.—When wool is treated with solutions of aluminum sulfate, $Al_2(SO_4)_3 \cdot 18H_2O$, less than 5 per cent on the wool, the bath is exhausted completely, all the alumina and the sulfuric acid being adsorbed.[4] At higher salt concentrations, more and more remains in the bath. Knecht[5] believes that both hydrous oxides and true basic aluminum salts are deposited by the mordanting process, since the spent liquors on dyeing well-washed wool with alizarin always possess an acid reaction. This evidence of basic salt formation is inconclusive, since adsorbed sulfuric acid would be displaced quite as readily as acid in definite chemical combination. Fürstenhagen and Appleyard[6] give data to show that the amount of sulfate taken up by wool remains constant when the fiber is mordanted from potash alum solutions containing 10 to 20 per cent of alum referred to the wool. According to Havrez[7] and to von Georgievics,[8] the amount of alumina taken up by wool from relatively dilute potash alum solutions is greater than the amount of sulfuric acid; but with increasing salt concentrations, the amount of sulfuric

[1] *J. Soc. Chem. Ind.*, **2**, 537 (1883); *cf.* also SCHLUMBERGER: *Bull. soc. chim.*, (3) **13**, 41 (1895); BÖTTINGER: *Liebig's Ann. Chem.*, **244**, 224 (1888).

[2] MILLER: *U. S. Pub. Health Repts.*, **38**, 1995 (1923); WILLIAMSON: *J. Phys. Chem.*, **27**, 284 (1923).

[3] See p. 379.

[4] LIECHTI and SCHWITZER: *Mitt. techn. Gewerbe-Museums in Wien, Sektion für Färberei*, **3**, 47 (1886).

[5] KNECHT, RAWSON, and LOWENTHAL: "A Manual of Dyeing," 237 (1916).

[6] *J. Soc. Dyers Colourists*, 105 (1888).

[7] *Chem. Zentr.*, 696 (1874).

[8] *J. Soc. Chem. Ind.*, **14**, 653 (1895).

acid taken up increases relatively to the alumina until at 24 per cent alum referred to the wool, the alumina and acid are taken up in the same relative amounts as they occur in aluminum sulfate.[1] Recently, Paddon,[2] in Bancroft's laboratory, determined the amounts of both alumina and sulfuric acid removed from potash alum baths at different concentrations. In these experiments, 2-gram samples of well-washed wool were boiled for 1 hour in the alum solutions, after which the wool was removed and aliquot portions of the several baths were analyzed in the usual gravimetric manner for aluminum and sulfate. The adsorption of alumina and sulfuric acid is given in Tables XXVI and XXVII and shown graphically in Figs. 23 and 24, respectively. Both curves are

TABLE XXVI.—ADSORPTION OF ALUMINA BY WOOL

Per cent potash alum on weight of wool	Original concentration Al_2O_3, milligram mols per liter	End concentration Al_2O_3, milligram mols per liter	Milligram mol Al_2O_3 adsorbed per gram of wool
5.12	0.438	0.137	0.377
10.25	0.881	0.395	0.607
15.37	1.319	0.842	0.597
20.50	1.761	1.362	0.500
25.62	2.200	1.863	0.421
30.75	2.645	2.403	0.303

TABLE XXVII.—ADSORPTION OF SULFURIC ACID BY WOOL

Per cent potash alum on weight of wool	Original concentration SO_3, milligram mols per liter	End concentration SO_3, milligram mols per liter	Milligram mol SO_3 adsorbed per gram of wool
5.12	1.730	1.120	0.068
10.25	3.460	2.550	0.113
15.37	5.185	4.075	0.139
20.50	6.915	5.705	0.153
25.62	8.650	7.305	0.168
30.75	10.375	9.055	0.165

[1] *Cf.* THENARD and ROARD: *Ann. Chim.*, **74**, 267 (1810).
[2] *J. Phys. Chem.*, **26**, 790 (1922).

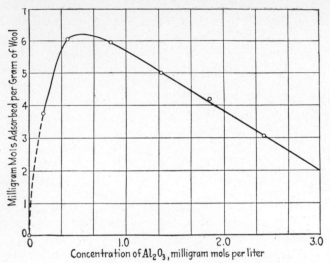

FIG. 23.—Adsorption of hydrous alumina by wool.

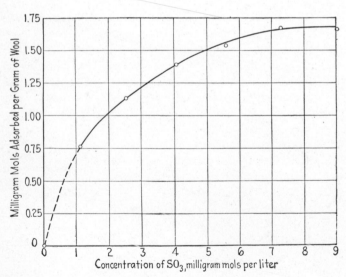

FIG. 24.—Adsorption of sulfate by wool.

smooth and free from sudden breaks, indicating that the mordanting of wool with potash alum does not lead to the formation of definite chemical compounds on the fiber; but that the process is strictly an adsorption phenomenon, involving both alumina and sulfuric acid. It is probable that the acid is adsorbed both by the alumina and by the wool.

The alumina curve passes through a maximum due to the precipitation of considerable alumina on boiling the solutions of higher concentrations, thereby cutting down the concentration of alumina so far as the wool is concerned. The adsorption of SO_3 follows a continuous course, approximating saturation in the neighborhood of 20 per cent of alum on the weight of the wool. Above this concentration, the amount adsorbed is necessarily approximately constant; hence, this should not be construed as indicating the adsorption of a definite basic salt on the fiber.

The purpose of the mordant is to have something on the fiber which will adsorb and hold the coloring matter. It is, therefore, important to have the mordant taken up under such conditions that it will be held most tenaciously by the cloth, have the maximum transparency, and adsorb the greatest amount of dye. As Bancroft[1] points out, one would not ordinarily expect to obtain the mordant in such a form that it will satisfy all these requirements to the maximum degree, simultaneously; but the aim should be to get the mordant in the form which is most generally useful. One objection to alum or aluminum sulfate for mordanting wool is that sulfate ion coagulates alumina too readily, thereby precipitating perceptible amounts of the hydrous oxide in the bath or superficially on the wool in a form that does not hold well. This is particularly true with more concentrated baths, as noted by Havrez[2] and by Paddon.[3] The former recommends a bath containing less than 10 per cent alum referred to the amount of wool, otherwise the mordant washes off readily and the wool is not dyed deeply when treated with the coloring matter. As one would expect, the so-called basic solutions of aluminum sulfate cannot be used at all with wool, since the precipitation of

[1] J. Phys. Chem., **18**, 399 (1914).
[2] Dinglers polytech. J., **205**, 491 (1872).
[3] J. Phys. Chem., **26**, 791 (1922).

the hydrous oxide is altogether too rapid. Liechti and Suida[1] claim that alum does not give as good a mordant as aluminum sulfate. This may be due to one or more of the following causes: the increase in the hydrolysis of aluminum sulfate by the presence of sodium sulfate;[2] the detrimental precipitating action of the excess sulfate in alum; and the increasing of the relative amount of sulfate adsorbed. Addition of sulfuric acid to alum causes the mordant to penetrate more thoroughly and to be fixed better than when the normal sulfate is used.[3] This is because the cutting down of the hydrolysis by the increased acidity is more pronounced than the agglomerating action of the increased concentration of sulfate.

The rapid precipitation of hydrous oxide in a loose condition on the surface of the cloth can be obviated by using an aluminum salt of a weak acid, such as aluminum oxalate, tartrate, or lactate. Although these salts hydrolyze more readily than sulfate, the resulting hydrous oxide is held in a more highly peptized state. Accordingly, the mordanting is deeper and more uniform from a solution of aluminum tartrate or oxalate; or from a solution of aluminum sulfate to which a mordanting assistant such as cream of tartar, tartaric acid, or oxalic acid is added. Some observations of Miller[4] are of interest in this connection: Portions of a solution $0.005\ M$ with respect to aluminum chloride and $0.0075\ M$ with respect to potassium oxalate were treated with gradually increasing amounts of alkali. No precipitate was formed until the pH value of the solution reached 8.8. Below this value, a slightly opalescent sol was formed but no floc. In striking contrast to this, a $0.0025\ M$ solution of potash alum formed a good floc at as low a pH value as 4.3 and up to 8.9. Obviously, the tendency of hydrous alumina to agglomerate under these conditions is much less in the presence of oxalate than of sulfate. It is probable that the behavior of tartrate is similar to that of oxalate, since the mordant obtained in the presence of the former is even more satisfactory than in the presence of the latter.

[1] *J. Soc. Chem. Ind.*, **5**, 526 (1886).
[2] LIECHTI and SUIDA: *J. Soc. Chem. Ind.*, **2**, 537 (1883).
[3] LIECHTI and SCHWITZER: *J. Soc. Dyers Colourists*, 161 (1886).
[4] *U. S. Pub. Health Repts.*, **40**, 351 (1925).

The beneficial influence of organic acids on the mordanting process has received widely diversified interpretations from time to time. Thus, Knecht, Rawson, and Löwenthal[1] claim that the aluminum salts of tartaric and oxalic acids possess a certain resistance to the dissociating action of wool; this is, of course, inaccurate, as the salts of the weaker acids hydrolyze more readily than sulfate. Beech[2] says that the addition of a little oxalic acid, cream of tartar, or tartaric acid to the mordanting bath helps in the decomposition of the metallic salt by the wool fiber; but this seems improbable, as the addition of an acid cuts down the hydrolysis. Herzfeld[3] offers no explanation of the phenomenon, but he recognizes clearly that the loose and uneven character of the mordant obtained with aluminum sulfate alone is due to the rapidity with which the salt decomposes; and that the presence of cream of tartar, oxalic acid, or lactic acid causes the precipitation to take place more slowly and regularly, thereby giving a more satisfactory mordant.

Mordanting of Silk.—Silk adsorbs hydrous alumina somewhat less strongly than wool and must, therefore, be mordanted from slightly more basic solutions. The solutions employed are aluminum sulfate,[4] alum,[5] and the sulfate-acetate and nitrate-acetate mixtures. Hermann[6] has made observations which leave little room to doubt but that the real mordants are the hydrous oxides, at least in the case of silk. In these experiments, both raw and boiled-off[7] silk were treated with various mordanting baths at 30°, and the mordanted fiber was analyzed for both metallic oxide and acid radical. The results have been collected in Table XXVIII.

Hermann looks upon mordanting as a catalytic process in which the fiber decomposes the mordanting salts catalytically, giving hydrous oxides that become fixed on the fiber and acids

---

[1] "A Manual of Dyeing," 236 (1910).

[2] "The Principles and Practice of Wool Dyeing," 71 (1902).

[3] "Das Färben und Bleichen der Textilfasern," 58 (1900).

[4] GANSWINDT: "Theorie und Praxis der modernen Färberei," **2,** 18 (1903).

[5] KNECHT, RAWSON, and LÖWENTHAL: "A Manual of Dyeing," 238 (1916).

[6] *J. Soc. Chem. Ind.*, **23,** 1143 (1904).

[7] Immersed in a good neutral Marseilles or olein soap solution at 90 to 95°, in order to remove the silk gum or pericine from the fibers.

TABLE XXVIII

Mordanting solution	Nature of silk	Ratio of adsorbed oxide to adsorbed acid radical
Stannic chloride..................	Raw	155 SnO_2:1 Cl
Stannic chloride..................	Boiled off	143 SnO_2:1 Cl
Ferric sulfate (basic)..............	Raw	111 Fe_2O_3:1 SO_3
Ferric sulfate (basic)..............	Boiled off	91 Fe_2O_3:1 SO_3
Chromic chloride..................	Raw	40 Cr_2O_3:1 Cl
Chromic chloride..................	Boiled off	44 Cr_2O_3:1 Cl
Aluminum acetate.................	Raw	Al_2O_3 only adsorbed
Aluminum acetate.................	Boiled off	Al_2O_3 only adsorbed

that remain in the bath. While the hydrolysis of the mordanting salts is increased, owing to strong adsorption of the hydrous oxides by the fiber, the process is not catalytic, as a given amount of fiber can increase the decomposition of only a limited amount of salt, and the mordanted fiber is not in the same condition after the process as before.

The mordanting of silk may be carried out satisfactorily at 15 to 20°. At as low a temperature as 0 to 5°, the mordanting salts do not penetrate the fiber well, and the adsorption of the hydrous oxides takes place slowly and irregularly.[1]

Mordanting of Cotton.—It has been recognized for a long time that normal aluminum sulfate and alum cannot be used as a mordant for cotton.[2] This is because the cotton adsorbs hydrous alumina much less strongly than wool or silk and so does not decompose solutions which are distinctly acid. If the acidity of the alum solutions is reduced by the addition of sodium carbonate, they can be used to mordant cotton. Liechti and Suida[3] showed that the amount of alumina fixed is greater the more basic the mordanting solutions. Since cotton adsorbs hydrous alumina less strongly than wool, the mordant is fixed less strongly by

[1] HERMANN: *J. Soc. Chem. Ind.*, **22**, 623 (1903); **23**, 57 (1904).

[2] *Cf.* BANCROFT: "Philosophy of Permanent Colors," **1**, 357; **2**, 148, 242 (1813).

[3] *J. Soc. Chem. Ind.*, **2**, 538 (1883); *cf.* KEITSCHERA and UTZ: *Mitt. techn. Gerwerbe-Museums in Wien, Sektion für Färberei*, **3**, 110 (1886).

cotton than by wool;[1] accordingly, we should expect the relatively large amounts of mordant taken up from highly basic solutions to rub off readily.   Recently, Tingle[2] claimed that hydrous alumina is adsorbed neither from aluminum sulfate nor basic aluminum sulfate solutions.   His results with aluminum sulfate confirm those of everybody else, but the observations with basic aluminum sulfate cannot be generally true, since such solutions have been used in mordanting cotton without a fixing agent.[3]

Aluminum acetate appears to be the best mordanting bath for cotton.   Fifty years ago, Napier[4] pointed out the advantages of acetate over sulfate:

First, the acetic acid is not so hurtful in its action upon the vegetable coloring matters; second, it holds the alumina with much less force than sulfuric acid, and consequently yields it much more freely to the cloth; and third, being volatile, a great portion of the acid flies off during the process of drying.

Another way of putting it is that aluminum acetate hydrolyzes readily, giving the hydrous oxide in the form of a finely divided sol which can penetrate into the fiber and be adsorbed.   The use of aluminum formate[5] and aluminum lactate[6] in place of aluminum acetate has been suggested; but the principle is the same with all salts of weak organic acids.   Cotton is not mordanted from a solution of "sodium aluminate," but the latter is used to pad on hydrous alumina in calico printing.[7]   This is accomplished by precipitating hydrous alumina on the cloth by adding ammonium chloride to the aluminate bath.

Cotton may be mordanted with alumina by first treating the fiber with a substance like tannin which is adsorbed strongly by the fiber and, in turn, adsorbs hydrous alumina strongly.   This will be referred to again in the section on fixing agents.

[1] BANCROFT: *J. Phys. Chem.*, **26,** 501 (1922).

[2] *J. Ind. Eng. Chem.*, **14,** 198 (1922).

[3] KNECHT, RAWSON, and LÖWENTHAL: "A Manual of Dyeing," 233 (1916).

[4] "A Manual of Dyeing," 121 (1875); *cf.* BANCROFT: "Philosophy of Permanent Colors," **1,** 365 (1813).

[5] SCHWALBE: *Kolloid-Z.*, **5,** 129 (1907).

[6] BOEHRINGER and SONS: *Z. Färben-Ind.*, **9,** 237, 253 (1910).

[7] GANSWINDT: "Theorie und Praxis der modernern Färberei," **2,** 212 (1903).

It is interesting to note that mercerized cotton adsorbs substantive dyes[1] and takes up basic mordants[2] more strongly than ordinary cotton does. This is not because the mercerized cotton is a definite chemical compound between cotton and sodium hydroxide[3] as Ganswindt[4] assumes; but is probably due to the retention of sodium hydroxide in the channel of the cotton fiber or to a change in structure of the cotton as a result of the mercerization process.

CHROME

Mordanting of Wool.—Chrome is by far the most important mordant used with wool. More than twenty years ago Ganswindt[5] claimed that 98 per cent of all the mordanting of wool is done with chromic oxide; and Matthews[6] stated recently that "chrome mordant is used for dyeing practically all of the alizarin, mordant, and acid mordant or after-chromed dyes; it is also the principal mordant used in conjunction with the natural logwoods."

It is interesting to note that the mordanting bath most generally used is an acid solution of bichromate instead of a chromic salt.[7] Before the war, the readily crystallized potassium bichromate was commonly used, but the demand for a cheaper product led to the development of a pure crystalline form of sodium bichromate which has displaced the potassium salt for mordanting purposes.[8]

From the bichromate solution, wool adsorbs chromic acid which is subsequently reduced to chromic oxide, the real mordant. Chromic acid is not held very strongly[9] by the fiber and practically all of it can be removed by washing.[10] Wool itself

[1] MATTHEWS: "Application of Dyestuffs," 165, 278 (1920).

[2] SCHAPOSCHNIKOFF and MINAJEFF: *Z. Färben-Ind.*, **3**, 165 (1904); **4**, 81 (1905).

[3] LEIGHTON: *J. Phys. Chem.*, **20**, 188 (1916).

[4] "Theorie und Praxis der modernen Färberei," **2**, 215 (1903).

[5] "Theorie und Praxis der modernen Färberei," **2**, 69 (1903).

[6] "Application of Dyestuffs," 334 (1920).

[7] KNECHT, RAWSON, and LÖWENTHAL: "A Manual of Dyeing," 255 (1916).

[8] MATTHEWS: "Application of Dyestuffs," 344 (1920).

[9] LIECHTI and HUMMEL: *J. Soc. Chem. Ind.*, **12**, 244 (1893).

[10] BANCROFT: *J. Phys. Chem.*, **26**, 737 (1922); *cf.*, however, WHITELEY: *J. Soc. Chem. Ind.*, **6**, 131 (1887).

has been shown to reduce chromic acid,[1] but this involves more or less waste,[2] so that a reducing agent is usually added either by itself or in the form of a dye, such as logwood[3] or alizarin;[4] and under these conditions, the wool is not attacked appreciably.   Chromic acid mordants wool more strongly than either neutral chromate or bichromate,[3] so that, in practice, a suitable amount of acid is added to the bichromate bath.   Within limits, increasing the acid concentration increases the amount of chromic acid adsorbed.[5] This is less marked with sulfuric acid than with either hydrochloric or nitric acid, probably because sulfuric acid is more strongly adsorbed by wool than hydrochloric or nitric acid and so is more effective in cutting down the adsorption of chromic acid.[6] The importance of sulfate ion is further indicated by the fact that a mixture of sodium chloride and sulfuric acid behaves like sulfuric acid and not like hydrochloric. The presence of sulfuric acid is more effective than an equivalent amount of either hydrochloric or nitric acid in causing the oxidation of wool by chromic acid.   Since the oxidizing power of chromic acid is greater the higher the concentration of acid, and since sulfuric acid is adsorbed by wool more strongly than hydrochloric or nitric acid, Bancroft[7] attributes the greater effect of the former to higher acid concentration at the surface of the wool.

A bichromate bath acidified with sulfuric acid is objectionable, not only because the reduction of chromic acid takes place at the expense of the wool, but because some chromic oxide remains in the mordant and oxidizes such colors as alizarin blue, alizarin yellow, etc., producing weak shades that may be undesirable.[8] As a matter of fact, the more customary thing is to use an organic acid or acid salt such as cream of tartar, tartaric acid, oxalic acid, formic acid,[9] and lactic acid.[10]   As these

[1] LIECHTI and HUMMEL: *J. Soc. Chem. Ind.*, **12**, 244 (1893).

[2] DURFEE: *Am. Dyestuff Rep.*, **9**, No. 10, Tech. Sec. 20–23 (1921).

[3] MATTHEWS: "Application of Dyestuffs," 477 (1920).

[4] LIECHTI and HUMMEL: *J. Soc. Chem. Ind.*, **12**, 244, 246 (1893).

[5] HUMMEL and GARDNER: *J. Soc. Chem. Ind.*, **14**, 452 (1895).

[6] BANCROFT: *J. Phys. Chem.*, **26**, 743 (1922).

[7] *J. Phys. Chem.*, **26**, 744 (1922).

[8] BEECH: "The Principles and Practice of Wool Dyeing," 116 (1902).

[9] KAPPF: *Z. Färben-Ind.*, **4**, 159 (1905); WHITTAKER: "Dyeing with Coal Tar Dyestuffs," 50 (1919).

[10] KNECHT, RAWSON, and LÖWENTHAL: "A Manual of Dyeing," 173, 256 (1916).

so-called assistants are oxidized by chromic acid, it is probable that there is little, if any, oxidation of the wool in their presence. Moreover, they bring about a uniform deposit of the mordant in a form highly satisfactory for receiving the dye.[1]

Solutions of chromium salts undergo hydrolysis to a greater or lesser degree, depending on the basicity of the solutions, the concentration, and the temperature.[2] Wool adsorbs hydrous chromic oxide from such solutions in the same manner as hydrous aluminum oxide is adsorbed from aluminum salts. If chrome alum is used, the fiber takes up sulfuric acid as well as the hydrous oxide. Liechti and Hummel claim that a part of the acid is taken up as a basic salt having the formula $3Cr_2O_3 \cdot 2SO_3$. Their data do not justify this conclusion, but the absence of a basic salt has not been proved. Williamson[3] obtained a gel of approximately constant composition by precipitating chrome alum below a certain pH value which was not determined. The amorphous mass was assigned the formula $7Cr_2O_3 \cdot 4SO_3$. It will be recalled that Williamson[4] and Miller[5] obtained a gel of approximately constant composition, $5Al_2O_3 \cdot 3SO_3$, by adding alkali to alum below pH = 5.5. For reasons already given,[6] I do not consider the alumina sulfuric acid gel to be a definite basic salt and the same applies to the chrome sulfuric acid gel. However, at least one definite crystalline basic sulfate of the formula $[Cr(OH)_2(H_2O)_4]_2 \cdot SO_4$ has been prepared;[7] so the formation of a basic salt on the fiber must be regarded as a possibility.

It is claimed that chrome alum cannot be used for a mordanting bath, because the mordant is not adsorbed evenly and the subsequent dyeing is uneven. Since a good mordant can be obtained with aluminum alum, it would appear that the difficulty with chrome alum could be corrected by suitable adjustment of the temperature or of other conditions of mordanting. The addition of cream of tartar, oxalic acid, or tartaric acid to the

[1] KNECHT, RAWSON, and LÖWENTHAL: "A Manual of Dyeing," 256 (1916); BEECH: "The Principles and Practice of Wool Dyeing," 117 (1902).

[2] LIECHTI and SCHWITZER: *J. Soc. Chem. Ind.*, **4**, 586 (1885).

[3] *J. Phys. Chem.*, **27**, 384 (1923).

[4] *J. Phys. Chem.*, **27**, 280 (1923).

[5] *U. S. Pub. Health Repts.*, **38**, 1995 (1923).

[6] *Cf.*, pages 339, 379.

[7] WERNER: *Ber.*, **41**, 3447 (1909).

alum bath gives a satisfactory mordant as does chromium oxalate[1] or chromium tartrate but not chromium acetate or chromium fluoride.[2]

Liechti and Hummel[3] observed increased mordanting with increasing concentration of chrome alum, just as would be expected. They also claimed to get an increased amount of chromium taken up by increasing the sulfuric acid content of the alum bath; but this is improbable, if not impossible, unless the heating is conducted in such a manner that a precipitate forms in the bath and is padded on the fibers. The reported increase in adsorption with increasing sulfuric acid content is contradicted by the further observation of Liechti and Hummel that the bath is exhausted less completely the greater the concentration of sulfuric acid.

Wool is mordanted very slightly from solutions of chromic chloride or chromic nitrate,[4] probably because the degree of hydrolysis is less and the peptizing action of these solutions for hydrous chromic oxide is too great to yield the mordant to the fiber. If this be true, the addition of a suitable amount of soda to chromic chloride solution should give a satisfactory mordanting bath.

Mordanting of Silk.—Silk adsorbs chromic oxide less strongly than wool.[5] In practice, it is mordanted from a bath of chrome alum[6] or chromic chloride but not from bichromate.[7] To preserve the luster of silk, Whittaker[8] recommends mordanting the silk overnight in a cold bath of chromic chloride, followed by treating with sodium silicate, which fixes the mordant on the fiber.

Mordanting of Cotton.—Cotton adsorbs hydrous chromic oxide very much less readily than either wool or silk, as evidenced by the observation that no mordanting whatsoever results on heating cotton with a 10 per cent chrome alum solution. Apparently, no completely satisfactory chrome mordant for dyeing cotton,

---

[1] TAGLIANI: *Color Trade J.*, **11**, 158 (1922); *Textile Colorist*, **44**, 650 (1922).

[2] LIECHTI and HUMMEL: *J. Soc. Chem. Ind.*, **13**, 356 (1894).

[3] *J. Soc. Chem. Ind.*, **13**, 222, 356 (1894).

[4] LIECHTI and HUMMEL: *J. Soc. Chem. Ind.*, **13**, 224 (1894).

[5] GANSWINDT: "Theorie und Praxis der modernen Färberei," **2**, 19 (1903).

[6] LIECHTI and HUMMEL: *J. Soc. Chem. Ind.*, **13**, 223 (1894).

[7] KNECHT, RAWSON, and LÖWENTHAL: "A Manual of Dyeing," 258 (1916).

[8] "Dyeing with Coal Tar Dyestuffs," 50 (1919).

especially cotton yarns, has been found.[1]   The most satisfactory
bath is the colloidal solution of hydrous chromic oxide in alkali,
the so-called alkali chromate bath.[2]   This cannot be used for
yarns on account of the caustic action on the hands of the work-
men; nor can it be used on oiled material, since the oil would
be stripped from the fiber.   A bath of chromic acetate is fairly
successful, as the acetic acid may be removed by heating.

Iron Mordants

Mordanting of Wool.—At one time, ferrous sulfate was widely
used for mordanting wool; but it has been largely replaced by
chrome mordants.   The iron mordant is still of importance in
dyeing logwood blacks, since the latter on chrome mordant are
likely to turn green on exposure to light.   Moreover, it is claimed
that cloth mordanted with copperas posesses a "kinder" and
softer handle than cloth mordanted with chrome.   In general,
iron mordants tend to "sadden" or darken the shade of most
dyes, and they are, therefore, used chiefly for dark colors, especially browns and blacks.

A copperas black may be obtained either by mordanting
before dyeing or mordanting after dyeing.   The latter process,
which is usually employed, consists essentially in boiling the wool
in a decoction of dyewoods for a time and then adding copperas
directly to the bath.   When the fiber is mordanted before dyeing,
it is necessary to add comparatively large quantities of tartar or
oxalic acid to prevent unequal precipitation of the oxide of iron
on the fiber.   Before placing the mordanted cloth in the dye
bath, better results are obtained by allowing it to lie for several
hours in the air, whereby hydrous ferrous oxide is oxidized more
or less completely to the ferric state.   From this, it would appear
either that hydrous ferric oxide is a better adsorbent than ferrous oxide or that the oxidation of the mordant following dyeing
may have a detrimental effect on the final product.

Mordanting of Silk.—Iron salts are quite extensively used in
mordanting silk for dyeing black, especially with logwood.
Alumina and tin mordants are of minor importance and chrome

[1] KNECHT, RAWSON, and LÖWENTHAL: "A Manual of Dyeing," 252 (1916).

[2] KOECHLIN: *Dinglers polytech. J.*, **254**, 132 (1884).

is seldom used as a mordant for logwood; nor is logwood used to produce any color on silk other than black. For the dyeing of silk, mordants are applied in sufficient amount not only to take up the dye but to add appreciably to the weight of the silk. Raw silks adsorb the hydrous oxide fairly strongly; but it is customary to impregnate the fiber with tannin before putting it in the iron bath which is usually ferrous acetate. By repeated treatment in the tannin and salt baths, the weight of the silk fiber may be increased as much as 400 per cent. If a ferric salt such as basic ferric sulfate is employed, the fiber is first mordanted with the hydrous oxide which is subsequently "fixed" in a tannin bath.

While raw silk adsorbs and holds the hydrous iron oxides fairly strongly, boiled-off silk possesses but a slight adsorption capacity for the mordant. The latter is, therefore, dipped in the iron liquor and subsequently put into a boiling soap solution containing olein soap and a little soda, which precipitates hydrous ferric oxide on the fiber in an aged condition. This operation may be repeated several times according to the amount of weighting desired.

Mordanting of Cotton.—Cotton shows a much weaker adsorption for hydrous ferric oxide than either wool or raw silk. It is, therefore, mordanted by a process similar to that employed with boiled-off silk, namely by saturating in a solution of basic ferric sulfate followed by treating with lime water or soda solution, which precipitates the hydrous oxide in the cloth. If ferrous sulfate is employed, the fiber is first mordanted with tannin, which adsorbs the hydrous oxide strongly; and any sulfate adsorbed is subsequently removed by washing with lime water. After mordanting, the adsorbed hydrous oxide is allowed to oxidize in the air before placing in the dye bath.

Tin Mordants[1]

Mordanting of Wool.—Although wool is seldom mordanted with tin mordant, when this is done, the bath consists of stannous chloride in conjunction with oxalic acid or tartaric acid. Considerably more acid is said to be taken up from stannic salt baths than from stannous salt baths, which accounts for the use

[1] *Cf.* p. 210.

of the latter in practice. As in the case of alumina mordanting, tin salts require the presence of an organic acid to prevent rapid and uneven deposition of the hydrous oxide on the fiber. Stannous tartrate and stannic tartrate alone are said to be unsatisfactory; but it is possible that the addition of an excess of either tartaric acid or oxalic would made a good mordanting bath if there were any point in avoiding the use of chloride. The hydrous oxide of tin is sometimes "fixed" with alum.

Mordanting and Weighting of Silk.—The most important use of tin salts in the dyeing industry is in the mordanting and weighting of silk.[1] For this purpose, stannic chloride is the salt generally employed. The cloth is first steeped in a solution of this salt, and after rinsing, is put into a bath of sodium phosphate and subsequently into one of sodium silicate. In order to give the silk the desired weight,[2] the process must be repeated several times.

If the silk is weighted excessively by the tin-phosphate-silicate process, serious faults may develop in the goods. Thus, heavily weighted silk frequently becomes quite tender when exposed even for a short time to direct sunlight.[3] Moreover, reddish-colored tender spots often appear in pieces, after storing. Gnehm, Roth, and Thomann[4] first attributed the formation of these tender spots to the action of perspiration; but this cannot be true, as unused goods frequently show the damaged spots. Sisley[5] pointed out that the only constituent of perspiration which has an injurious effect is the salt; and Meister[6] showed that the deterioration of the silk is due to active chlorine produced by the catalytic action of copper which is always present in small quantities as a result of careless handling during spinning and weaving. As a preventive, Knecht[3] suggest padding the goods in a very weak solution of ammonium thiocyanate; but this is not infal-

---

[1] HEERMANN: *J. Soc. Dyers Colourists*, 1903–1906; NEUHAUS: Knecht, Rawson, and Löwenthal's "A Manual of Dyeing," 279 (1916).

[2] GNEHM and BAENZIGER: *J. Soc. Dyers Colourists*, 40 (1897).

[3] KNECHT, RAWSON, and LÖWENTHAL: "A Manual of Dyeing," 279 (1916).

[4] *J. Soc. Dyers Colourists*, 256 (1902).

[5] *J. Soc. Dyers Colourists*, 276 (1902).

[6] *J. Soc. Dyers Colourists*, 192 (1905).

lible.   The use of thiourea and its salts has been patented for the same purpose.[1]

Since silk adsorbs hydrous stannic oxide, leaving most of the hydrochloric acid in the bath, the latter becomes strongly acid by continued use.   To keep the bath in good condition, stannic chloride must be replaced and the excess hydrochloric acid neutralized with ammonia from time to time.   After the ammonium chloride content of the liquor becomes too high for satisfactory mordanting, a fresh bath must be employed.

Mordanting of Cotton.—Stannic salts are sometimes used to mordant cotton; but on account of the usual weak adsorption of cotton for the hydrous oxides, the fiber must first be mordanted with tannin.   When sodium stannate is used, the cloth is first impregnated with a solution of the salt and is then passed through a very dilute solution of sulfuric acid or of aluminum sulfate. Hydrous stannic oxide or, if an aluminum salt is employed, a mixture of the hydrous oxides of tin and aluminum are precipitated and constitute the mordant.

TANNIN

Having considered the most important basic mordants, it seems advisable to point out the essential characteristics of a typical acid mordant.   The class of substances known as the tannins, to which tannic acid belongs, is seldom employed in mordanting wool but finds its chief use in mordanting cotton and linen, in "fixing" the hydrous oxide mordants on cotton, and in weighting silk with hydrous ferric oxide, as noted in an earlier paragraph.

Both wool and cotton adsorb tannin from its colloidal solution in water, the amounts taken up varying continuously with the concentration of the sol, as shown by the curves in Fig. 25 constructed from the data of Pelet-Jolivet[2] on the adsorption by wool and of Sanin[3] on the adsorption by cotton.

The adsorption of tannin by wool is not very marked, especially at ordinary temperatures; but it increases with the temperature;

---

[1] *J. Soc. Dyers Colourists*, 51 (1907).
[2] "Die Theorie des Färbeprozesses," 79 (1910).
[3] *Kolloid-Z.*, **10**, 82 (1912).

on the other hand, the adsorption by cotton apparently decreases with increasing temperature of the bath.[1]   If mixed cotton goods containing wool are mordanted at ordinary temperature, the cotton only is mordanted to any appreciable extent.

Since tannin is an acid mordant, one might expect the adsorption to be reduced in alkaline solution and increased in acid solution.   As a matter of fact, the adsorption of tannin is cut down almost to zero in the presence of alkali; and acetic acid increases the adsorption[2] which, however, passes through a

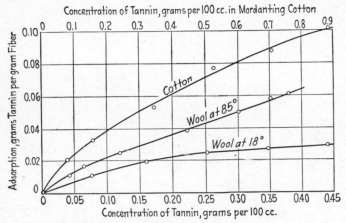

FIG. 25.—Adsorption of tannin by wool and cotton.

maximum at high concentration.[3]   Sulfuric acid, on the other hand, cuts down the adsorption, and hydrochloric acid has little effect.   This behavior with different acids is probably due to the difference in the adsorption of the acids by cotton.   We know, for example, that sulfuric acid is adsorbed by cotton more strongly than hydrochloric,[4] which would account for the adsorption of tannin being cut down more by the former than by the latter.   Different salts added to the bath all seem to increase

[1] KNECHT and KERSHAW: *J. Soc. Dyers Colourists*, 40 (1892); GANSWINDT: "Theorie und Praxis der modernen Färberei," 2, 216 (1903).

[2] KNECHT, RAWSON, and LÖWENTHAL: "A Manual of Dyeing," 1, 188 (1916).

[3] DREAPER: "The Chemistry and Physics of Dyeing," 161 (1906).

[4] LEIGHTON: *J. Phys. Chem.*, 20, 188 (1916).

the adsorption of tannin, possibly because they decrease the stability of the sol.

Although tannin is adsorbed quite strongly by cotton, it must be "fixed" on the fiber before the dyeing process. The best fixing agents are antimony salts; but salts of tin, aluminum, and iron are used in special cases.

FIXING AGENTS

Whenever a mordant is not fixed sufficiently strongly by a fiber, it is necessary to add a so-called fixing agent to bring about the desired results. For example, sodium phosphate is used for fixing alumina and tin; sodium arsenate, soap, and tannin for iron; sodium silicate and tannin for chrome and tin; salts of antimony, tin, and aluminum for tannin; etc. In other words, arsenates, silicates, phosphates, fatty acid salts, and tannin are used as fixing agents for the basic or metallic mordants while the latter are used for fixing the acid mordants, tannin, and the fatty acid compounds. The question arises as to whether the fixing process consists in the formation of definite chemical compounds, such as antimony tannate, iron arsenate, tin phosphate, etc., as is generally assumed, or whether the fixed mordants are mixtures of indefinite composition. The latter view seems much the more reasonable in the light of the evidence. For example, it is known that precipitated hydrous ferric oxide is peptized as a positive sol on washing and that tannin is peptized by water as a negative sol. If the two are brought in contact, there is mutual adsorption and each keeps the other from being peptized; in other words, there is a mutual "fixing." The so-called iron tannates are not definite compounds.

The case of the action between antimony salts and tannin has been studied by Sanin[1] who believes there are at least three definite antimony tannates. These cannot be obtained pure; but at first, Sanin preferred to regard different products as mixtures of two or more antimony tannates rather than as substances of continuously varying compostion. Later,[2] he concluded that adsorption does occur when tannin and potassium

[1] Z. Farben-Ind., **9**, 2, 17, 49 (1910).

[2] SANIN: Kolloid-Z., **13**, 305 (1913).

antimony tartrate are mixed; but that tannates are formed during the technical procedure used in mordanting with tannin. While no one can question the possibility of forming a true antimony tannate under special conditions, it is altogether improbable that the varied conditions in technical practice are such as to yield a definite salt.

Wislicenus and Mutte[1] studied the action of tannin on fibrous alumina. The amount taken up was found to increase rapidly at first, with increasing concentration of the sol and then to reach an approximately constant value. This constant value is the limiting value of adsorption[2] for the particular alumina and does not indicate the formation of aluminum tannate. Had a different alumina been used, the saturation value would have been found at a different point. Von Schröder[3] showed that the taking up of tannin from solution in alcohol and from the aqueous sol is a typical adsorption phenomenon and no tannate is formed.

It is a moot question whether the fixing of iron oxide or alumina by oil mordants is due to the formation of salts of fatty acids. Knecht[4] says:

The amount of iron which is taken up by the fiber depends less on the strength of the mordanting liquor than on the amount of oil that has already been fixed in the material; the oil attracts the oxide of iron with great energy, so that it is not readily stripped from the fiber even by comparatively concentrated sulfuric acid or hydrochloric acid.

This behavior is more nearly what one would expect if the ferric oxide were adsorbed by the oil than if a ferric salt of a fatty acid were formed; but there is no proof either way.[5] Turning to the fixing of metallic mordants by phosphates, silicates, etc., we know that compounds are not formed, in many cases. Thus, hydrous aluminum oxide adsorbs arsenic acid;[6]

[1] *Kolloid-Z.*, **2**, 2d Supplement, XVIII (1908).
[2] SCHMIDT: *Z. physik. Chem.*, **74**, 699 (1910).
[3] *Kolloidchem. Beihefte*, **1**, 1 (1909).
[4] KNECHT, RAWSON, and LÖWENTHAL: "*A Manual of Dyeing*," **2**, 597 (1916).
[5] *Cf.* BANCROFT: *J. Phys. Chem.*, **19**, 50 (1915).
[6] LOCKEMANN and PAUCKE: *Kolloid-Z.*, **8**, 273 (1911).

hydrous ferric oxide adsorbs arsenious acid[1] and arsenic acid; hydrous stannic oxide adsorbs phosphoric acid;[2] and beryllium oxide adsorbs arsenious acid.[3]   In none of these cases is a definite compound formed; and it is probable that many more of the alleged phosphates, stannates, and silicates of the heavy metals are not obtained under ordinary conditions.   However, this does not preclude the formation of definite compounds under special conditions.   Thus, crystalline aluminum orthophosphate[4] results on treating a concentrated solution of sodium aluminate with an excess of phosphoric acid and heating in a sealed tube at 250° for several hours.

It was claimed for a long time, that alizarin would dye alumina only in the presence of lime salts, the color on the mordanted cloth being attributed to a calcium aluminum alizarate.[5]   This is now known to be true only in case the hydrous oxide contains sulfate.   Hydrous alumina prepared from aluminum acetate takes up alizarin in the absence of calcium salts.[6]   The purpose of the calcium is not to fix the alumina to the fiber or the dye to the mordant, but to remove sulfate, which cuts down the adsorption of the alizarin.[7]

Color Lakes

In the dyeing of mordanted cloth, the color is taken up chiefly by the mordant giving a color lake on the fiber.   For a long time, all lakes were believed to be definite compounds between the metallic oxide and the dye.   This view was questioned by Biltz and Utescher,[8] who investigated the behavior of alizarin with hydrous chromic oxide and hydrous ferric oxide.   With the former, the amount of dye taken up increases continuously with increasing concentration of solution, giving no indication whatsoever of the formation of a chromium alizarate.   On the other

---

[1] BILTZ: *Ber.*, **37**, 3138, 3151 (1904).

[2] MECKLENBURG: *Z. physik. Chem.*, **74**, 207 (1912).

[3] BLEYER and MÜLLER: *Arch. Pharm.*, **251**, 304 (1913).

[4] DE SCHULTEN: *Compt. rend.*, **98**, 1853 (1884).

[5] LIECHTI and SUIDA: *J. Soc. Chem. Ind.*, **5**, 525 (1886).

[6] DAVISON: *J. Phys. Chem.*, **17**, 737 (1913).

[7] BANCROFT: *J. Phys. Chem.*, **18**, 10 (1914).

[8] *Ber.*, **38**, 4143 (1905).

hand, with hydrous ferric oxide, there is a rather marked increase in the amount of dye taken up with relatively small change in the concentration of the bath, leading Biltz to conclude that iron and alizarin combine in a definite ratio of 1 molecule of iron to 3 of alizarin.[1] But since the amount of alizarin taken up by the iron oxide is so far in excess of that necessary to form alizarate, one is confronted by the necessity of assuming either that alizarate adsorbs the excess dye or that the whole phenomenon is a case of adsorption of dye by the hydrous oxide.

If sodium alizarate reacts with hydrous ferric oxide to form a ferric alizarate, it must follow that sodium hydroxide will be liberated by the reaction; while if the sodium alizarate is adsorbed by the hydrous oxide, there should be no accumulation of alkali in the solution. Bull and Adams[2] investigated the phenomenon quantitatively. It was necessary, first of all, to determine the adsorption of sodium hydroxide by hydrous ferric oxide, since ferric alizarate might form and still leave little alkali behind in case the latter were sufficiently strongly adsorbed by the excess oxide. Observations were then made on the amount of alkali remaining in solution on shaking the hydrous oxide with sodium alizarate prepared by dissolving resublimed alizarin in a very slight excess of the theoretical quantity of alkali. The relative quantities of dye and oxide were so chosen that practically complete adsorption of the dye occurred even at the highest concentrations. The results are given in Tables XXIX and XXX and shown graphically in Fig. 26.

TABLE XXIX.—ADSORPTION OF NaOH BY HYDROUS Fe_2O_3

$N/10$ NaOH at start, cubic centimeters	$N/10$ NaOH at end, cubic centimeters	$N/10$ NaOH adsorbed, cubic centimeters
1.20	0.20	1.00
2.40	0.56	1.84
3.60	1.07	2.53
4.80	1.52	3.28
6.00	2.13	3.87

[1] *Cf.* also LIECHTE and SUIDA: *J. Soc. Chem. Ind.*, **5,** 523 (1886).
[2] *J. Phys. Chem.*, **25,** 660 (1921).

TABLE XXX.—ADSORPTION OF SODIUM ALIZARATE BY HYDROUS FE₂O₃

Sodium alizarate solution, cubic centimeters	$N/10$ NaOH equivalent to the alizarate, cubic centimeters	$N/10$ NaOH in bath, cubic centimeters	$N/10$ NaOH adsorbed, cubic centimeters
5.00	1.25	0.15	1.10
10.00	2.50	0.25	2.25
15.00	3.75	0.30	3.45
20.00	5.00	0.35	4.65
25.00	6.25	0.35	5.90

If ferric alizarate were formed, alkali would be liberated as given in column 2 of Table XXX. Much smaller quantities of this are found, and there is also much less sodium hydroxide present in the baths than would be found if the calculated amount

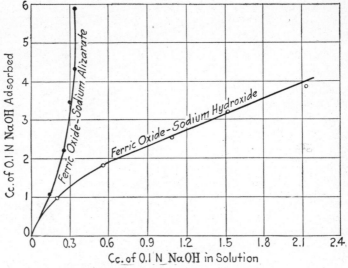

FIG. 26.—Adsorption by hydrous ferric oxide.

of alkali were formed and subsequently adsorbed by the ferric oxide as shown in Table XXIX. The small quantities of alkali recorded in column 3 of Table XXX are due to hydrolysis of the adsorbed sodium alizarate, producing in solution the amounts of alkali shown, while the insoluble alizarin remains on the fiber. The first two values are lower than the hydrolysis value because the amount of hydrolysis will be determined to some extent by the intensity of adsorption. Further experiments were carried out, which eliminated the possibility that the adsorption of alkali was increased by the presence of sodium alizarate. In the light of these observations and the continuous curve obtained by Biltz, it seems altogether probable that the iron-alizarin lake is an adsorption complex and not ferric alizarate.

Liechti[1] claims that a definite aluminum alizarate is obtained when hydrous aluminum oxide and sodium or ammonium alizarate are brought together. This claim was found to be altogether without foundation by Williamson[2] who investigated the matter in much the same way as Bull and Adams did the iron-alizarin lakes.

Marker and Gordon[3] studied the influence of hydrogen ion concentration on the amount of the basic dyes, crystal violet, and methylene blue, and the acid dyes, orange II, and metanyl yellow, taken up by hydrous ferric oxide, alumina, and silica. The different hydrogen ion concentrations were obtained by the addition of sulfuric acid or sodium hydroxide. Some data are given in Tables XXXI and XXXII. In all cases, it will be seen that the amount of dye taken up increases with increasing pH for basic dyes and decreases with increasing pH for acid dyes. Throughout the range investigated, the pH-adsorption curves appear continuous for the adsorption of crystal violet and metanyl yellow by alumina and of crystal violet for ferric oxide. On the other hand, the amount of methylene blue taken up increases greatly between pH = 11 and 12, and the same is true for orange II between pH = 3.2 and 2.3; so that these curves are drawn with a sharp break at approximately pH = 11 and pH = 3.2, respectively. Since crystalline salts of a number of metals, including iron and aluminum, can be obtained by the action of the sulfonic acid, orange II, on the respective oxides, it is concluded that the breaks in the pH adsorption curves show the lakes investigated to be definite compounds. While certain ones

[1] *J. Soc. Chem. Ind.*, **4**, 587 (1885); **5**, 523 (1886).
[2] *J. Phys. Chem.*, **28**, 891 (1924).
[3] *J. Ind. Eng. Chem.*, **16**, 1186 (1924); **15**, 818 (1923).

TABLE XXXI.—ADSORPTION OF DYES BY HYDROUS FERRIC OXIDE

(Adsorption in milligrams dye per gram of gel)

Basic dyes				Acid dyes			
Methylene blue		Crystal violet		Orange II		Metanyl yellow	
pH	Adsorption	pH	Adsorption	pH	Adsorption	pH	Adsorption
1.96	27.6	2.06	23.2	2.30	429.0	1.92	361.0
2.33	29.0	2.94	33.0	3.20	75.0	2.30	340.0
5.95	30.0	5.02	42.3	5.27	70.0	3.38	255.0
9.85	32.1	9.01	50.6	10.14	52.0	7.46	211.0
11.12	33.8	10.95	56.1	11.02	50.0	11.60	80.7
12.00	131.0						

TABLE XXXII.—ADSORPTION OF DYES BY HYDROUS ALUMINA

(Adsorption in milligrams dye per gram of gel)

Basic dyes				Acid dyes			
Methylene blue		Crystal violet		Orange II		Metanyl yellow	
pH	Adsorption	pH	Adsorption	pH	Adsorption	pH	Adsorption
1.96	65.6	1.50	3.0	2.30	452.0	1.92	703.0
2.23	66.1	5.44	8.0	3.20	186.0	2.30	460.0
5.95	67.5	9.18	45.0	5.27	179.0	7.46	276.0
9.85	77.0	10.70	282.0	10.14	162.0	9.67	226.0
11.12	82.7	11.12	413.0	11.02	136.0	11.60	115.0
12.00	279.0						

of the lakes may be definite salts, I cannot see how this can be deduced from the adsorption data or the curves constructed therefrom. Consider the orange II lake with either alumina or ferric oxide: If the amount of dye taken up by a definite amount of oxide were independent of the concentration of the dye bath at a certain pH value, then the assumption that the lake is a definite salt might be justified. But the above data show only that a change in pH value from 5.2 to 3.2 causes a much smaller

increase in adsorption than a change in pH value from 3.2 to 2.3.
If the equilibrium

$$\mathrm{NaX} \underset{}{\overset{\mathrm{H^{.}}}{\rightleftharpoons}} \mathrm{HX} \underset{}{\overset{\mathrm{Fe_2O_3}}{\rightleftharpoons}} \mathrm{FeX_3},$$

(where X is the acid dye anion) exists as assumed by Marker and
Gordon, there is nothing to indicate why the velocity to the right
should proceed regularly with decreasing pH to a certain point,
and then jump abruptly. Had the adsorption been determined
at two or three points between pH = 3.2 and 2.3, it is probable
that the adsorption curve would prove to be a continuous one
with a sharp bend, instead of a broken one that has no apparent
significance. It is possible that the marked increase in adsorption above pH = 3.2 is due to the concentration of hydrogen ion
being sufficiently great to cause some peptization of the oxide
on boiling for an hour. If the experiments were repeated with a
freshly formed gel, I should expect the amount adsorbed for a
given pH value to show considerable variation from the values
obtained by Marker and Gordon.

The effect of the concentration of dye on the amount taken up
at various constant pH values should be investigated. Marker
and Gordon determined the amounts of dyes left over on treating
different concentrations of orange II with an excess of hydrous
oxide at constant pH. They fail to give the important thing,
namely, the constant pH value of the solution; but one is pretty
safe in assuming that it was low, as all the dye anion was taken up
except a constant small amount, the equilibrium concentration.

For methylene blue to form a salt, hydrous ferric oxide must
function as an acid. Until someone shows that a very weak base
like that of methylene blue will react with ferric oxide to give a
stable salt even under special conditions, there seems no ground
for assuming that the iron-methylene blue lake as ordinarily
obtained is ever a definite compound. Pelet-Jolivet[1] showed
that methylene blue is adsorbed by silica, the amount taken up
depending upon the previous history of the hydrous oxide.

That it is unsafe to assume a lake to be a true compound simply
because the constituents in question can form a definite salt under
special conditions is further emphasized by the work of Gilbert[2]

[1] "Die Theorie des Färbeprozesses," 71, 205 (1910).
[2] *J. Phys. Chem.*, **18**, 586 (1914).

on the copper lakes of eosin. Gilbert prepared a definite crystalline copper eosinate; but found it to be a different substance from the precipitate obtained by the interaction of copper sulfate and sodium eosinate. Although the precipitated lake has a fairly constant composition, it always contains an excess of copper when an excess of copper salt is employed. By shaking hydrous copper oxide with varying concentrations of an ether solution of eosin, a typical adsorption isotherm is obtained, showing no evidence of compound formation. The maximum amount of eosin adsorbed under these conditions is only about one-tenth of that necessary to form copper eosinate. Starting with colloidal hydrous copper oxide and colloidal eosin acid, lakes were obtained varying in composition between 2 molecules of copper to 1 of eosin and 2 molecules of eosin to 1 of copper. All the lakes behave like the one in which copper and eosin are in equivalent quantities, and all can be carried into colloidal solution. In the presence of ether, small amounts of certain salts decompose the lakes. This is because the adsorption of the anions of the salts by hydrous copper oxide is sufficiently great to displace the adsorbed eosin. The order of displacing power of the anions is the usual order of adsorption: $SO_4'' > Br' > Cl' > NO_3'$.

The taking up of crystal ponceau by wool mordanted with alum was shown by Pelet-Jolivet[1] to be a clear case of adsorption when the process is carried out at room temperature; but at 90°, the amount taken up is practically independent of the concentration of the dye bath, when the latter contains more than 700 milligrams per liter, the lowest concentration employed. It is probable that, in this instance, a definite aluminum salt of crystal ponceau is formed. Pelet-Jolivet prepared such a salt in crystalline form.

Bayliss[2] found that hydrous alumina adsorbs Congo red acid from its deep-blue colloidal solution in water. If this adsorption complex is washed, suspended in water, and heated, the color changes from blue to red. Since Congo red salts are red, Bayliss attributed this change in color to the formation of an aluminum salt. The experiments were extended to the precipitates obtained by mixing the negative sol of Congo red acid with the positive sols

[1] "Die Theorie des Färbeprozesses," 213 (1910).
[2] *Proc. Roy. Soc.*, **84***B*, 881 (1911).

of the hydrous oxides of aluminum, zirconium, and thorium. The blue adsorption complex became red on heating in every case, provided the hydrous oxide sols were dialyzed until practically free from acid. A small amount of acid is sufficient to prevent the color change. Assuming that the color change is due to the formation of a Congo red salt, Bancroft[1] fails to see why a trace of acid should prevent the change, provided there is an excess of hydrous oxide with which the Congo red can react. Blucher and Farnau[2] attempt to get around this difficulty by assuming that hydrous alumina adsorbs and stabilizes the free red Congo acid which is instable in aqueous suspension. This raises the question why a trace of free mineral acid should prevent the adsorption and alleged stabilization of the red Congo acid. The whole phenomenon should be reinvestigated quantitatively, paying attention to the relative concentrations of both the positive and negative sols and their respective pH values. In this connection it may be mentioned that Schaposchnikoff and Bogojawlenski[3] have isolated the metastable red Congo acid by allowing the pyridine salt to effloresce.

Considering the acid mordant, tannin, for a moment, we find Dreaper[4] stating that magenta and tannic acid form a definite salt; but no proof is offered for the statement, and the admission is made that 100 parts of the alleged salt will take up at least 160 parts of tannin when the latter is present in excess. Sanin[5] likewise states that basic dyes form definite salts with tannin when the dyes are in excess; but when tannin is in excess, the latter is adsorbed. In no case is any proof of compound formation presented except the fact that a formula for the alleged product can be written.

In conclusion, one seems justified in saying that mordants function by adsorbing dyes in indefinite proportions depending on the conditions. In certain cases, definite salts may be formed, but these constitute the exceptions to the general rule.

[1] *J. Phys. Chem.*, **19**, 57 (1915).
[2] *J. Phys. Chem.*, **18**, 634 (1914).
[3] *J. Russ. Phys.-Chem. Soc.*, **44**, 1813 (1913).
[4] "The Chemistry and Physics of Dyeing," 244 (1906).
[5] SANIN: *Z. Farben-Ind.*, **10**, 97 (1911).

CHAPTER XVII

WATER PURIFICATION

All natural waters are contaminated to a greater or lesser degree by the materials with which they come in contact. Thus, waters from regions of old rocks like granite are relatively low in mineral content; while waters from regions of limestone are hard. Surface waters flowing through districts containing readily peptizable material like clay are more or less turbid, and those from swampy regions are highly colored.

The purification of water on a large scale is carried out with one or more of the following objects in view: first, to render the supply safe and suitable for drinking; second, to reduce the amounts of mineral ingredients which are injurious to boilers; and third, to remove substances injurious to the machinery or the manufactured product in industrial processes. The colloidal matter in surface waters consists of finely divided particles of clay, sand, organic coloring matter, and bacteria. Such material can usually be removed by agglomeration and filtering under suitable conditions. Undesirable dissolved substances such as the bicarbonates and sulfates of calcium and magnesium can be eliminated only by resorting to chemical precipitation. Many of the largest artificial water purification plants are operated solely to provide potable water without special attention to its use for industrial purposes. In other instances, the water is not only rendered potable but is softened at the same time. A notable example of the latter is the purification plant at New Orleans where hard, colored, turbid, sewage-polluted water from the Mississippi River is rendered suitable for industrial as well as domestic consumption.

The most important requirement in the purification of a municipal water supply is the elimination of bacteria, especially those causing disease, and the removal of turbidity; but a perfectly acceptable drinking water is free from objectionable odor,

366

taste, and color. Small amounts of the mineral constituents commonly found in water are not objectionable, as a rule, but certain ones are highly undesirable. Thus, the presence of as little as 2 p.p.m. of iron renders the water unpalatable to some people and causes trouble by discoloring washbowls and tubs, and by producing rust stains on cloth. It is needless to say that drinking water must contain no more than a trace of salts of barium, copper, zinc, and lead, because of their poisonous character. Fortunately, the occurrence of harmful amounts of the latter salts in the ordinary water supply is quite rare.

FILTRATION

Surface water is rendered potable by filtration, sometimes accompanied by disinfection with ozone, chlorine, or hypochlorite which destroy disease-producing organisms, and by the addition of an algicide such as copper sulfate to kill organisms responsible for objectionable tastes or odors. Chemical treatment alone is not a substitute for purification by filtration, since it does not remove colloidal matter which causes turbidity and color, or dissolved organic matter which produces swampy tastes and odors.

Two general types of filters are employed in purifying municipal water supplies: slow sand filters and mechanical filters.

Slow Sand Filtration.—In slow sand filtration the water is caused to pass through a suitable layer of sand which removes the undesirable suspended matter. The method was inaugurated by Simpson in England in 1829 and is frequently referred to as the English system. The filter is a very large water basin containing filtering material 1.5 to 2 meters in thickness. The upper layer consists of fine sand approximately 1 meter in thickness supported on coarser sand, and this in turn, on a layer of graded gravel, the coarest material at the bottom. Drains are installed below the gravel to carry off the filtered water.

The process of slow sand filtrations is about as follows: The raw water containing suspended material, together with colloidal clay, bacteria, microscopic plants, etc., is run into a sedimentation basin where part of the impurities settle out under the influence of gravity. The removal of microorganisms by the filter is not very efficient until the surface layer of the sand becomes coated with a slimy protoplasmic deposit called the "schmutzdecke." This protoplasmic filtering layer consists essentially of myriads of living forms—diatoms, fungi, blue and green algæ, protozoa, and bacteria—together with silt, mud, and other colloidal matter. Although the greater part of the impurities are retained in the surface layer, thick filter beds have been found to be more efficient than thinner ones, indicating that each particle of sand contributes to the purification.[1] Obviously, the rate at which the filtration is carried out has an important bearing on the efficiency of the process. In practice, from two to four million gallons of water per acre per day are rendered substantially free from suspended matter, including bacteria. When the protoplasmic film has become clogged so that the rate of filtration is unduly retarded, the water is allowed to subside below the surface, about ½ inch of sand is scraped off, and the filtering resumed. The sand is used over again after washing free from impurities.

The slow sand filter is suited to purification of waters containing relatively small amounts of color, suspended matter, and animal pollution. This type of filter has been in use in Europe for years and has proved most efficient; on the other hand, but few American waters can be treated successfully and economically by this process. In some places where the slow sand filter has been adopted and has not proved entirely satisfactory, the normal biological action of the filter is supplemented by the use of coagulants, such as aluminum sulfate. The trivalent aluminum ion causes agglomeration of the negatively charged colloidal particles and hydrous aluminum oxide, which subsequently settles out, carries down with it a large portion of the impurities. Thus, at Washington, the Potomac River water is treated with aluminum sulfate before it enters the Georgetown reservoir, which acts as a sedimentation basin. After partial clarification by sedimentation, the water is conducted to the filter bed, where the undesirable impurities are further reduced. Clark[2] suggests loading the sand with coagulant as a means of supplementing

---

[1] PIEFKE: *Z. Hyg.*, **7**, 115, 170 (1889).

[2] *J. Am. Water Works Assoc.*, **36**, 385 (1922); *Public Works*, **53**, 197 (1922).

the action of the slow sand filter. From 75 to 225 tons of aluminum sulfate per acre have been used in practice.

Aeration, preferably by spraying, before filtration brings about the precipitation of dissolved iron as hydrous ferric oxide. Objectionable odors and tastes are likewise best removed by aeration, either before or after filtration.

Mechanical Filtration.—The method of rapid sand filtration was developed in America and is, therefore, referred to as the American system. The process is characterized by the artificial formation of a surface filtering layer consisting essentially of hydrous aluminum or ferric oxide, by the method of cleaning the filters, and by the rapid rate of filtration which may be as much as fifty times that in slow filters. The method is eminently suited to the treatment of turbid and highly colored waters, and is commonly used where softening as well as filtration is necessary. The process is substantially as follows: The raw water passes through a meter which measures the volume of water passing and at the same time regulates the rate of addition of coagulant to the flow of water. If the water is to be softened, it is next passed to a set of weirs where it is divided, one small fraction receiving the charge of lime and a second the requisite amount of soda ash. These portions are subsequently mixed with the main body of water, which is then allowed to stand until the body of the precipitate settles out. The water is next conducted to the filters, which consist of concrete or wooden basins having a filtering area of 50 to 120 square meters. The top layer of a filter is of fine sand about 75 centimeters thick followed by a 30-centimeter layer of graded gravel, which rests on perforated brass strainers connected with the drain system. The small residual amount of suspended hydrous oxide quickly forms a filtering layer on the sand, which entrains the remaining impurities. Usually after 8 to 12 hours' operation, the filters become clogged and must be washed. This is accomplished by forcing clean water up through the strainers, thus dislodging the impurities which pass over the top of the filters with the wash water. Both gravity and pressure filters are in use, but the principle is the same in each.

The precipitate of hydrous alumina or ferric oxide adsorbs and entangles practically all suspended matter including bacteria;

but where the raw water has a very high bacterial count, it may be necessary to sterilize the water with chlorine, hypochlorite, or ozone as an added precaution against transmitting such diseases as typhoid fever and Asiatic cholera.

Flinn, Weston, and Bogert[1] summarize the applicability of slow sand and rapid sand filters, as follows:

For a water having a turbidity[2] less than 30 p.p.m.[3] or a color[4] less than 20 p.p.m., slow filters without coagulation give excellent results. For waters having a turbidity of more than 50 p.p.m. or a color of more than 30 p.p.m., mechanical filters give unquestionably better results. They not only produce an equally safe water but one of far better appearance. Between these extremes is a region where either the mechanical filter or the slow filter with coagulants may be used equally well. Under ordinary conditions, the latter is far more expensive than the former.

THE ACTION OF COAGULANTS

When a coagulant such as aluminum sulfate is added to polluted water, several colloidal processes take place, most important of which are the neutralization of colloidal particles by adsorption of ions, followed by agglomeration; and the adsorptive action of the highly gelatinous aluminum oxide. The strongly adsorbed aluminum ion has a marked precipitating action on colloidal clay, bacteria, and coloring matter. Observations of the effect of multivalent cations on the sedimentation of clay and on the agglutination of bacteria date back to the pioneer work of Bodländer[5] and Bechhold,[6] respectively. More recently, Saville[7]

---

[1] "Waterworks Handbook," 734 (1918).

[2] The standard of turbidity is a water which contains 100 p.p.m. of precipitated fuller's earth in such a state of fineness that a bright platinum wire 1 millimeter in diameter can just be seen when the center of the wire is 100 millimeters below the surface of the water and the eye of the observer is 1.2 meters above the wire. The turbidity of this standard water is 100.

[3] Parts per million.

[4] The standard color solution, having a color of 500, contains 1.246 grams K_2PtCl_6, 1 gram $CoCl_2 \cdot 6H_2O$ and 100 cubic centimeters of concentrated HCl in 1 liter.

[5] *Jahrber. Mineral.*, **2**, 147 (1893).

[6] *Z. physik. Chem.*, **48**, 385 (1904).

[7] *J. New Engl. Water Works Assoc.*, **31**, 78 (1917).

showed that the color taken up by water originating in swamps
or peaty soils is due almost exclusively to negatively charged
colloidal particles which are coagulated by the cations of the
coagulant. Miller[1] confirmed this result and demonstrated further that the decolorizing action on the so-called humic acid
colors is due, for the most part, to the agglomerating action of
aluminum ion, hydrous alumina alone playing an unimportant
rôle in the process. The precipitating action of hydrogen ion
on the negatively charged impurities is much less than that of
aluminum ion of the same concentration.[2] The high precipitating power of sulfate ion neutralizes any positively charged
colloids that may be present in the water; but the most important
function of a multivalent negative ion is to prevent the formation
of a positive sol of hydrous aluminum oxide.

The highly gelatinous hydrous alumina which precipitates
under suitable conditions adsorbs and entangles the finely divided
impurities, leaving the water relatively clear and uncontaminated
as it settles out. Because of the outstanding role of the hydrous
oxide in the purification process, it is important to know what
constitutes the most satisfactory floc and how the desired product
may be obtained. Some waters contain sufficient iron to produce
a good floc when lime or soda ash is added; others have normally
sufficient alkali to precipitate hydrous alumina on the addition
of aluminum sulfate; still others require the addition of both
sulfate and alkali. If ferrous sulfate is added, lime must always
be used to bring about satisfactory precipitation. In practice,
the coagulant most used is commercial aluminum sulfate, commonly called filter alum or alum. A great deal of empirical
information regarding the use of coagulants has been collected;
but the principles underlying their proper use have received but
little attention until recent years. In this connection, the
important work of Clark, Thierault, and Miller in the Hygienic
Laboratory of the United States Public Health Service deserves
special mention.

Formation of Alumina Floc.—It is well known that hydrous
aluminum oxide does not separate from an aluminum sulfate
solution when the final solution is either too acid or too alkaline.

[1] *U. S. Pub. Health Repts.*, **40**, 1472 (1925).
[2] *Cf.* BANERJI: *Indian J. Med. Research*, **11**, 695 (1924).

In other words, there is a comparatively narrow range of hydrogen ion concentration in which a precipitate forms and the range of complete precipitation is still narrower. The ideal conditions should result in the rapid and complete formation of a floc that settles readily.

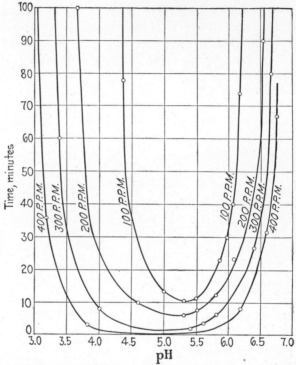

Fig. 27.—Relation between time required for the appearance of floc in solutions buffered at various pH values when the total salt concentration is constant and the alum concentration is varied: 1 = 400 p.p.m.; 2 = 300 p.p.m.; 3 = 200 p.p.m.; 4 = 100 p.p.m.

In any precipitation process, the highest rate of precipitation will result under otherwise constant conditions, when the highest concentration of separable material above the equilibrium concentration is attained. In the present instance, the degree of supersaturation of water with hydrous aluminum oxide can be varied either by increasing the total amount of aluminum sulfate added at a given final pH value or by varying the pH value with a constant amount of aluminum sulfate. The maximum degree of supersaturation and rate of precipitation of hydrous alumina under varying conditions was first studied by Thierault and Clark.[1] The procedure was as follows: A definite volume of a solution of known composition was treated with varying amounts of aluminum sulfate in dilute solution. After rapid mixing, the liquid was poured into a 100-cubic-centimeter cylinder, and the time necessary for the first appearance of a floc was noted. The visibility of the floc was increased by slight agitation of the cylinder. In Fig. 27 is given the time required for the first appearance of a floc in solutions buffered at various pH values, when the total salt concentration is constant and the alum is varied. The concentration of aluminum sulfate in parts per million is 400, 300, 200, and 100 for curves 1, 2, 3, and 4, respectively. The optimum pH value for producing a floc in minimum time increases slightly as the concentration of alum decreases. In curves 1, 2, 3, and 4, it is at pH = 4.95, 5.10, 5.25, and 5.40, respectively. With less than 100 p.p.m. of aluminum sulfate, the optimum pH value is close to 5.5, which is significant since the amount used in practice is ordinarily considerably less than 100 p.p.m. Moreover, as the concentration of aluminum sulfate decreases, the width of the curves decreases, the optimum zone, using 100 p.p.m., being less than one pH unit.

Attention is called to the fact that the floc which appears first in a series of experiments is always the best so far as the flocculent appearance is concerned. Also, the floc formed in minimum time is most abundant and settles most rapidly.

The actual time required for the appearance of a floc depends on the size of the vessel. This difference is quite marked, a precipitate forming within a minute in a large vessel and often requiring hours to become visible in a small one. Apparently this "volume effect" is only the effect of the volume-surface ratio upon circulation, since mechanical circulation decreases the time required for the appearance of a floc.[2] Gentle agitation was found to influence only the time of flocculation and not the amount of precipitate or the optimum pH value for maximum rate.

[1] *U. S. Public Health Repts.*, **38**, 181 (1923).
[2] *Cf.* HOOVER: *J. Am. Water Works Assoc.*, **11**, 582 (1924).

Since the two branches of the curve relating pH value to floccu-lation time, tend to become parallel, no floc is likely to appear for a very long time in laboratory vessels if the pH value is beyond the asymptote to either branch. Moreover, since the two branches come closer together the more dilute the solutions, the region in which a floc appears may be quite narrow for extremely dilute solutions. Thierault and Clark found that if a floc does not appear within a few hours with slight occasional agitation, it will not appear within a greatly reduced time with mechanical agitation. This indicates the necessity for rigid control of the final pH values under large volume conditions, in order to secure floc formation in a reasonable time from highly dilute aluminum sulfate solutions.

The above method of determining the optimum conditions for a satisfactory floc was found to be applicable to natural waters containing carbonates. A slight but definite buffer action is obtained in the region of pH = 5.5 with aluminum sulfate and a hydroxide. At as low a pH value as this, the carbon dioxide of the air is not so effective in disturbing the equilibrium of dilute solutions as it is in such solutions nearer neutrality. Accordingly, it is possible to obtain mixtures of aluminum sulfate and calcium hydroxide having definite pH values in the range 4.6 to 6.0. Using $M/500$ calcium hydroxide without the use of supplemen-tary buffers and varying the amount of aluminum sulfate, the optimum pH value is between 5 and 6; with $M/500$ sodium hydroxide and varying amounts of aluminum sulfate, the best floc is obtained at pH = 5.2; and with constant amount of aluminum sulfate and varying amounts of alkali, the optimum value is about pH = 5.8. These observations would indicate that a hydrogen ion concentration between pH = 5 and 6 is best suited for the coagulation of aluminum sulfate even in natural waters. This proves to be approximately true in many cases but not in all. A minimum in residual alum in filter effluents under commercial conditions was found by Buswell and Edwards[1] at pH = 6; by Baylis[2] between pH = 5.5 and 7.0; and by Hatfield[3] between pH = 5.8 and 7.5. The latter

[1] *Chem. Met. Eng.*, **26**, 826 (1922).
[2] *J. Am. Water Works Assoc.*, **10**, 365 (1923).
[3] *J. Am. Water Works Assoc.*, **11**, 554 (1924).

values are for Lake St. Clair water in which the maximum rate of flocculation is between pH = 6.1 and 6.3. Dallyn and Delaporte[1] found the optimum condition for coagulation to be pH = 5.5 and 6.5 for soft colored, and for clear Great Lakes water, respectively; and Mum[2] obtained the most favorable results with Triliwong River water at pH = 5.5 to 6. On the other hand, Hatfield[3] obtained most satisfactory results at Highland Park, Mich., when the pH value of the treated water was between 7.2 and 7.3; and similar conditions exist in other places.[4] Obviously, therefore, the hydrogen ion concentration most favorable for coagulation varies with the nature of the water. In this connection, the importance of research being carried out under the conditions which obtain in actual practice cannot be emphasized too strongly. Different waters present their individual problems which very frequently cannot be solved simply by referring to data obtained with pure chemicals. Some of the factors which influence the optimum hydrogen ion concentration for obtaining a good floc will be considered in order.

The observations recorded in the preceding paragraphs were all carried out with aluminum sulfate. The range of hydrogen ion concentration over which flocculation occurs might be expected to vary with the nature of the anion. Thus, it will be recalled that colloidal hydrous alumina is formed by dialysis of a solution of aluminum chloride to which ammonium hydroxide is added short of precipitation; aluminum sulfate cannot be substituted for aluminum chloride on account of the strong precipitating action of sulfate ion. This is illustrated further by some observations of Miller[5] on the effect of various anions on the zone of precipitation of hydrous alumina. For example, 0.005 M solutions of aluminum chloride and aluminum sulfate were treated with varying amounts of alkali, and after precipitation, the hydrogen ion concentration of the supernatant solution and the amount of aluminum in the precipitate were determined.

[1] *Contract Record,* **37,** 343 (1923); *cf.* CATLETT: *J. Am. Water Works Assoc.,* **11,** 887 (1924).

[2] *Mededeel-Burgerlyken Geneeskund. Nederland-Indie,* Part 1, 27 (1925).

[3] *J. Ind. Eng. Chem.,* **14,** 1038 (1922).

[4] BANERJI: *Indian J. Med. Research,* **11,** 695 (1924).

[5] *U. S. Pub. Health Repts.,* **40,** 351 (1925).

Referring to Fig. 28, it will be seen that with aluminum sulfate, practically complete precipitation occurs between pH values of about 5.3 and 8.7;[1] while with aluminum chloride, flocculation occurs only in the narrow range between pH = 7.8 and 8.6. It should be emphasized that these ranges represent zones of flocculation and not of insolubility. The insoluble hydrous oxide formed in the presence of chloride remains in colloidal solution throughout the lower pH values on account of the strong stabilizing action of hydrogen ion and the weak precipitating power of

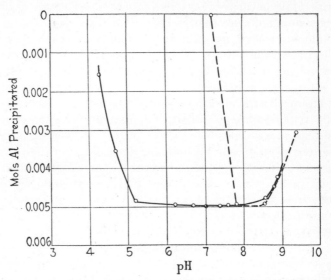

Fig. 28.—Zones of hydrogen ion concentration in which flocculation occurs for alum and aluminum chloride.

chloride ion. Similar observations were made by Miller with more dilute solutions approaching those used in the actual operation of water purification. It is quite evident, therefore, that the nature and precipitating power of the anions present in solution are equal in importance to that of the hydrogen ion concentration in controlling the formation of a suitable precipitate of hydrous alumina. From the results of observations with various anions, Miller reports that sulfate yields a floc best suited to successful water clarification. The range of concentration over which

[1] *Cf.* Greenfield and Buswell: *J. Am. Chem. Soc.*, **44**, 1435 (1922).

precipitation occurs is broad and the floc is of good quality, rapid settling, and shows least tendency to become colloidally dispersed.

Since the maximum rate of flocculation of pure aluminum sulfate in dilute alkali is at pH = 5.5, Thierault and Clark suggest that this value may represent the isoelectric point[1] of hydrous aluminum oxide. Hatfield[2] likewise refers to his values of pH = 6.1 to 6.3 as indicating the "apparent" isoelectric point of the hydrous oxide. As a matter of fact, the zone of maximum rate of flocculation is of no significance whatsoever as a direct experimental method of determining the isoelectric point of hydrous alumina, since the zone can be varied at will by varying the anions present in solution. Miller confirmed Thierault and Clark's value of pH = 5.5 as the approximate point of maximum precipitation for aluminum sulfate; but the maximum is at pH = 8 for aluminum chloride.

In addition to the effect of the negative ion content of natural waters, the presence of colloidal inorganic or organic matter, which may function as a protective colloid, will cause variation in the zone of hydrogen ion concentration in which flocculation occurs. Thus, colloidal silica[3] prevents the formation of hydrous alumina under certain conditions; and sewage-polluted water requires more coagulant than an unpolluted water having the same turbidity and color.

Instead of adding aluminum sulfate directly to water, Coxe[4] suggests adding a colloidal solution[5] prepared by mixing 40 grams of crystalline aluminum sulfate in 80 cubic centimeters of water with 10 grams of sodium carbonate in 40 cubic centimeters of water. This sol is precipitated simply by dilution, and it is claimed to have certain advantages as a clarifying agent over aluminum sulfate and alkali added separately. Thus, clarification can be brought about without softening, if desired; and the carbon dioxide content of the water is not increased as a result of decomposition of aluminum sulfate in the water treated. The clearest advantage would appear to be in the very short time

---

[1] *Cf.* HEYROVSKY: *J. Chem. Soc.*, **117**, 11, 695, 1013 (1920).

[2] *J. Am. Water Works Assoc.*, **11**, 554 (1924).

[3] SMITH: *J. Am. Chem. Soc.*, **42**, 460 (1920).

[4] *Chem. Met. Eng.*, **29**, 279 (1923).

[5] *Cf.* SPENCER: *Chem. Age*, **32**, 31 (1924).

necessary for the formation of the floc, as compared with the usual process.   On account of the low concentration of aluminum ion, the sol would probably be unsuited for treating waters containing large amounts of negatively charged coloring matter.

In view of the importance of aluminum ion in the coagulation and removal of coloring matter, it would appear advantageous to treat highly colored waters at a low pH value where aluminum ions exist in solution as such, followed by increasing the pH value in order to precipitate all the aluminum.   This is exactly what Norcom[1] does with Cape Fear River water at Wilmington, N. C.   The desired result is accomplished by connecting two sedimentation basins in series, treating the water with alum at a low pH value in the first basin, and increasing the pH value in the second basin by the addition of alkali.

Finally, it may be said that successful water purification by alum depends on the presence of a certain minimum quantity of aluminum ion; the presence of an anion of high precipitating power, such as sulfate; and the proper adjustment of the hydrogen ion concentration.[2]

Composition of the Alumina Floc.—When aluminum sulfate is added to water, an equilibrium is set up that may be represented by the following equation:

$$Al_2(SO_4)_3 + xH_2O = Al_2O_3 \cdot xH_2O + 6H^{\cdot} + 3SO_4''$$

The addition of alkali displaces this reaction to the right, complete precipitation of the aluminum resulting when approximately 2.5 equivalents of hydroxyl to 1 of aluminum are added. Miller[3] determined the composition of the precipitate formed at various final pH values: Liter quantities of 0.005 M solution of potassium alum were added to varying quantities of sodium hydroxide. The pH values of the resulting solutions were determined, and the precipitates were analyzed for their aluminum and sulfate content, after thorough washing.   The results are given in Fig. 29.   From the lowest pH value at which a precipitate forms up to pH = 5.5, the composition of the precipitate

[1] *J. Am. Water Works Assoc.*, **11**, 97 (1924); *cf.* MILLER: *U. S. Pub. Health Repts.*, **40**, 1479 (1925).

[2] MILLER: *U. S. Pub. Health Repts.*, **40**, 365 (1925).

[3] *U. S. Pub. Health Repts.*, **38**, 1995 (1923).

remains constant and may be represented approximately by the formula $5Al_2O_3 \cdot 3SO_3$.[1] Above pH = 5.5, which corresponds to 2.4 equivalents of alkali to 1 of aluminum, the sulfate content of the precipitate decreases gradually, becoming zero at pH = 9 when exactly 3 equivalents of alkali to 1 of aluminum have been added.

The constancy of composition of the precipitate thrown down below pH = 5.5 suggests that it may be a basic salt. This view

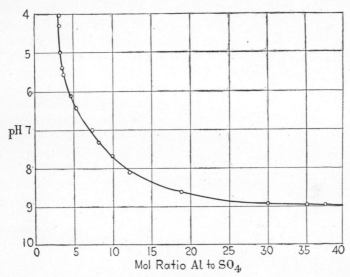

Fig. 29.—Composition of the precipitate from alum at varying hydrogen ion concentration.

is rendered improbable by the ease with which the sulfate is displaced by washing the hydrous oxide containing sulfate, with solutions of negative ions of equal or greater valence.[2] Dyes containing two or more acid groups such as the di-, tri-, and tetrapotassium sulfonates of indigo likewise displace sulfate. From a study of the reciprocal displacement of oxalate and sulfate ions, Miller[3] suggests that the negative ions are in solid

[1] WILLIAMSON: *J. Phys. Chem.*, **27**, 284 (1923); *cf.*, however, HOPKINS: *J. Am. Water Works Assoc.*, **12**, 425 (1924).

[2] CHARRIOU: *Compt. rend.*, **176**, 679, 1890 (1923).

[3] *U. S. Pub. Health Repts.*, **39**, 1502 (1924).

solution in the hydrous oxide. This question was considered in an earlier chapter[1] and the conclusion was reached that the carrying down of ions by hydrous alumina is an adsorption phenomenon rather than a case of solid solution in which the ions form an integral part of the space lattice of the microcrystals. A possible explanation of the constancy of adsorption of sulfate ion below pH = 5.5 is that the adsorption of hydrogen ion by the hydrous oxide reaches the saturation value at approximately this point. If such be the case, the amount of sulfate ion which must be adsorbed to neutralize the adsorbed hydrogen ion will be constant below pH = 5.5. Above this value, the adsorption of hydrogen ion falls off, and there is a corresponding gradual decrease in the adsorption of sulfate until it becomes zero at pH = 9 and above.

It will be recalled that Thierault and Clark obtained the best and most rapid flocculation in very dilute aluminum sulfate solutions near pH = 5.5, where the precipitation of aluminum first approaches completion on the addition of alkali and where the greatest proportion of sulfate is found in the precipitate. Miller likewise found the precipitate to be more dense, more rapid settling, more opaque, less gelatinous in appearance, and less voluminous in the more acid portion of the flocculation range than at the higher pH values. It would appear that the best floc for commercial water clarification should be sufficiently gelatinous to adsorb and entangle all impurities but sufficiently dense to settle rapidly.

The Ferric Oxide Floc.—Ferrous sulfate in conjunction with lime is a very good coagulant for turbid alkaline waters such as those of the Missouri and Ohio basins. If ferrous sulfate is added to such water, the action with calcium bicarbonate may be represented as follows:

$$FeSO_4 + Ca(HCO_3)_2 = Fe(HCO_3)_2 + CaSO_4$$

Ferrous bicarbonate oxidizes and precipitates too slowly for practical use, and so lime must be added which precipitates hydrous ferrous oxide thus:

$$Fe(HCO_3)_2 + Ca(OH)_2 + xH_2O = FeO \cdot xH_2O + Ca(HCO_3)_2$$

[1] P. 127.

By adding sufficient lime, the calcium is also precipitated as carbonate. Hydrous ferrous oxide is slightly soluble; but it is oxidized by the oxygen dissolved in the water, giving hydrous ferric oxide, the coagulant desired. This oxide may be obtained directly from ferric sulfate but the latter salt is much more expensive than the ferrous salt.

Hydrous ferric oxide forms a denser coagulum than hydrous alumina, and ferrous sulfate is considerably cheaper than aluminum sulfate. On the other hand, ferrous sulfate must always be used in conjunction with lime and the mixture is not suitable for soft waters, because any surplus lime gives the water a caustic alkalinity. Moreover, hydrous ferric oxide does not remove coloring matter so well as hydrous alumina and so is not suitable for clarification of waters which are high in color or which are alternately turbid and colored. The failure of ferrous sulfate to remove coloring is probably due to the relatively low precipitating power of ferrous ion as compared with aluminum ion and the rapidity with which the former is removed from solution when used in conjunction with lime.

Miller[1] extended the study of aluminum compounds to the corresponding compounds of iron and found the same factors which determine the optimum conditions for forming an alumina floc to apply equally to ferric oxide floc. The floc from ferric alum is precipitated almost completely near pH = 3, approximately 2.5 pH units below the zone of maximum precipitation of hydrous alumina from sulfate solution. Like aluminum chloride, ferric chloride forms a sol at lower pH values, complete flocculation occurring at approximately pH = 5.0; but unlike alumina, hydrous ferric oxide is insoluble at higher pH values. The zone of precipitation of hydrous ferric oxide is, therefore, much wider than that of hydrous alumina, a circumstance which may be of distinct advantage under certain conditions.

[1] *U. S. Pub. Health Repts.*, **40**, 1413 (1925).

CHAPTER XVIII

CEMENT

The term cement, as ordinarily used at the present time, refers to mortars which possess the property of hardening in water as well as in air. Reference has already been made to hydraulic cements in which magnesia or zinc oxide is the most important constituent, so that this chapter will deal for the most part, with what is known as Portland cement.

Portland Cement

The need for a cementing material to bind sand and small stones together was recognized from the time man started to build. In some of their constructions, the Assyrians and Babylonians are known to have used moistened clay, which was probably the first cementing material ever used for building purposes. Such a binder is not sufficiently durable or hard for building massive constructions, and the next development appears to have been the discovery by the Egyptians of the cement now known as plaster of Paris, which was mixed with sand to make the mortar used in the construction of the Pyramids. The discovery that the application of heat to certain rock minerals, such as gypsum, would give a cementing substance was later employed by the Greeks in making lime from limestone or marble. The Greeks prepared some very satisfactory mortars by mixing lime with sand or with sand and volcanic earths known as pozzolana. The development of pozzolana mortars was brought to a high state of perfection by the Romans, as evidenced by many of their imposing structures which still exist. The so-called Roman or pozzolana cements were similar in many respects to the modern Portland cement.

The art of cement making declined with the fall of Rome and was not revived until 1756 when John Smeaton discovered that a clayey limestone found in Cornwall would give an hydraulic lime, when burned. This product was mixed with pozzolana to prepare the mortar used in constructing the Eddystone lighthouse. Because of the scarcity of pozzolana, which is found only in a few volcanic regions, subsequent investigations were carried out in an attempt to produce an artificial Roman cement. The invention of a satisfactory process is attributed to Joseph Aspdin of Leeds, who took out a patent in 1824 for making a cement by heating an intimate mixture of limestone and clay at the temperature ordinarily used in burning lime. To this product, Aspdin gave the name Portland cement, since its color, after hardening, was similar to that of Portland stone, a famous English building stone. Aspdin's original cement was not what is now known as Portland cement, as the temperature of burning was not high enough; but a year later, in 1825, the importance of heating the mass to incipient fusion was recognized. From this beginning, a century ago, there has developed the modern Portland cement industry, the importance of which in our present-day civilization is difficult to overestimate.

Formation.—Portland cement is produced by heating a mixture of compounds containing suitable amounts of aluminum, calcium, and silicon together with small amounts of iron and magnesium. In the early stages of the development of the industry, the method of procedure employed in making a satisfactory cement was determined by the method of trial and error. Now, it is known that certain definite compounds impart the desired properties to cement and that a uniform product made up of these compounds results only when the raw material containing calcium, aluminum, and silicon in rather definite proportions is ground to a fine powder and the intimate mixture heated to a minimum temperature.

Typical raw materials employed in cement manufacture are limestone and clay, both of which are found in large deposits of uniform composition. In some places, there exist deposits of clayey limestone, called cement rock, containing all three of the essential constituents; but as a rule, either limestone or clay must be added to get the desired composition for good Portland cement. The alumina and silica are sometimes derived from blast-furnace slag and the calcium oxide from sea shells. From whatever source the material is obtained, the separate constituents are first mixed in the proper proportions and then thoroughly pulverized. If the raw materials are rocks, the grinding is commonly carried out in the dry way. On the other hand, soft materials, such as marl and clayey mud which are gathered by dredging operations, are usually ground wet and are kept suspended until dried out in the kiln.

The burning process is carried out in cylindrical kilns, 100 to 300 feet in length and 6 to 12 feet in diameter, built of steel plates and lined with highly refractory material. The drums are held in a slightly inclined position by friction rollers and are rotated slowly. The process is continuous, the raw mix entering at one end of the kiln and the cement clinker leaving it at the other. The heat is derived from pulverized coal, fuel oil, or gas which is blown into the lower end of the kiln by compressed air, giving a flame 30 to 40 feet in length. The time of passage through the kiln is from 1.5 to 2 hours, during which the raw material is subjected to a gradually increasing temperature that reaches a maximum of about 1425°. In the first stage of the burning process, the raw material is thoroughly dried; in the second stage, carbon dioxide and organic matter are driven off; and in the final stage, the alumina, silica, and lime react to form the cement clinker. The latter consists of partially sintered masses of particles from 0.5 to 6 centimeters in diameter. After adding a small amount of gypsum which regulates the rate of setting, the particles of clinker are ground to a fine powder which is the Portland cement of commerce.

Composition.—The limits of composition within which cements of good quality usually fall are set down in Table XXXIII as given by Meade.[1] This, of course, gives only the percentage amount of the several components and does not indicate the nature of the compounds present. It will be seen that more than 90 per cent of the average Portland cement consists of calcium, aluminum, and silicon, referred to the oxides; hence, it is reasonable to suppose that its properties are due chiefly to compounds of these three constituents. As a matter of fact, Richardson[2] demonstrated that a good Portland cement can be prepared by starting with lime, silica, and alumina in a pure state.

Many workers have been concerned with the constitution of Portland cement since Le Chatelier published the results of his

[1] "Portland Cement" (1925).
[2] *Cement*, **5**, 314 (1904).

TABLE XXXIII.—COMPOSITION OF PORTLAND CEMENT

Constituent	Limits of composition, per cent	Average composition, per cent
Lime.....................................	60.0 to 64.5	62.0
Silica....................................	20.0 to 24.0	22.0
Alumina..................................	5.0 to 9.0	7.5
Magnesia.................................	1.0 to 4.0	2.5
Iron oxide...............................	2.0 to 4.0	2.5
Sulfur trioxide...........................	1.0 to 1.75	1.5

classic investigations four decades ago.[1] In most of the work, the evidence offered in support of the alleged reactions which take place during the burning process and of the compounds formed is not convincing, since the criteria used to define a compound were either indefinite or insufficient. The solution of many questions connected with the constitution and setting of Portland cement has been brought about by the thorough systematic investigations carried out in the Geophysical Laboratory and the United States Bureau of Standards. Thus Rankin and Wright[2] made a complete phase-rule study of the ternary system $CaO-Al_2O_3-SiO_2$ which necessitated the investigation of about 1000 different compositions and fully 7000 heat treatments and microscopical examinations. The results of these observations are summarized in the triangular concentration diagram shown in Fig. 30. In this diagram, the pure components are represented by the apices of the triangle; the binary mixtures, $CaO-Al_2O_3$, $Al_2O_3-SiO_2$, and SiO_2-CaO, respectively, by points on the three sides; and ternary mixtures by points within the triangle. Each side of the triangle is divided into 100 parts and all compositions are given as percentage weights of the components. The lines within the large triangle divide the latter into 14 small triangular spaces which enclose all possible mixtures of the three components whose compositions are represented by the apices of the respective triangles. The com-

[1] "Experimental Researches on the Constitution of Hydraulic Mortars" (1887), translated by Hall (1905).

[2] *Am. J. Sci.*, (4) **39**, 1 (1915); SHEPHERD, RANKIN, and WRIGHT: *J. Ind. Eng. Chem.*, **3**, 211 (1911); RANKIN: *Ibid.*, **7**, 466 (1915).

pounds within each small triangle are represented by symbols in which C = CaO, A = Al₂O₃, and S = SiO₂. Thus the compound $5CaO \cdot 3Al_2O_3$ is formulated: C_5A_3.

Richardson finds that a good cement clinker can be made from mixtures of the three oxides in the proportion represented by the points at P in Fig. 30. Since all the points lie within the triangle whose apices are $3CaO \cdot SiO_2$, $3CaO \cdot Al_2O_3$, and $2CaO \cdot SiO_2$,

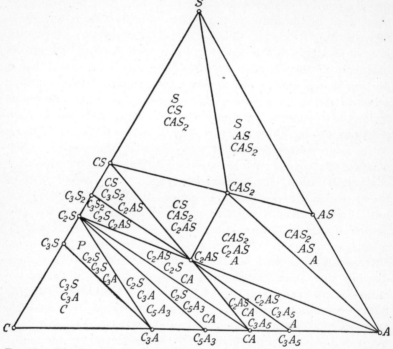

Fig. 30.—Diagram showing final products of crystallization of solutions of CaO, Al₂O₃ and SiO₂.

it follows that a cement clinker made by burning the three pure components in this proportion until equilibrium is reached should consist of these three compounds only. If, however, equilibrium were approached but not reached, there should be, in addition, only the compounds $5CaO \cdot 3Al_2O_3$, and CaO, as these are the only other constituents present in the adjacent triangles. As will be shown subsequently, observations on commercial Portland cement clinker confirm these conclusions.

As a result of precise investigations of the conditions of formation and the optical properties of each of the four compounds individually, Rankin[1] deduces the mode and order of their formation in the burning of a cement clinker made up from the pure oxides. The first step in the process is the union of lime with the other components to give the readily formed compounds, $5CaO \cdot 3Al_2O_3$ and $2CaO \cdot SiO_2$, probably in this order, since the melting point of the former is lower than the latter; subsequently, these compounds unite in part with more lime to give $3CaO \cdot SiO_2$ and $3CaO \cdot Al_2O_3$. The formation of the last two compounds is a slow process in mixtures of their own composition but is hastened in the ternary mixtures by the circumstance that a portion of the charge has already melted and acts as a flux or solvent. Since $3CaO \cdot SiO_2$ is the most important constituent in Portland cement, the necessity for burning at a high enough temperature to sinter the raw materials is readily understood. At a temperature somewhat above 1335°, the conversion of $5CaO \cdot 3Al_2O_3$ to $3CaO \cdot Al_2O_3$[2] is complete and the important compound $3CaO \cdot SiO_2$ is forming rapidly. At 1475°, most of the lime has entered into combination but a complete melt is not obtained until around 1900°. The final products of crystallization of this melt are: $3CaO \cdot SiO_2$, $2CaO \cdot SiO_2$ and $3CaO \cdot Al_2O_3$.

Investigations carried out on commercial Portland cements disclose that their composition is essentially the same as the clinker made from pure oxides. This is best illustrated by the data recorded in Table 34 for (1) pure cement; (2) a commercial white cement; and (3) the more common gray variety of commercial Portland cement. All three are made up largely of the same constituents. It is of interest that the optical characteristics of the essential compounds persist even when these compounds are formed in the presence of small amounts of magnesia, iron oxide, etc. The magnesia and alkalies are apparently taken

[1] *J. Ind. Eng. Chem.*, **7**, 466 (1915).

[2] NOTE: CAMPBELL [*J. Ind. Eng. Chem.*, **9**, 943 (1917)] claims that tricalcium aluminate should be regarded either as a metastable saturated solid solution of CaO in $5CaO \cdot 3Al_2O_3$ or as $5CaO \cdot 3Al_2O_3$ with four molecules of CaO of crystallization rather than as a stable phase in the strict sense of the word.

up in solid solution by tricalcium aluminate and dicalcium silicate,[1] and the iron oxide combines with lime to give ferrite.[2]

The minor constituents play an important part in the burning of the cement clinker, since their presence results in the formation of a flux at a lower temperature, thereby hastening the combination of lime with alumina and silica. This is evidenced by the

TABLE XXXIV.—COMPOSITION OF PORTLAND CEMENTS[1]

Type	Actual constituents		Relative to content of CaO, Al_2O_3,- SiO_2	Burning temperature, degrees	Compounds in resulting cements
Pure..	CaO 68.4 Al_2O_3 8.0 SiO_2 23.6	100.0	CaO 68.4 Al_2O_3 8.0 SiO_2 23.6	1650	$2CaO \cdot SiO_2$ $3CaO \cdot SiO_2$ $3CaO \cdot Al_2O_3$
White.	CaO 66.2 Al_2O_3 6.4 SiO_2 25.0	97.6	CaO 67.9 Al_2O_3 6.5 SiO_2 25.6	1525	$2CaO \cdot SiO_2$ $3CaO \cdot SiO_2$ $3CaO \cdot Al_2O_3$ Small amount of CaO
	MgO, Fe_2O_3, Na_2O, and K_2O	2.4			
Gray..	CaO 63.2 Al_2O_3 7.7 SiO_2 22.4	93.3	CaO 66.7 Al_2O_3 9.0 SiO_2 24.3	1425	$2CaO \cdot SiO_2$ $3CaO \cdot SiO_2$ $3CaO \cdot Al_2O_3$ Small amounts of $5CaO \cdot Al_2O_3$, CaO, and ferrites
	MgO, Fe_2O_3, Na_2O, K_2O, and SO_3	6.7			

[1] RANKIN: *J. Ind. Eng. Chem.*, **7,** 466 (1915).

data given in Table XXXIV. It should be pointed out, however, that the temperatures are not strictly comparable, since the reactions of the white and gray products are incomplete. In these cases, it is probable that the temperatures necessary for equilibrium would be somewhat higher than the values recorded.

[1] RANKIN and MERWIN: *J. Am. Chem. Soc.*, **38,** 568 (1916); *cf.* KLEIN and PHILLIPS: *Eighth Int. Cong. Applied Chem.*, **5,** 81 (1912).

[2] SOSMAN and MERWIN: *J. Wash. Acad. Sci.*, **6,** 15 (1916); CAMPBELL: *J. Ind. Eng. Chem.*, **11,** 116 (1919).

Setting and Hardening.—When finely pulverized Portland cement is mixed with water, a plastic mass results which becomes solid in the course of a few hours. This process, which is called setting, is followed by a gradual increase in strength or hardening of the mass. While a good cement becomes very hard in the course of a few weeks, it may require years to attain its full strength.

According to Le Chatelier,[1] the setting and hardening of Portland cement consist in the dissolution in water of the anhydrous silicates and aluminates, which subsequently become hydrated. Since the hydrates are less soluble than the anhydrous salts, the solutions become supersaturated with respect to the former and deposit an entangling mass of needles, thereby giving the cement its characteristic hardness. This theory of the hardening process was not questioned until Michaelis[2] recognized the formation not only of crystals but of a gel which increased gradually until it filled the interstices between the crystalline needles as well as those between the cement particles. The cementing gel was supposed to be calcium monosilicate and the crystals tricalcium aluminate and calcium hydroxide. According to this hypothesis, the cement particles and crystals become embedded in a common sheath of gelatinous substance which imparts a degree of hardness that could not be attained by the felting of crystalline needles alone.

More or less successful attempts were made to distinguish the various products of hydration of Portland cement by the use of organic dyes which stain colloidal and zeolitic minerals selectively.[3] Such experiments led Blumenthal[4] to conclude that crystalline monocalcium silicate and tricalcium aluminate are among the first products of hydration and that a gelatinous silicate forms subsequently. From this, he concludes that the setting is due to crystallization alone, the later hardening process consisting of the binding together of the crystals and the filling of the pores by means of a gel.

---

[1] "Experimental Researches on the Constitution of Hydraulic Mortars" (1887), translated by Hall (1905).

[2] *Kolloid-Z.*, **5**, 9 (1909); **7**, 320 (1910); *Chem. Ztg.*, **17**, 982 (1893).

[3] KEISERMANN: *Kolloidchem. Beihefte*, **1**, 423 (1910).

[4] *Silikat Z.*, **2**, 43 (1914); Thesis, Jena (1912).

A systematic investigation of the setting and hardening process was possible only after the constitution of cement had been definitely established. Knowing that cement consists essentially of $3CaO \cdot Al_2O_3$, $3CaO \cdot SiO_2$, and $2CaO \cdot SiO_2$, investigations were carried out by Klein, Phillips, and Bates[1] in the U. S. Bureau of Standards to determine what happens when each of the constituents separately is brought in contact with water. The results of these and later observations are as follows:

Tricalcium Aluminate.—When $3CaO \cdot Al_2O_3$ is mixed with water, a gelatinous hydrous material is first formed which sets so rapidly that it is almost impossible to make test pieces. It never attains a tensile strength much beyond 100 pounds per square inch. When mixed with silicate, it affects the latter more markedly in the time of set than in the strength, tending to hasten the former and retard the latter. With the limited amount of water in cement pastes, it is converted into and remains a gel during the first 24 hours, at least.[2] With more water, crystallization takes place fairly rapidly. Pulfrich and Linck[3] isolated crystals having the composition $3CaO \cdot Al_2O_3 \cdot 7H_2O$, which were claimed to be identical with those in cement. Duchez[4] claims that all calcium aluminates in cement hydrate to $3CaO \cdot Al_2O_3 \cdot 12H_2O$. If lime aluminates of lower basicity are present, a quantity of hydrous alumina is liberated which in turn combines with $Ca(OH)_2$ from the hydrolysis of calcium silicates, forming the duodecahydrate.

It is an interesting fact that $3CaO \cdot Al_2O_3$, the single aluminate present in Portland cement, is the only one that does not possess hydraulic properties.[5] This is probably because the action of water on aluminates other than $3CaO \cdot Al_2O_3$ gives some hydrous $3CaO \cdot Al_2O_3$, which later crystallizes, and gelatinous alumina which is the real cementing agent in aluminous cements.

Dicalcium Silicate.—The compound $2CaO \cdot SiO_2$ sets very slowly with water, and it is only after long intervals that sufficient

[1] KLEIN and PHILLIPS: *U. S. Bur. Standards, Techn. Paper* 43 (1914); BATES and KLEIN: *Ibid.*, **78** (1916).

[2] BATES: *J. Am. Ceram. Soc.*, **2,** 708 (1919).

[3] *Kolloid-Z.*, **34,** 117 (1924).

[4] *Rock Products*, **27,** No. 18, 62 (1924).

[5] BATES: *J. Am. Ceram. Soc.*, **1,** 679 (1918); *U. S. Bur. Standards, Techn. Paper* 197 (1921).

gelatinous material is produced to cement the granules of compound together into a solid mass. After 14 days, a test piece broke at less than 60 pounds per square inch; but at the end of a year, a sample developed a tensile strength of 600 pounds per square inch. The cementing material is hydrous monocalcium silicate,[1] which, together with calcium hydroxide, is formed by the slow hydrolysis of the silicate.

Tricalcium Silicate.—$3CaO \cdot SiO_2$ is the only one of the three major constituents which reacts with water within a reasonable time to give a mass comparable to Portland cement in hardness and strength. The end products of the reaction are hydrous monocalcium silicate and calcium hydroxide, as in the case of dicalcium silicate; but unlike the latter, tricalcium silicate hydrolyzes very readily to give the essential binding gel and so is the most important constituent in Portland cement.

Summary.—When water is added to a mixture of the three constituents as they occur in Portland cement, the initial set is due to the formation of a gel of tricalcium aluminate and possibly a small amount of monocalcium silicate. Pulfrich and Linck[2] emphasized the importance of gel formation in the initial stage by showing that crystallization does not take place at the outset in the presence of the amount of water used in technical practice. Their observations were made in glycerin solutions in order to get the necessary dilution for microscopic examination; and the glycerin may have inhibited the crystallization. This, however, merely emphasizes the contention that setting is not necessarily occasioned by the formation of microscopically visible crystal needles. It is true, of course, that some crystallization takes place in time; but the only crystalline bodies which form ordinarily[3] are calcium hydroxide[4] and a crystalline hydrate derived from tricalcium aluminate, probably the duodecahydrate.

Whereas the initial set results primarily from the formation of tricalcium aluminate gel, the subsequent fairly rapid increase in

---

[1] MICHAELIS: *Kolloid-Z.*, **5,** 9 (1909); **7,** 320 (1910); DUCHEZ: *Rock Products*, **27,** 18, 62 (1924).

[2] *Kolloid-Z.*, **34,** 117 (1924).

[3] *Cf.*, however, GLASENAPP: *Zement*, **11,** 446 (1922); KÜHL: *Ibid.*, **13,** 362, 375 (1924.)

[4] *Cf.* BAIKOV and RAGOZINSKII: *J. Russ. Phys.-Chem. Soc.*, **47,** 761 (1916).

cohesive strength and hardness is due in large measure to the liberation of hydrous monocalcium silicate by the hydrolysis of the tricalcium silicate and dicalcium silicate. It is a pity that dicalcium silicate does not hydrolyze more rapidly, for it is formed at a lower temperature than tricalcium silicate, and yields ultimately a higher percentage of the important binding material, monocalcium silicate.

As already noted, gypsum is added to cement clinker before grinding, in order to retard the time of set. The gypsum may function by diminishing the solubility of tricalcium aluminate or by precipitating calcium sulfoaluminate,[1] thus removing lime from solution which would otherwise be available for the formation of tricalcium aluminate gel.

Tippermann[2] is of the opinion that the presence of gypsum serves two functions; it retards crystallization and aids the formation of colloids. This opinion is based on the observation that sulfate-free cements to which no gypsum is added, undergo rapid and extensive crystal formation, but no colloidal material is present at the end of a year. The addition of gypsum to such cements cuts down the rate of crystallization; but swelling, together with gel formation, takes place at once. Tippermann attributes the action of gypsum to the sulfate ion and not to calcium ion, since in the sulfate-free cement, the concentration of calcium ion varies from zero to saturated solution without gel formation entering in. These observations should be confirmed and extended.

Since gypsum is softer than clinker, it is probable that the gypsum particles are ground considerably finer than the cement particles. It has been suggested that the more finely divided gypsum particles coat the coarser cement particles, thereby acting to some extent as a protecting film and so delaying the chemical process involved in setting.[3]

The addition of salts influences the time of set to a greater or lesser degree. Gadd[4] reports the results of recent observations with a large number of compounds including the carbonate,

[1] Kühl: *Prot. ver. D. P. C. F.*, **45,** 98 (1922).

[2] *Zement*, **13,** 135, 147 (1924).

[3] Fink: *J. Phys. Chem.*, **21,** 32 (1917); Briggs: *Ibid.*, **22,** 216 (1918).

[4] *British Portland Cement Research Assoc.*, Pamphlet 1 (1922).

nitrate, chloride, sulfate, borate, and hydroxide of sodium, ammonium, aluminum, zinc, cobalt, and chromium. Of the various compounds studied, the nitrates appear to have little effect on the rate of setting, whereas all the other compounds except gypsum and plaster of Paris accelerate the set. In view of the influence of electrolytes on jelly formation,[1] it is not surprising to find that their presence has an effect on the rate of setting of cement.[2] One would expect the addition of salts[3] to have either a retarding or accelerating action, depending on whether they have a coagulating or stabilizing action on the colloids formed by the action of water on the cement particles.

The addition to cement of calcium chloride or "Cal"[4] materially accelerates the rate of hardening of Portland cement mixtures. This is probably due to the precipitation of a calcium chloraluminate of the composition $3CaO \cdot Al_2O_3 \cdot CaCl_2 \cdot 18H_2O$,[5] with an accompanying decrease in the pH value. This reduction in pH accelerates the hydrolysis of the silicates and so hastens the hardening process. Platzmann,[6] on the other hand, attributes the action mainly to the hygroscopicity of calcium chloride which, by absorption of moisture during the first few weeks, prevents the shrinking and cracking of the cement and protects it from too rapid a loss of moisture.

Cements Related to Portland Cement

Iron-Portland Cement.—A cement may be prepared in which iron is substituted for aluminum. It is manufactured in much the same way as ordinary Portland cement; and as in the latter, the chief hydraulic constituent is tricalcium silicate. The area occupied by cements rich in iron oxide in a triaxial diagram of the system lime-silica-iron oxide is in nearly the same position as

---

[1] See p. 26.

[2] ROHLAND: *Kolloid-Z.*, **8,** 251; **9,** 21 (1911).

[3] *Cf.* BENSON, NEWHALL, and TREMPER: *J. Ind. Eng. Chem.*, **6,** 795 (1914).

[4] A material resulting from the interaction of lime and calcium chloride in water.

[5] LAFUMA: "Le Ciment," 174 (1925); *cf.*, however, KÜHL and ULRICH: *Zement*, **14,** 859, 880, 898 (1925); GASSNER: *Chem. Ztg.*, **48,** 157 (1924).

[6] *Zement*, **10,** 499 (1921); **11,** 137 (1922); *Chimie & industrie*, **7,** 943 (1922); **8,** 614 (1922).

that of Portland cement in the system lime-silica-alumina.[1]
Iron-Portland cement with its lower lime content[2] contracts more
on setting than does Portland cement.   The addition of calcium
chloride to iron-Portland or blast-furnace cements causes them
to swell, so that the natural shrinkage is counteracted or takes
place only after a long time.[3]

In Germany, up to 30 per cent of blast-furnace slag is added to
Portland cement clinker giving what is called Eisen-Portland
cement.   This produces a superior product for sea-water construction, possibly because the added slag unites with any free
lime, thereby preventing it from acting with the sea water to
form calcium hydrosilicates[4] or such compounds as magnesium
hydroxide[5] or calcium sulfoaluminate,[6] which are active in producing cracks.

Aluminous Cement.—Cements in which the alumina content is
equal to or greater than that of the silica content are known
commercially as "aluminous," "fused," or "electrofused"
cements.   They are produced by fusion, because calcium aluminates soften readily, and clinkering is very difficult.[7]   As previously mentioned, Bates[8] found that all the alumina compounds
in the lime-alumina-silica system possess hydraulic properties
except $3CaO \cdot Al_2O_3$.   The compound $5CaO \cdot 3Al_2O_3$ sets very
rapidly indeed; while both $3CaO \cdot 5Al_2O_3$ and $CaO \cdot Al_2O_3$ set
slowly but harden rapidly, developing great strength in 24 hours.
Very good cements may be had with 55 to 75 per cent alumina in
lime-alumina burns.   Aluminous cements are manufactured
extensively in France; but the chief drawback to their wide commercial use is the lack of a widely distributed supply of hydrous
alumina and the consequent high cost of raw materials.

[1] Kühl: *Zement*, **10**, 361, 374 (1921).

[2] Campbell: *J. Ind. Eng. Chem.,* **11**, 116 (1919).

[3] Guttmann: *Zement*, **9**, 310, 429 (1920).

[4] *Cf.* Gassner: Practical Questions Concerning Concrete in Sea Water,
Zement, **14**, Nos. 21 to 25 (1924).

[5] Lewis: *Engineering*, **109**, 626 (1920); Gary: *Mitt. Material-prüfungsamt*,
37, 12 (1919).

[6] Grün: *Zement*, **12**, 297, 307, 317, 326 (1924).

[7] Bied: *Techn. moderne*, **14**, 508 (1922); *Rev. métal.*, **19**, 759 (1922).

[8] *J. Am. Ceram. Soc.*, **1**, 679 (1918); *U. S. Bur. Standards, Techn. Paper*
197 (1921); *cf.* Endell: *Zement*, **8**, 319, 334, 347 (1919).

The setting and subsequent hardening of aluminous cements result from the formation of tricalcium aluminate gel and hydrous alumina.[1] The early hardening is due to the relatively high rate of hydrolysis of the aluminates. Advantages claimed for aluminous cement over Portland cement are: the more rapid rate of hardening; greater strength; and the higher temperature developed on setting, usually sufficient to permit normal hardening even in severe weather.[2]

[1] Kühl and Thuring: *Zement*, **13**, 109, 243 (1924); Platzmann: *Rock Products*, **27**, No. 19, 23 (1924).

[2] Gueritte: *Contract Record*, **38**, 1197 (1924); Anon.: *Eng. News-Record*, **94**, 320 (1925).

CHAPTER XIX

THE SOIL

In his classic work on adsorption by the hydrous oxides, van Bemmelen[1] advances the idea that the inorganic colloids in the soil are similar in general nature to the gelatinous oxides. This idea has persisted, and according to Whitney:[2] "It is now coming to be quite generally believed that the inorganic colloidal material of the soil is essentially the same as the artificial gels of silica, iron, and alumina, which have been prepared." There are, however, a number of people[3] who champion the view that a considerable portion of soil colloids consists of complex acid aluminosilicates rather than a mixture of the hydrous oxides. In any event, it would seem that a volume devoted to the hydrous oxides would be incomplete without some reference to the colloidal matter of the soil.

Composition of the Soil Colloid

The colloidal matter of the soil is derived from both organic and mineral sources. The organic colloidal matter consists of the remains of animal and vegetable life, together with the soil bacteria and fungi. In such organic soils as the so-called peats and mucks, the colloids are chiefly organic; but in most agricultural soils, the colloidal matter is of mineral origin, derived in large measure from the hydrolysis of silicates.

It is difficult, if not impossible, to separate all the colloidal matter from a soil. The earlier investigators merely rubbed up the soils with a considerable amount of water and estimated as colloidal matter the amount that remained suspended for a

---

[1] "Die Absorption," 114 (1910); LANDER: Ber. Stat., **23**, 265 (1879).

[2] Bogue's "Colloidal Behavior," **2**, 468 (1924).

[3] SHARP: Univ. Calif. Publ. Agr. Sci., **1**, 291 (1916); BRADFIELD: Colloid Symposium Monograph, **1**, 369 (1923); J. Am. Soc. Agron., **17**, 253 (1925); TRUOG: Colloid Symposium Monograph, **3**, 228 (1925).

given length of time. Schlösing[1] is of the opinion that the material which remains longest in suspension differs essentially from material which does not remain suspended so long and so estimates the colloid content of soils to be only 0.5 to 1.5 per cent.[2] Hilgard[3] and Williams[4] reported much higher percentages based on the amount of material that does not settle in a 24-hour period. Since the amount of soil that will remain suspended depends on the degree of peptization of a gel and the time of settling, methods of estimating the colloid content of soils based on such procedures[5] are necessarily inaccurate. Other methods that have been employed are based on determination of the adsorption capacity of the soil for malachite green,[6] water, and ammonia. Gile[7] and his coworkers determine the adsorption capacity of a sample of soil and of the colloidal material extracted frcm the soil, and from these data, calculate the percentage colloidal matter. After correcting for the possible alteration in adsorptive capacity of the colloid produced by extraction, the percentages of colloidal matter indicated by adsorption of malachite green, water, and ammonia show fairly good agreement among themselves[8] and with the percentages estimated gravimetrically and microscopically. As would be expected, the colloidal content of different soils varies widely. Assuming that all particles less than 1μ in diameter are colloidal, the sandy soils contain but a few per cent of colloids; while the loam soils may contain 15 to 25 per cent, and the clays 40 to 50 and up to 90 per cent colloidal matter.

The method of procedure employed in the Bureau of Soils, U. S. Department of Agriculture, for separating samples of colloids from the rest of the soils is essentially as follows: The soil is suspended in distilled water or in water containing enough ammonia to impart a pH of 7 to 8. After allowing to settle for

[1] *Compt. rend.*, **70**, 1345, 1870; **78**, 1276; **79**, 473 (1874).

[2] *Cf.* EHRENBERG: "Die Bodenkolloide," Dresden, 99 (1922).

[3] *Am. J. Sci. Arts*, (3) **106**, 288, 333 (1873); "Soils," New York, 333 (1919).

[4] *Forsch. Gebiete Agrikuitur-Physik.*, **18**, 225 (1895).

[5] SCALES and MARSH: *J. Ind. Eng. Chem.*, **14**, 52 (1922).

[6] ASHLEY: *U. S. Geol. Survey Bull.* **388**, 65 (1909).

[7] GILE, MIDDLETON, ROBINSON, FRY, and ANDERSON: *U. S. Dept. Agr. Bull.* 1193 (1924).

[8] *Cf.* DAVIS: *J. Am. Soc. Agron.*, **17**, 277 (1925).

18 hours, the turbid supernatant liquid is passed through a supercentrifuge where each particle is exposed to a force of approximately 17,000 gravity for 3 minutes. The colloid which passes through the supercentrifuge is collected on the outside of a Pasteur-Chamberlain filter by sucking off the water. The average diameter of the particles obtained by this procedure is 0.1 to 0.15μ, the largest being about 0.3μ. The residue appears distinctly gelatinous and dries to a hard, horn-like mass.

To give some idea of the composition of the soil colloids, there are given in Table XXXV the analyses of a number of such colloids

TABLE XXXV.—COMPOSITION OF SOIL COLLOIDS

Substance	Soil type							
	1	2	3	4	5	6	7	8
SiO_2	50.49	50.13	44.94	48.04	42.40	36.26	31.30	15.86
TiO_2	0.51	0.46	0.47	0.65	0.56	0.65	1.01	3.54
Al_2O_3	16.73	21.70	22.15	25.19	24.71	32.85	33.64	34.38
Fe_2O_3	10.77	8.70	8.91	8.80	15.27	12.44	11.66	22.67
MnO	0.121	0.035	0.126	0.032	0.138	0.160	0.070	0.068
CaO	2.36	1.48	1.12	1.29	1.18	0.44	0.56	0.21
MgO	5.32	2.54	1.95	1.53	2.59	0.18	0.78	0.29
K_2O	2.24	1.86	2.07	0.89	2.39	0.36	1.71	0.27
Na_2O	0.54	0.24	0.19	0.38	0.51	0.47	0.58	0.33
P_2O_5	0.37	0.69	0.70	0.14	0.25	0.36	0.24	0.26
Organic matter	1.79	3.83	7.94	4.52	3.49	4.15	6.33	5.96
Combined H_2O	8.26	8.73	8.92	9.23	7.22	12.73	11.79	15.63

1. Fallon loam, soil, Nevada
2. Sharkey clay, soil, Mississippi
3. Marshall silt loam, soil, New York
4. Carrington loam, subsoil, Iowa
5. Ontario loam, subsoil, New York
6. Vega Baja clay loam, soil, Porto Rico
7. Cecil loamy fine sand, soil, Georgia
8. Aragon clay, deep subsoil, Costa Rica

from widely different types of soils. This table was compiled from data obtained in the Bureau of Soils of the U. S. Department of Agriculture.[1] Although the composition of the colloids from different sources may show wide variation, these differences may be relatively small in soils from similar climatic regions.[2] Investigations on a large number of representative soils disclosed

[1] *Cf.* GILE: *Colloid Symposium Monograph*, **3**, 218 (1925); ROBINSON and HOLMES: *U. S. Dept. Agr. Bull.* 1311 (1924).

[2] BRADFIELD: *J. Am. Soc. Agron.*, **17**, 253 (1925).

that the composition of the colloids, as compared with that of the whole soil, was much higher in alumina, ferric oxide, organic matter, water, magnesia, phosphorus, and sulfur, and lower in silica. In the ageing process to which the soil is subjected, there appears to be a tendency either for the silica to be transformed into secondary quartz or to move below the soil layer, while iron oxide and alumina accumulate in the soil colloids.

The colloidal mineral matter of soils appears to be formed by the action of water on hydrated silicates of igneous origin. Whitney[1] believes the soil colloids are formed by the bombardment of soil particles by water molecules when the former are of the order of magnitude of 0.0001 millimeter in diameter; while Gordon[2] considers that the outer layer of all silicate particles is constantly subjected to hydrolytic action. By these weathering influences, there are formed the insoluble hydrous oxides of iron, aluminum, and silicon, and the soluble salts of sodium, potassium, calcium, and magnesium, which are adsorbed in part by the hydrous oxide gels. There appears to be no conclusive evidence as to whether the hydrous oxides remain as such in the soil, retaining more or less of the adsorbed soluble constituents, or whether in the course of time there are formed complex aluminosilicates of definite composition. On account of the variability in the proportion of alumina to silica, it is obvious that no one fixed proportion would account for all the alumina or all the silica in every colloid. It is necessary, therefore, either to postulate the existence of several complex silicates or to assume that a portion of the hydrous oxides remain as such. Until the question is definitely settled, I subscribe to the simpler assumption that the inorganic soil colloids consist essentially of variable amounts of the hydrous oxides of iron, alumina, and silica with varying amounts of adsorbed salts. For the most part, the so-called aluminosilicates are adsorytion complexes of indefinite composition, formed by the mutual precipitation of negatively charged hydrous silica and positively charged hydrous alumina. It is probable that the organic material[3] and the

[1] *Science*, **54**, 656 (1921).

[2] *Science*, **55**, 676 (1922).

[3] EHRENBERG: *Z. angew. Chem.*, **41**, 2122 (1908); WIEGNER: *Kolloidchem. Beihefte*, **2**, 238 (1910); FODOR and SCHOENFELD: *Kolloidchem. Beihefte*, **19**, 1 (1924).

hydrous silica keep the colloidal soil material in a dispersible state. As Gile[1] put it: "In most soils, colloidal material has probably persisted several thousand years, undergoing some changes, but remaining nevertheless a dispersible colloid. The experiment will never be performed; so it is safe to predict that pure inorganic gels would not preserve their characteristics over the same period of time." Bradfield[2] points out that mixtures of artificial colloids having the same composition as colloids found in the soil do not have the same properties as the soil colloids. This, in itself, offers no proof that the soil colloids do not consist essentially of the hydrous oxides of iron, aluminum, and silicon together with colloidal organic matter and adsorbed salts. It would seem impossible to prepare a synthetic soil that even approaches the properties of a true soil until one can duplicate very closely the conditions of formation of the hydrous oxides and the influence of salts, organic matter, and other soil conditions which enter into soil formation.

The organic colloids introduced into the soil in the form of plant and animal residues are subjected to the action of bacteria and other lower forms of life which cause porfound changes. Under aerobic conditions, that is, under conditions of good aeration such as exist in cultivated soils, the organic matter is oxidized fairly completely, giving water and carbon dioxide and the phosphates, carbonates, nitrates, and sulfates of sodium, potassium, calcium, and magnesium which are made available for new plant growth. On the other hand, under anaerobic conditions such as obtain in poorly drained and hence poorly aerated marshes and swamps, a part of the organic matter is decompsoed with the formation of a colloidal substance known as humic acid or humus. This product is a dark, waxy mixture of many complex compounds.[3]

The so-called humic acids are formed also in drained prairie soils which are covered with a dense growth of grass. The sod provides what amounts to partial anaerobic conditions by preventing rapid aeration, so that dead roots, stems, and leaves of grass are in part converted into humic acid. In the presence of

[1] *Colloid Symposium Monograph*, **3**, 227 (1925).
[2] *Missouri Agr. Exp. Sta., Res. Bull.* 60 (1923).
[3] SCHREINER and SHOREY: *U. S. Bur. Soils Bull.* 74 (1910).

considerable calcium, the organic matter may be quite black. The dark color of prairie soils is probably due to a coating of the black organic substance on the particles of mineral matter. After the humus substance is once formed, it resists decomposition when exposed to aerobic conditions, as evidenced by the fact that the cultivation of black prairie land for many years does not cause it to lose its black color.

The bacteria and other living organisms constitute a very important part of the colloidal matter of the soil; but they represent a very minute proportion of the total weight.

Relation between Properties and Composition of Soil Colloids

Although colloidal soil material contains a number of constituents in variable proportions, the three major constituents in the colloids from soil other than peat soils are silica, alumina, and ferric oxide. As a result of investigations carried out in the U. S. Bureau of Soils,[1] it has been demonstrated that the properties of soil colloids vary fairly regularly with the contents of the major constituents as expressed by the molecular ratio of silica to alumina plus ferric oxide. This is well illustrated in Table XXXVI, compiled by Anderson and Mattson.[2] In this table, a series of colloids extracted from different soils is arranged in ascending order of the molecular ratio, silica to alumina plus ferric oxide. In columns 3 and 4, respectively, are given the heats of wetting in calories per gram of colloid and the amounts of ammonia gas adsorbed per gram of colloid. In columns 4, 5, and 6, the data of 2, 3, and 4 are expressed relatively, in order to make the relationships more apparent and to bring out individual exceptions. The evidence indicates that the correlation between heat of wetting and ammonia adsorption will hold fairly well for practically all soil colloids,[3] whereas the relationship between the molecular ratio of silica to alumina plus ferric oxide and the

---

[1] Anderson: *J. Agr. Research,* **28,** 927 (1924); Gile, *et al.*: *U. S. Dept. Agr. Bull.* 1193 (1924); Robinson and Holmes: *U. S. Dept. Agr. Bull.* 1131 (1924).

[2] *Science,* **62,** 114 (1925).

[3] *Cf.* Bouyoucos: *Soil Science,* **16,** 320 (1924).

Table XXXVI.—Relation between Composition and Properties of Soil Colloids

Source of colloidal material	Actual values for			Relative values for		
	$\dfrac{SiO_2}{Al_2O_3 + Fe_2O_3}$	Heat of wetting, calories	NH_3 adsorbed, grams	$\dfrac{SiO_2}{Al_2O_3 + Fe_2O_3}$	Heat of wetting	NH_3 adsorbed
Cecil subsoil......	1.20	4.5	0.0192	0	0	3
Cecil soil.........	1.34	6.2	0.0230	7	13	12
Chester soil.......	1.77	7.2	0.0293	28	21	26
Norfolk subsoil...	1.84	6.0	0.0295	32	11	27
Huntington soil...	1.86	8.3	0.0319	33	29	32
Sassafras subsoil..	1.89	9.8	0.0340	34	40	37
Hagerstown sub-soil...........	1.89	7.9	0.0299	34	26	28
Susquehanna sub-soil...........	1.98	5.3	0.0177	40	6	0
Miami subsoil....	2.66	11.8	0.0358	72	56	41
Marshall soil.....	2.82	14.2	0.0536	80	74	82
Stockton soil.....	2.85	16.3	0.0617	81	90	100
Wabash soil......	3.16	17.6	0.0614	97	100	99
Sharkey soil......	3.23	16.3	0.0609	100	90	98

heat of wetting or ammonia adsorption is subject to some marked exceptions. Thus, the Susquehanna subsoil shows good agreement between heat of wetting and ammonia adsorption, and poor agreement between silica ratio and either heat of wetting or ammonia adsorption.

A fairly good correlation has also been found[1] to exist between the ratio $\dfrac{SiO_2}{Al_2O_3 + Fe_2O_3}$ and the ratio $\dfrac{CaO + Na_2O}{Al_2O_3 + Fe_2O_3}$ for a series of soils. It thus appears that chemical constitutents other than those which enter into the silica ratio correlate with the properties of the soil colloids. As an example, some properties appear to be closely related to the percentage of calcium or to the total exchangeable monovalent and bivalent bases.

Such information as contained in Table XXXVI on the relationship between composition and properties of the soil colloids is of practical value in enabling one to predict qualitatively the general behavior of the colloids without making complete chemical analyses or extensive physical tests.[2]

[1] Robinson and Holmes: *U. S. Dept. Agr. Bull.* 1311 (1924).
[2] *Cf.* Anderson and Mattson: *Science,* **62,** 114 (1925).

The Rôle of the Soil Colloids

Adsorption of Salts.—On accuont of the high specific surface of the colloidal material in the soil, it is the colloids chiefly which adsorb certain mineral constituents, especially the so-called plant foods, and yield them up to growing plants as required. This is illustrated by some observations of Gordon[1] on the adsorption of calcium acid phosphate by the hydrous oxides of silicon, iron, and aluminum, Table XXXVII. Sulfate and nitrate are also adsorbed, but less strongly than phosphate. Since the

Table XXXVII.—Adsorption of Calcium Acid Phosphate by Hydrous Oxides

Concentration of solution	Milligrams Ca adsorbed per gram of gel			Milligrams PO₄ adsorbed per gram of gel		
	Silica	Alumina	Ferric oxide	Silica	Alumina	Ferric oxide
$N/10$.........	0.12	84.9	121.4	0.08	610.2	609.9
$N/20$.........	0.12	51.4	83.3	0.04	393.4	421.6
$N/40$.........	0.11	32.7	54.5	0.01	272.6	266.6

amount adsorbed is in equilibrium with a solution of certain concentration, leaching with water should remove a portion of the adsorbed salt. Gordon finds that 40,000 cubic centimeters of water must be passed through the gel before the filtrate fails to give a test for phosphate. By this procedure, most of the adsorbed salt is leached out from the particular sample of silica; but the alumina and ferric oxide still retain a large portion of the salt, as shown in Table XXXVIII. It thus appears that below a certain concentration, rain will leach out but very small quantities of phosphate from a soil made up of hydrous oxides. To determine whether salts which can be removed only in extremely small amounts by leaching are available for plant growth, Gordon[2] prepared a synthetic soil by mixing the leached hydrous oxides with pure quartz sand and used this in investigations on plant growth. Unmistakable evidence was obtained that plants derive all the phosphorus required for their nourishment from the

[1] Lichtenwalner, Flenner, and Gordon: *Soil Science*, **15**, 157 (1923).
[2] Wiley and Gordon: *Soil Science*, **15**, 371 (1923).

TABLE XXXVIII.—EFFECT OF LEACHING ON THE PHOSPHATE CONTENT OF
GELS

	Milligrams PO$_4$ adsorbed per gram of	
	Ferric oxide	Alumina
Before washing.................	25.9	162.4
After washing.................	16.4	117.5

hydrous oxides containing adsorbed phosphates. Apparently, the roots of the plant in intimate contact with the colloidal oxides take up the very slight equilibrium concentration of soluble phosphorus which is replaced continuously. Obviously, the equilibrium concentration decreases as the amount of adsorbed phosphate in the soil decreases, so that plants are not well nourished if the phosphate content is too low. As Gordon points out, it is immaterial whether the plants take up the phosphate from CaH$_4$(PO$_4$)$_2$ or from some complex compound; the concentration of salt in equilibrium with the adsorbed phosphate determines the amount available at a given time.

Nitrogen in the form of nitrate is preferred by most plants; but, as already noted, the element cannot be stored as nitrate since the latter is so weakly adsorbed by the soil colloids that it is readily leached out and lost. The original source of nitrogen for plants, other than the legumes, is organic matter which is changed by the action of bacteria into ammonia and subsequently into the relatively strongly adsorbed ammonium salts. The latter transformation is a result of the soil acidity which is derived in large measure from the hydrolysis of salts and the relatively stronger adsorption of base than of acid by the soil colloids. Under the influence of bacteria, the small equilibrium concentration of ammonium salt is oxidized slowly to nitrate and becomes available for plant food.

Soluble potassium salts are sufficiently strongly adsorbed[1] that they are conserved in the soil and are gradually given up to plants as needed. The relative adsorbability by hydrous oxides of the ions from solutions of sulfates and of the primary phos-

[1] BOGUE: *J. Phys. Chem.*, **19**, 665 (1915).

phates of potassium magnesium and calcium is recorded in Table XXXIX, compiled from data by Gordon.[1] It will be seen that the adsorption is similar to that of calcium and considerably stronger than that of magnesium.   The last two rows of

TABLE XXXIX.—ADSORPTION OF IONS BY HYDROUS FERRIC OXIDE AND ALUMINA

Milligrams ions adsorbed per gram Fe_2O_3						Milligrams ions adsorbed per gram Al_2O_3				
KH_2PO_4		$Mg(H_2PO_4)_2$		$Ca(H_2PO_4)2$			$Mg(H_2PO_4)_2$		$Ca(H_2PO_4)_2$	
K	PO_4	Mg	PO_4	Ca	PO_4		Mg	PO_4	Ca	PO_4
43.8	165.4	21.7	165.0	50.7	235.6		14.0	165.0	47.0	239.0
K_2SO_4		$MgSO_4$		$CaSO_4$		K_2SO_4		$MgSO_4$		$CaSO_4$
K	SO_4	Mg	SO_4	Ca	SO_4	K	SO_4	Mg	SO_4	Ca	SO_4
11.4	13.6	7.6	21.1	12.9	36.0	11.0	19.0	6.2	26.3	5.7	12.0
29.0	....	25.0	....	24.0	....	16.1	....	11.1	....	13.1	

figures represent the adsorption of ions before adding phosphate and after adding phosphate, respectively.   The more strongly adsorbed phosphate ion displaces completely the sulfate ion and, at the same time, increases greatly the adsorption of the cations.

Using a sandy loam soil as adsorbent instead of the pure hydrous oxides, Harris[2] obtained the results recorded in Table XL.

TABLE XL.—ADSORPTION OF CATIONS BY A SOIL

Solution	Adsorption of cation by 50 grams of soil	
	Grams	Equivalents
$AlCl_3$.......................	0.113	0.00125
KCl..........................	0.0395	0.00101
$CaCl_2$.......................	0.0134	0.00067
$MnCl_2$.......................	0.0177	0.00064
$MgCl_2$.......................	0.0057	0.00047
NaCl..........................	0.0041	0.00013

[1] LICHTENWALNER, FLENNER, and GORDON: *Soil Science*, **15**, 158 (1923).
[2] *J. Phys. Chem.*, **21**, 454 (1917).

In these experiments 50-gram samples of soil were shaken frequently with 125-cubic-centimeter portions of the salts during a period of 24 hours. The salts are arranged in the order of adsorbability of the cations. It will be seen that potassium ion is adsorbed more strongly than the divalent ions and almost as strongly as trivalent aluminum. The adsorbed potassium ion is displaced by other ions as given in Table XLI. The soil was first treated with potassium chloride, thoroughly washed, and dried, after which 50-gram portions were treated for 72 hours with the

TABLE XLI.—DISPLACING OF POTASSIUM ION FROM SOIL BY OTHER CATIONS

Fifty-gram samples treated with 200 cubic centimeters of distilled water	Grams of potassium ion	
	Found in solution	Displaced
Distilled water............................	0.0076	
$N/10$ AlCl$_3$................................	0.0512	0.0436
$N/10$ NH$_4$Cl..............................	0.0471	0.0395
$N/10$ MnCl$_2$..............................	0.0426	0.0350
$N/10$ CaCl$_2$..............................	0.0424	0.0348
Water containing 1.2 grams CaSO$_4$ · 2H$_2$O....	0.0423	0.0347
$N/10$ MgCl$_2$..............................	0.0343	0.0267
$N/10$ NaCl................................	0.0326	0.0250

solutions listed in the table and the adsorption measured. As would be expected, the order of the displacing power of the cations is approximately the same as the order of adsorbability given in Table XL. Particular attention should be called to the strong adsorbability of ammonium ion as evidenced by a displacing power second only to that of aluminum ion.

Thus, we may look upon the inorganic and organic colloids as a reservoir which adsorbs[1] and so conserves the plant foods and yields them up as needed to the growing plants. Another point of view is that the soil colloids are amphoteric compounds which bind the mineral constituents as definite complex salts possessing the necessary solubility to supply food to the plants as required. Until it has been proved that the inorganic soil col-

[1] SCHLÖSING: Ann. chim. phys., 5, 2 (1874); SCHREINER and FAILYER: U. S. Bur. Soils Bull. 32 (1906).

loids are largely complex silicates which combine with the so-
called plant foods, yielding complex salts with all the necessary
properties, I prefer the simpler hypothesis that the inorganic
colloidal material is chiefly the hydrous oxides whose adsorption
capacity for salts is well known.

Adsorption of Water.—The capacity of the colloidal content of
the soil to adsorb and retain water is second only in importance
to the adsorbing capacity for salts. Indeed, Gile and his
coworkers have found that 95 per cent the adsorptive capacity

TABLE XLII

Type of soil	Hygroscopic coefficient,[1] per cent	Heat evolved[2] by 50 grams of soil, calories
Quartz sand	....	0.0
Coarse sand	0.5	0.2
Fine sand	1.5	0.8
Sandy loam	2.3	10.8
Fine sandy loam	6.5	15.0
Loam	9.8	172.8
Silt loam	....	205.2
Clay loam	11.8	391.5
Clay	14.6	607.5

[1] Briggs and Shantz: *U. S. Dept. Agr., Bur. Plant Ind.*, 230 (1912).

[2] Bouyoucos: *Mich. Agr. Exp. Sta., Tech. Bull.* 42 (1918); *cf.* Müntz and Gaudechon: *Ann. sci. agron.*, (3) **4**, 393 (1919).

of the soil is due to its colloidal material and only 5 per cent to
the non-colloidal material. If dry soils are placed in a saturated
atmosphere, they adsorb water until a condition of approximate
equilibrium is attained. The amount of adsorbed water and the
heat of adsorption increase with the fineness of the particles, as
shown in Table XLII. These observations were made by different investigators and on different soils which come under the
same general soil type.

Bouyoucos[1] has proposed the phenomenon of heat of wetting
as a means of estimating the colloidal content of the soil. As
would be expected, the colloids of different soils vary widely in
their heat of wetting, owing to the difference in their physical

[1] *Soil Science*, **16**, 320 (1924).

character.   Heating to 750° is said to decrease the heat of wetting of soils to zero.   This cannot be strictly true, for the adsorptive capacity of ignited soils may be 30 to 50 per cent of the value before ignition.   Because of this loss of adsorptive capacity on ignition, Alway[1] questions the reliability of the water-adsorption method of estimating the colloid content of the soil.   This seems to be beside the point, since one might reasonably expect the coalescence accompanying ignition to decrease materially the amount of colloidal matter.   The validity of the water-adsorption method depends primarily on whether non-colloidal material in unheated soil adsorbs an appreciable amount of water under the conditions of determination.

The total water-holding capacity of a soil is influenced to a considerable extent by the height of the soil column and by the mode of packing of the particles; but the colloidal content is by far the most important factor in determining the moisture-holding capacity.   Bouyoucos[2] found that some ordinary clays will hold as much as 75 per cent of water as compared to only 20 per cent in some coarse sands.   The best method of increasing the colloid content and, hence, the water-holding capacity of sandy farming land is to increase the organic matter by the application of good farming methods.

Not only do the colloidal particles adsorb and conserve water for times of drouth, but the freezing point of water is lowered very appreciably when it is adsorbed.[3]   As in the case of the hydrous oxide gels,[4] a part of the adsorbed water is not frozen until the temperature is reduced several degrees below zero. This is doubtless of importance in preventing complete desiccation of the soil by freezing and the consequent destruction of the soil bacteria.

Plasticity.—Certain colloidal material acts as a binder, and if present in suitable amount, it holds the particles of soil together

[1] ALWAY: *Colloid Symposium Monograph*, **3**, 241 (1925); PURI, CROWTHER, and KEEN: *J. Agr. Sci.*, **15**, 68 (1925).

[2] *Colloid Symposium Monograph*, **2**, 132 (1924); *cf.* KING: *Wis. Agr. Exp. Sta., Sixth Rept.*, 189 (1889); ALWAY and KING: *J. Agr. Research*, **14**, 27 (1917).

[3] BOUYOUCOS and McCOOL: *Mich. Agr. Exp. Sta., Tech. Bull*, 31 (1916); 36 (1917); PARKER: *J. Am. Chem. Soc.*, **43**, 1011 (1921).

[4] FOOTE and SAXTON: *J. Am. Chem. Soc.*, **38**, 588 (1916).

in a granular structure, thus preventing them from being blown
or washed away and providing for aeration. The quantity of
colloidal matter in a soil does not differ greatly, as a rule, from
the quantity of the "clay fraction" given by various systems of
mechanical analysis. Gile[1] points out, however, that in certain
cases the nature of the clay fraction may be a more important
factor in determining how a soil will act than the quantity of this
fraction.[2] It is possible to increase the colloidal content of
sandy soil by the direct addition of a plastic clay and to cut down
the plasticity of a clay soil by the addition of sand; but this method
of controlling the relative proportion of suitable colloidal to
non-colloidal material is too expensive to use in the ordinary
farming operations. Sand-clay roads, however, are constructed
by mixing sand with plastic clay, which serves as a binder.

Acidity of the Soil.—The so-called acidity of the soil is probably due in large measure to selective adsorption. If one shakes
fuller's earth with distilled carbon-dioxide-free water and filters,
the filtrate is neutral to litmus and to phenolphthalein, showing
the absence of soluble base or acid. Now, if a dilute sodium
chloride solution is shaken with fuller's earth and filtered, the
filtrate is acid to litmus or the phenolphthalein. Obviously,
this is not because the fuller's earth is acid, but because it adsorbs
the base from the sodium chloride solution more strongly than
the acid, giving the solution an acid reaction. Similarly, if a
piece of litmus paper is pressed against moistened fuller's earth,
the paper turns red, and if fuller's earth is added to a faintly
alkaline solution of phenolphthalein, the red color disappears.[3]
Bancroft reports that the adsorbing power of fuller's earth is so
great that an acre-foot, as soil, would adsorb 30,000 pounds of
lime, thus making the fuller's earth about equivalent in acidity
to a 2 per cent solution of sulfuric acid. Not only do clays and
certain hydrous oxides, such as hydrous silica and manganese
dioxide,[4] show this selective adsorption, but van Bemmelen[5]

[1] *Cf. Proc. Am. Soc. Civil Eng.*, **51**, 892 (1925).

[2] MIDDLETON: *J. Agr. Research*, **28**, 499 (1924).

[3] CAMERON: *J. Phys. Chem.*, **14**, 400 (1910); BANCROFT: "Applied Colloid Chemistry," 121 (1921).

[4] VAN BEMMELEN: "Die Absorption," 445 (1910).

[5] "Die Absorption," 454 (1910).

reports that colloidal humus substance decomposes small amounts of solutions of ammonium chloride, carbonate, phosphates, and borates, the base being adsorbed more strongly than the acid, giving the solution an acid reaction. The same results are obtained by digesting either a humus-rich or a clay-rich soil with a solution of ammonium chloride. Gile[1] showed conclusively that silica gel has a beneficial action on the growth of plants supplied with rock phosphate by increasing the quantity of phosphoric acid in solution. This is due to decomposition of the rock phosphate by stronger adsorption of hydroxyl ion than of hydrogen ion by the silica gel.

In the light of these observations, it appears evident that a part and possibly the larger part of the so-called soil acidity results from selective adsorption of the basic constituent of certain salts.[2] This view has been supported by Salter and Morgan[3] as a result of recent observations on the change in acidity of certain soils with variation in the soil-water ratio. In general, it was found that the variation in hydrogen ion concentration agrees with the distribution of hydrogen ions between soil and solution which could be expected if controlled by an adsorption mechanism. The conclusion is reached that the reaction of a soil is dependent on three factors: the total dissociated acid present; the adsorptive capacity of the soil for hydrogen ion; and the soil-water ratio.

The selective adsorption theory of soil acidity is opposed by those who believe that the acidity is due to aluminosilicic acids and humic acid which are relatively insoluble but are soluble enough to give the soil solution an acid reaction. Bradfield[4] gets a kind of end point on titrating dilute solutions of strong bases with acid colloidal clays by either the conductivity or hydrogen electrode method. This is considered as proof of a neutralization reaction between a strong base and weak soil acid, the anion of which is a particle of colloidal dimensions.

[1] Gile and Smith: *J. Agr. Research*, **31**, 247 (1925).

[2] Harris: *J. Phys. Chem.*, **18**, 335 (1914); Noyes: *J. Ind. Eng. Chem.*, **11**, 1040 (1919); Kappen: *Landw. Vers.-Sta.*, **96**, 306 (1920); Mattson: *Kolloidchem. Beihefte*, **14**, 296 (1922).

[3] *J. Phys. Chem.*, **27**, 117 (1923).

[4] *J. Am. Chem. Soc.*, **45**, 2669 (1923).

Returning to the case of fuller's earth and salt referred to at the beginning of this section, one may write the equation for the hydrolysis of sodium chloride as follows:

$$Na^{\cdot} + Cl' + H_2O \leftrightarrows Na^{\cdot} + OH' + H^{\cdot} + Cl'$$

Since fuller's earth adsorbs hydrxhyl ion more strongly than hydrogen ion, it displaces this equilibrium to the right, giving the solution an acid reaction. Now if one adds a base, it will tend to displace the equilibrium in the opposite direction, and one will obtain what amounts to an end point when the amount of alkali added just neutralizes the increased tendency of sodium chloride to hydrolyze as a result of preferential adsorption of hydroxyl ion by the fuller's earth. But this is an entirely different thing from fuller's earth itself being a weak acid that is neutralized by a strong base. Stating the matter in another way: In the presence of a certain concentration of hydroxyl ion, the adsorption capacity of the fuller's earth is satisfied for this ion, and the hydrolysis of the sodium chloride remains the same as in the absence of fuller's earth. The concentration of all strong bases required to bring about this result would be the same, provided the cations of all bases are adsorbed equally and have the same effect on the adsorption of hydroxyl ion. Actually, the cations of strong bases are not all adsorbed to the same extent, and the concentration will not be identical for different bases. For the present at least, there appears no reason for regarding the so-called end point in the titration of acid soils as proof of the existence of a definite soil acid which yields a colloidal anion.

It should be mentioned in passing, that pseudo end points are not infrequently encountered in adsorption phenomena. Thus, in the exchange adsorption with strongly polar adsorbents[1] such as kaolin, one gets what might be termed end points at quite similar concentrations of different salts of the same cation. Moreover, when the value $\dfrac{1}{n}$ in the Freundlich adsorption formula[2] is small, the adsorption curve may bend relatively sharply and take a direction nearly parallel to the concentration

---

[1] FREUNDLICH: "Kapillarchemie," 279 (1922).
[2] FREUNDLICH: "Kapillarchemie," 156 (1922).

axis, thereby giving what might be interpreted as an end point above which the adsorption increases but little with increasing concentration.

Bradfield[1] determined the hydrogen ion concentration of varying concentrations of colloidal clay and compared the results

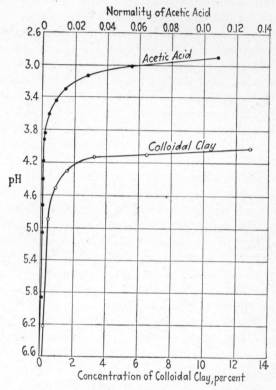

FIG. 31.—The effect of concentration of colloidal clay and acetic acid upon the hydrogen ion concentration.

with similar determinations on acetic acid. Colloidal material was extracted from an acid clay by the aid of the supercentrifuge, and a sol was prepared containing 12.8 per cent of oven-dried material. From this stock solution, dilutions containing 6.4, 3.2, 1.2, 0.8, 0.4, 0.2, 0.05, and 0.25 per cent were prepared and the hydrogen ion concentration determined. Various concentrations

[1] *J. Phys. Chem.*, **28**, 170 (1924).

of acetic acid from 0.000025 to 0.1 N were also prepared and their hydrogen ion concentrations determined. The results are plotted in Fig. 31. It will be seen that the relationship between concentration of acetic acid solution and its hydrogen ion concentration is nearly linear at very low concentrations and becomes exponential at higher concentrations. Similarly, the relationship for colloidal clay is about linear at high dilutions, exponential at intermediate dilutions, and almost constant at higher concentrations. The similarity in the two curves leads Bradfield to regard the colloidal clay as a weak acid which behaves like acetic acid. Personally, I cannot see how the evidence justifies this conclusion. It would seem that with equal propriety one might assume that the acid or mixture of acids formed as a result of preferential adsorption of hydroxyl ion behaves similarly to acetic acid as regards change in pH with increasing concentration.[1]

Truog[2] likewise supports the view that the acidity of soils is due to the presence of relatively insoluble aluminosilicic acids, but claims that the electrometric method is unsuitable for determining the hydrogen ion concentrations of the very slightly buffered solutions such as are obtained with relatively low soil-water ratios. "The reason for this is that slight diffusion of potassium chloride from the connecting bridge, slight contamination of alkali from glassware, slight impurities in the hydrogen, presence of nitrates in the soil, and slightly contaminated or so-called poisoned electrodes can easily effect the reaction of slightly buffered soil suspensions and solutions." He, therefore, determined the hydrogen ion concentration of soil-water extracts colorimetrically after filtering out all the colliodal matter with a special ultrafilter. When the soils were thoroughly washed to remove excess soluble salts, the hydrogen ion concentrations of the ultrafiltrates appeared to be fairly constant at soil-water ratios of 1 to 2, 1 to 20, and 1 to 50. Salter and Morgan failed to obtain a constant hydrogen ion concentration measured potentiometrically at varying salt-water ratios, and so concluded that soil acidity was not due to complex soil acids. The constancy in hydrogen ion concentration at varying soil-water ratios as

[1] WALPOLE: *J. Chem. Soc.*, **105**, 2521 (1914).
[2] *Colloid Symposium Monograph*, **3**, 228 (1925).

determined by Truog's method was offered as proof that acidity of the soil is due to colloidal acids.

Now if the acidity is due to relatively insoluble colloidal acids, the surface ionization will give hydrogen ion and a cation of colloidal dimensions, as claimed by Bradfield. When such a suspension is filtered through an ultrafilter which holds back all the negatively charged colloidal particles, it will obviously hold back their hydrogen ion equivalent, so that from this point of view, the hydrogen ion concentration determined as Truog does it is due entirely to the molecularly dissolved complex acid. Since the degree of dissociation of such an acid is probably very slight even at high dilutions, the solubility of "clay acid" necessary to get a pH value of 4 would be quite appreciable. Truog should make a careful investigation of his perfectly clear ultrafiltrates; for if he can show that these ultrafiltrates contain only complex aluminosilicic acid and humic acids in molecular solution, then the problem is solved. It is altogether unlikely that the alleged complex acids, if they exist, are as soluble as Truog's data would suggest. Until we know more of the nature and composition of Truog's ultrafiltrates, it is impossible to give an intelligent interpretation of his observations.

It should be mentioned, in conclusion, that Schreiner and Shorey,[1] Olin,[2] and others have demonstrated the existence in the soil of definite compounds possessing an acid character; but the cases in which these compounds are present in sufficient quantities to give an acid reaction are rare.

FLOCCULATION AND DEFLOCCULATION

A suspension of soil colloid is made up of negatively charged particles and is, therefore, flocculated readily by the addition of salts containing cations that are relatively strongly adsorbed. As a result of his investigations on the flocculation of kaolin, Bodländer[3] introduced the term "threshold value" of electrolytes, which was defined as the concentration necessary to cause rapid flocculation. Hall and Mouson[4] determined the precipitation

[1] *U. S. Bur. Soils, Bull.* 47, 70, 74, 77, 80, 83, 87, 88, 98.
[2] *Ber.*, **45**, 651 (1912).
[3] *Jahrb. Mineral.*, **2**, 141 (1893).
[4] *J. Agr. Sci.*, **2**, 251 (1907).

concentration of various chlorides, sulfates, and nitrates on colloidal clay. The order of precipitating power of the cations beginning at the greatest is: hydrogen, aluminum > calcium, barium, magnesium > potassium > sodium; and the order of stabilizing power of the anions is hydroxyl > sulfate > nitrate > chloride. The order of a series of acids beginning with hydrochloric, which has the greatest precipitating power, is: hydrochloric > nitric > sulfuric > mono-, di-, and tri-chloracetic > acetic > oxalic, tartaric > amido acetic, citric, phenol. The last three exert no precipitating action.

Since colloidal clays owe their charge to preferential adsorption of hydroxyl ion, one should expect the precipitation value of hydroxides to be higher than that of neutral salts. Bradfield[1] reports that 1.4 milliequivalents of potassium are required to coagulate a certain soil colloid when present as chloride, and 14 milliequivalents as hydroxide; while 10 milliequivalents are required with a mixture of 19 parts chloride and 1 part hydroxide; and 14 milliequivalents, with a mixture of 9 parts chloride and 1 part hydroxide.

The precipitation value of an electrolyte for a sol is that concentration which results in sufficient adsorption of the precipitating ion to neutralize the combined adsorption of the original stabilizing ion and the stabilizing ion added with the precipitating electrolyte or mixture of electrolytes.[2] The precipitation value of potassium chloride is much lower than of potassium hydroxide, since chloride ion is adsorbed much less strongly than hydroxyl ion by colloidal clay. Mixtures of potassium chloride and hydroxide cause coagulation at some value in between the values for the individual electrolytes. Obviously, the effect of hydroxyl ion will be much greater at relatively low concentrations on account of the relatively greater adsorption; and above the saturation value for the adsorption of hydroxyl ion which is reached fairly sharply in the case of a strong adsorbent for a strongly adsorbed ion such as clay for hydroxyl, the precipitation value of potassium ion is fairly constant. Another factor which may come in is that, above the normal saturation value, the presence of the strongly adsorbed hydroxyl ion may actually

[1] *J. Am. Chem. Soc.*, **45**, 1243 (1923).
[2] WEISER: *J. Phys. Chem.*, **25**, 680 (1921).

increase the adsorption of the precipitating cation to such a degree that the rate of precipitation in the presence of the mixture is greater than that of the same concentration of salt without any added hydroxide. This is apparently what happens in certain cases as observed by Mattson[1] in Ehrenberg's laboratory. Mattson finds the order of precipitating power of calcium compounds for a negatively charged colloidal clay to be: calcium chloride > calcium sulfate > calcium bicarbonate > calcium hydroxide; but when a concentration a little above the precipitation value of calcium hydroxide is attained, the rate of flocculation is faster than is observed for salt concentrations considerably above their respective precipitation values. Similarly, when small amounts of sodium hydroxide are added to the clay sol, the stability is increased, as evidenced by the higher concentration of calcium sulfate required for flocculation. But when the initial concentration is increased to 0.002 N, in a 1 per cent clay, the rate of precipitation is appreciably greater than with calcium sulfate alone, even though the concentration of the latter is considerably above its precipitation value in the absence of sodium hydroxide. It appears obvious that, above a certain concentration, the influence of hydroxyl ion in increasing the adsorption of the precipitating calcium ion predominates over its own stabilizing action. Mattson showed that the presence of hydroxyl ion increases enormously the adsorption of calcium ion by quartz. Comber[2] attributes the abnormal flocculating power of calcium hydroxide above a certain concentration to its coagulating action on emulsoid matter that tends to stabilize the clay sol.

Alkali hydroxides in low concentration have a stabilizing action on colloidal clay, while higher concentrations cause flocculation. In the ceramic industry, the so-called clay slip is prepared by deflocculating clay with sodium hydroxide, carbonate, or silicate. The slip can be readily poured or cast, even though it contains less water than a stiff mass of clay and water without alkali. Adding a little acid to a fluidified clay slip flocculates the mass which becomes so stiff that it will not fall from an inverted vessel. Clays carrying appreciable amounts of soluble salts, such as

---

[1] *Kolloidchem. Beihefte*, **14**, 241 *et seq.* (1922); *cf.* COMBER: *J. Agr. Sci.*, **11**, 450 (1922); FODOR and SCHOENFELD: *Kolloidchem. Beihefte*, **19**, 1 (1924).

[2] *J. Agr. Research*, **12**, 372 (1922).

the sulfates of calcium and magnesium, are difficult to defloccu-
late; while clays containing protective colloids, such as humus,
are readily peptized.

The deflocculating action of calcium hydroxide is not as marked
as that of the alkali hydroxides, because of the relatively strong
precipitating power of calcium ion. Nevertheless, it appears
that calcium hydroxide in low concentrations may have an appreciable stabilizing influence on colloidal clay. The addition of
lime to soil containing a large amount of deflocculated colloidal
material is intended to impart a crumbly flocculent structure to
the soil; but in certain instances, liming is reported to have an

TABLE XLIII.—FLOCCULATION AND DEFLOCCULATION OF CLAY BY LIME

Concentration in milliequivalents per liter of		Character of superna-tant solution
$Ca(HCO_3)_2$	$Ca(OH)_2$	
2.02	1.12	Clear
2.02	1.35	Slightly cloudy
2.02	1.57	Cloudy
2.02	1.80	Very cloudy
2.02	2.02	Very cloudy
2.02	2.25	Cloudy
2.02	2.47	Slightly cloudy
2.02	2.70	Clear
2.02	2.92	Clear
2.02	3.15	Clear

unfavorable effect on the structure. Mattson[1] flocculated a
colloidal clay with calcium bicarbonate and then treated it with
varying concentrations of lime water, with the results recorded in
Table XLIII. It will be seen that calcium hydroxide in certain
concentrations does have a peptizing action on clay containing
bicarbonate, and it is probable that a similar condition may be
encountered in a clayey soil if the lime has been used too sparingly. When lime is added to the soil, it is converted into the
hydroxide, a part of which is adsorbed and another part of which
is neutralized by the bicarbonate present. If the amount of lime
added is sufficient to neutralize the deflocculating bicarbonate

[1] *Kolloidchem. Beihefte*, **14,** 276 (1922).

and not enough to neutralize the adsorbed hydroxyl ion, then the lime will have an unfavorable influence on the soil structure.

Under certain conditions, sodium salts[1] in the soil are converted in part into soda which has a strong deflocculating action on the colloidal material. If 'the soil in question is permeable or sandy, the colloidal hydrous oxides and humus are washed down by the rain to a lower stratum, the depth of which is determined by the rainfall in the locality. There, the collected mass of colloidal material and fine sand hardens by desiccation forming an insoluble rock-like layer known as hardpan. This formation may shut off the soil beneath from air and water and, by interfering with drainage, may bring about swampy conditions. The addition of a suitable amount of gypsum to a soil containing soda, neutralizes the deflocculating action of the latter, owing to strong adsorption of calcium ion.

[1] HILGARD: "Soils," 62 (1906); EHRENBERG: "Die Bodenkolloide," 347 *et seq.* (1922).

AUTHOR INDEX

419

SUBJECT INDEX

A

"Acclimatization," 69, 70

Adsorption (see also this heading under several hydrous oxides).
capillary theory of, 183–185
effect of neutral salts, 328
influence of hydrogen ion concentration, 91–94, 316, 320, 321, 324
isotherms, 185, 186, 286, 324, 330, 331, 341, 355, 360
maxima in, 331, 332
mutual (see *Mutual adsorption*).
preliminary to chemical reaction, 245
reversibility, 332
theory of composition of sol, 48, 52, 53
of mechanism of mineral tanning, 325, 328
selective, in the soil, 409–411

Agar jellies, 5, 8, 12

Agate, 181

Agglomeration, prevention of, 71, 73

Albumin, 16, 65, 68, 70, 128, 298, 303, 334
adsorption by hydrous alumina, 128
of arsenious acid, 68
sol, 65, 70
mutual precipitation of ferric oxide sol and, 65
swelling, 16

Albumin-ferric oxide sol, 65

Alizarin, 268, 336, 358–361
adsorption of, 358–361
iron-alizarin lake, 359, 360
streaming double refraction, 268

Alum as coagulant in water purification, 370–380

Alumina mordant, 338–347

Aluminum oxide, anhydrous, 110–112
corundum gems, color of, 111, 112
modifications, 110

Aluminum oxide, hydrous, 103–129, 162, 285, 319, 337–346, 356, 361–363, 365, 369–380
adsorption by cotton, 345
wool, 340
adsorption of acid and basic dyes, 361–363
effect of hydrogen ion concentration, 362, 363
adsorption of arsenious acid, 68
albumin, 128
alizarin, 358, 361
ammonium ion, 406
calcium, 403, 404
casein, 128
chondrin, 128
chromate, 123, 126
Congo blue, 128
red, 364
ferrocyanide, 128
gum arabic, 126
hide, 333
magnesium, 405
phosphate, 405
potassium, 405
precipitating ions, 122–124
order of, 123, 124
sulfate, 405
tannin, 357
tuberculin, 128
ageing, 109, 160
composition, 103–107

435